MST124

Essential mathematics 1

Book D

This publication forms part of an Open University module. Details of this and other Open University modules can be obtained from the Student Registration and Enquiry Service, The Open University, PO Box 197, Milton Keynes MK7 6BJ, United Kingdom (tel. +44 (0)845 300 6090; email general-enquiries@open.ac.uk).

Alternatively, you may visit the Open University website at www.open.ac.uk where you can learn more about the wide range of modules and packs offered at all levels by The Open University.

To purchase a selection of Open University materials visit www.ouw.co.uk, or contact Open University Worldwide, Walton Hall, Milton Keynes MK7 6AA, United Kingdom for a brochure (tel. +44 (0)1908 858779; fax +44 (0)1908 858787; email ouw-customer-services@open.ac.uk).

The Open University, Walton Hall, Milton Keynes, MK7 6AA.

First published 2014.

Edited, designed and typeset by The Open University, using the Open University TeX System.

Printed in the United Kingdom by Page Bros, Norwich.

ISBN 978 1 7800 7362 0

1.1

Contents

Contents

Sequences and series

Introduction

This unit introduces the concept of a *sequence*, which is the mathematical name for a list of numbers arranged in a particular order. The list can stop at a particular number, or it can contain infinitely many numbers. Here are some of the sequences discussed in the unit:

$1, 3, 5, 7, \ldots$

$7.15, 10.50, 13.85, 17.20, \ldots, 245.00$

$1000, 950, 900, 850, \ldots, 0$

$1000, 1050, 1102.50, 1157.63, 1215.51$

$2000, 1400, 980, 686, 480.2, \ldots$

$1, 2, 6, 24, 120, \ldots$

$\dfrac{1}{4}, -\dfrac{1}{8}, \dfrac{1}{16}, -\dfrac{1}{32}, \ldots$

$1, 7, 21, 35, 35, 21, 7, 1.$

Here the three dots ... stand for 'and so on', to indicate that the list continues. If the dots are followed by a number, then that number terminates the sequence. Otherwise, the sequence continues indefinitely.

Several of the sequences above arise from practical situations, such as estimating the height of a bouncing ball on successive bounces. Each of them has a definite mathematical pattern, and you may like to try to spot the pattern now in each case. (However, do not spend longer than a few minutes on this. The patterns may become harder to spot as you move down the list.) You'll see later what pattern is associated with each sequence.

In Section 1 you'll meet two different ways, known as *closed forms* and *recurrence systems*, to specify sequences using formulas. A closed form is a formula for each *term* (individual number) in a sequence, whereas a recurrence system indicates what the first term is and how each subsequent term is related to the previous term in the sequence.

In Section 2 you'll study two special types of sequence, known as *arithmetic* and *geometric* sequences, which include the majority of the examples above.

Section 3 explores how sequences can be visualised, and how they behave in the long term, that is, when a large number of terms are considered.

In some cases, it's possible to calculate the sum of the terms of a sequence, even if there are infinitely many of them. An expression that's obtained by adding the terms of a sequence, such as $1 + 3 + 5 + 7 + 9$, is known as a *series*. Series are the subject of Section 4.

In Section 5 the focus moves from sequences to the *binomial theorem*. This important result enables you to multiply out expansions such as $(1 + x)^4$, $(a + b)^7$ and $(2y - 3)^5$ quickly.

1 What is a sequence?

In this section you'll meet some notation used for sequences, and two different ways to specify sequences using formulas.

1.1 Sequence notation

We frequently see lists of numbers arranged in order. For example, a list of numbers can be used to represent a quantity that's varying over time, such as the midday temperature (in °C) at a particular location, recorded each day for a week:

  13, 12, 10, 10, 10, 9, 8;

or the amount of money (in £) in a savings account on each 1 January over a five-year period:

  1000.00, 1050.00, 1102.50, 1157.63, 1215.51.

In mathematics, a list of numbers is called a **sequence**, and each number in the list is called a **term** of the sequence.

A sequence that has a finite number of terms (and hence has a last term as well as a first term) is called a **finite** sequence, whereas a sequence that has an infinite number of terms is called an **infinite** sequence.

For example,

  13, 12, 10, 10, 10, 9, 8

is a finite sequence, whose first term is 13 and whose last term is 8. On the other hand, the sequence of odd natural numbers,

  1, 3, 5, 7, 9, ...,

goes on forever, with first term 1 but no last term, so this is an infinite sequence. For each term in the sequence there is always a next term, an odd number 2 greater than the one before, so the sequence has no end.

Many sequences have a structure, or pattern, that allows us to give a concise description of the sequence and helps us to understand its behaviour. For example, the sequence $1, 3, 5, 7, 9, \ldots$ has a simple mathematical structure; each term is exactly 2 more than the previous term:

  $1 + 2 = 3, \quad 3 + 2 = 5, \quad 5 + 2 = 7, \quad 7 + 2 = 9, \quad \ldots.$

The savings account sequence 1000, 1050, ..., 1215.51 also has a simple structure, though this is less obvious. For this sequence, you can check that, to three significant figures:

$$\frac{1050}{1000} = 1.05, \quad \frac{1102.50}{1050} = 1.05, \quad \frac{1157.63}{1102.50} = 1.05, \quad \frac{1215.51}{1157.63} = 1.05,$$

so each term is 1.05 times the previous term (approximately, at least).

This pattern arises because the savings account pays compound interest of 5% per annum, and there have been no withdrawals. We consider this sequence again in Section 2.

The last two fractions above are not *exactly* equal to 1.05 because the numbers in the sequence have been rounded to two decimal places, that is, to the nearest penny. Without this rounding the sequence would be

$$1000.00, \quad 1050.00, \quad 1102.50, \quad 1157.625, \quad 1215.506\,25,$$

for which each term is exactly 1.05 times the previous term.

There's no reason to suppose that the temperature sequence above has any simple mathematical structure, since it is obtained by making independent measurements each day. In this unit, we'll investigate various types of sequence that *do* have simple underlying mathematical structures. Such sequences arise in various real-world situations and have many applications.

First, however, here's some notation associated with sequences. In elementary algebra, we use letters such as $a, b, c, x, y, z, A, B, C$, and so on, to represent variables. With a sequence, we represent the terms by using one particular letter with an attached subscript; this subscript is an integer that indicates which term of the sequence is referred to. Thus the sequence

$$a_1, \ a_2, \ a_3, \ \ldots, \ a_{10}$$

has 10 terms, the first being a_1 and the last being a_{10}. This notation is called **subscript notation** (or **suffix notation**). The terms above are read as: a-one (or a-sub-one), a-two (or a-sub-two), and so on. (You've seen subscripts used previously, for coordinates in Unit 2, and for vector components in Unit 5.)

Sometimes it is possible to choose an appropriate letter for a sequence. For example, you might use t for the temperature sequence. Since the first term is 13, you write $t_1 = 13$, and so on, giving

$$t_1 = 13, \quad t_2 = 12, \quad t_3 = 10, \quad t_4 = 10, \quad t_5 = 10, \quad t_6 = 9, \quad t_7 = 8.$$

You can use either upper- or lower-case letters to represent sequences. The use of appropriate letters can be helpful, especially when dealing with several sequences, but it is not necessary and indeed not always possible.

If you want to refer to a general term of a sequence, rather than a particular term, then you use a letter for the subscript as well, as follows:

a_n denotes the term of the sequence with subscript n.

Here n represents a natural number in the appropriate range; for example, for the sequence $a_1, a_2, \ldots, a_{10}$, the range of n is $1, 2, \ldots, 10$. In mathematics, the letter n often represents a natural number or, more generally, an integer; that is, one of the numbers $\ldots, -2, -1, 0, 1, 2, \ldots$. Other letters commonly used to represent integers are i, j, k, l, m, p and q.

The notation a_n denotes an individual term of a sequence – the term with subscript n. You can represent a whole sequence by using notation such as the following:

$(a_n)_{n=1}^{17}$ denotes the finite sequence $a_1, \ a_2, \ a_3, \ \ldots, \ a_{17}$

$(a_n)_{n=1}^{\infty}$ denotes the infinite sequence $a_1, \ a_2, \ a_3, \ \ldots$.

Because infinite sequences occur frequently, we use the abbreviated notation (a_n), with no subscript values, to mean $(a_n)_{n=1}^{\infty}$. That is,

(a_n) denotes the infinite sequence a_1, a_2, a_3, ...

The variable n in the notation for a sequence is sometimes referred to as the **index variable** for the sequence. It's a **dummy variable**: you can change it to any other variable name you like without changing the meaning. For example,

$(a_n)_{n=1}^{\infty}$, $(a_i)_{i=1}^{\infty}$ and $(a_k)_{k=1}^{\infty}$

all denote the same sequence $a_1, a_2, a_3, \ldots$. (The idea of a dummy variable featured also in Unit 8.)

Activity 1   Using sequence notation

Consider the infinite sequence

$(b_n)_{n=1}^{\infty}$ with terms 1, 4, 7, 10, 13, 16, 19, ...

(a) Write down the values of b_1 and b_4.

(b) For which value of n is $b_n = 16$?

(c) Can you write down the value of b_0?

1.2 Closed forms for sequences

The notation a_n is useful when you want to specify a sequence by giving a formula for the terms. For example, suppose that you want to specify the infinite sequence of *perfect squares*:

1, 4, 9, 16, 25, ...

If you choose to represent this sequence using the letter s (for square), then

$s_1 = 1^2$, $s_2 = 2^2$, $s_3 = 3^2$, $s_4 = 4^2$, ...

For a general natural number n, we have $s_n = n^2$, which is a formula for the general term, called the **nth term**, of the sequence. To complete the specification of the sequence, you need to state the range of values of the subscript n. You do this using brackets, as follows:

$s_n = n^2$ $(n = 1, 2, 3, \ldots)$.

Note that it's important to include the range of values of n here. It tells you that for this particular sequence the first term corresponds to $n = 1$ and that the sequence continues indefinitely, rather than stopping after some number of terms.

A formula like $s_n = n^2$, for defining a sequence in terms of the subscript n, is called a **closed form** (or a **closed-form formula**). A closed form for a sequence enables you to calculate any term of the sequence directly, once you're given the value of n. Unfortunately, however, not all sequences have such a formula.

Closed form for a sequence

A **closed form** for a sequence is a formula that defines the general term a_n as an expression involving the subscript n. To specify a sequence using a closed form, two pieces of information are needed:

- the closed form
- the range of values for the subscript n.

Example 1   *Using closed forms for sequences*

For each of the sequences specified by the following closed forms and ranges of values of n, find the first four terms and the 10th term.

(a) $a_n = 2^n - n^2$ $(n = 1, 2, 3, \ldots)$

(b) $b_n = 1/n^2$ $(n = 1, 2, 3, \ldots)$

Solution

🔍 Substitute in turn $n = 1, 2, 3, 4, 10$ into the closed form for each sequence. 💬

(a) $a_1 = 2^1 - 1^2 = 1$
$\quad\ a_2 = 2^2 - 2^2 = 0$
$\quad\ a_3 = 2^3 - 3^2 = -1$
$\quad\ a_4 = 2^4 - 4^2 = 0$
$\quad\ a_{10} = 2^{10} - 10^2 = 924$

(b) $b_1 = 1/1^2 = 1$
$\quad\ b_2 = 1/2^2 = 1/4$
$\quad\ b_3 = 1/3^2 = 1/9$
$\quad\ b_4 = 1/4^2 = 1/16$
$\quad\ b_{10} = 1/10^2 = 1/100$

Here are some examples for you to try.

Activity 2   *Using closed forms*

For each of the sequences specified by the following closed forms and ranges of values of n, find the first five terms and the 100th term.

(a) $a_n = 7n$ $(n = 1, 2, 3, \ldots)$ (b) $b_n = 1/n$ $(n = 1, 2, 3, \ldots)$

(c) $c_n = (-1)^{n+1}$ $(n = 1, 2, 3, \ldots)$ (d) $d_n = (-1)^n n$ $(n = 1, 2, 3, \ldots)$

(e) $e_n = (-2)^n$ $(n = 1, 2, 3, \ldots)$

Notice the device used in Activity 2(c)–(e) to specify a sequence whose terms alternate in sign (that is, are alternately positive and negative). The expression $(-1)^n$ has value -1 when n is odd and 1 when n is even, and the expression $(-1)^{n+1}$ has value 1 when n is odd and -1 when n is even. In part (e), $(-2)^n = (-1)^n 2^n$.

If you're given some terms of a particular sequence, then you may be able to spot a closed form for the sequence by recognising the pattern involved. It's helpful to consider questions such as the following.

- Is the nth term a constant multiple of n or of some fixed power of n?

- Is the nth term a constant multiple of the nth power of some fixed number?

- Do the terms alternate in sign?

Activity 3   *Spotting closed forms*

For each of the following sequences, given by the first four terms, try to spot a closed form for the sequence. Denote the nth term of the sequence by a_n in each case. Then use your closed form to find the 10th term in the sequence.

(Don't spend more than a short time attempting each part. Some of the closed forms are harder to spot than others.)

(a) 1, 2, 3, 4, ...   (b) 2, 4, 8, 16, ...   (c) −1, 1, −1, 1, ...

(d) 1, 8, 27, 64, ...   (e) 6, −6, 6, −6, ...   (f) $\frac{1}{2}$, $\frac{2}{3}$, $\frac{3}{4}$, $\frac{4}{5}$, ...

(g) 2, −4, 6, −8, ...

When you write down a closed form for a sequence, you should usually also write down the subscript range, as demonstrated in the solution to Activity 3, so that you have fully specified the sequence.

So far you've represented sequences using the subscript 1 for the first term. For example, you've seen that you can represent a sequence as $a_1, a_2, a_3, \ldots$. This seems natural and easy to remember, but there are occasions when it is convenient to be flexible about how you represent the first term. Consider, for example, the sequence

$$1, 2, 4, 8, 16, \ldots.$$

This is a sequence of powers of 2:

$$2^0, 2^1, 2^2, 2^3, 2^4, \ldots.$$

You can specify this sequence in closed form, using $a_n = 2^n$, but only if you start numbering the subscripts from 0 rather than from 1:

$$a_n = 2^n \quad (n = 0, 1, 2, \ldots).$$

In this case, the simplicity of the formula $a_n = 2^n$ generally outweighs any inconvenience of starting with a_0. There is the possibility of confusion in having a_0 as the first term of a sequence, with a_1 as second term, and so on, but with practice this should not cause difficulties. If it were considered essential to have the first term with subscript 1, then you could specify the sequence as follows:

$b_n = 2^{n-1}$ $(n = 1, 2, 3, \ldots)$.

Then, for example, $b_1 = 2^{1-1} = 2^0 = 1$.

Further flexibility about the subscript for the first term of a sequence is sometimes useful, as illustrated in the next activity.

Activity 4   *Using a subscript other than 1 for the first term*

(a) For each of the following closed forms and ranges of values of n, find the first three terms of the sequence specified.

(i) $a_n = 3^n$ $(n = 0, 1, 2, \ldots)$

(ii) $b_n = \dfrac{1}{n(n-1)}$ $(n = 2, 3, 4, \ldots)$

(iii) $c_n = \dfrac{1}{(n+1)n}$ $(n = 1, 2, 3, \ldots)$

(b) For each of the following sequences, given by the first four terms, try to spot a closed form for the sequence, using the notation specified. Then use your closed form to find the sixth term in the sequence. (Don't spend more than a short time attempting each part.)

(i)   1, 3, 9, 27, ...   (general term d_n, first term d_0)

(ii) $\dfrac{1}{5}, \dfrac{1}{6}, \dfrac{1}{7}, \dfrac{1}{8}, \ldots$ (general term e_n, first term e_5)

(iii) $\dfrac{1}{4}, -\dfrac{1}{8}, \dfrac{1}{16}, -\dfrac{1}{32}, \ldots$ (general term f_n, first term f_2)

The sequences in parts (a)(ii) and (a)(iii) of Activity 4 illustrate the fact that two sequences whose descriptions appear to be different at first sight can actually have exactly the same terms. This activity also highlights the importance of including the range of values of n in the definition of the sequence.

It's sometimes useful to convert a closed form for a sequence into a different closed form for the same sequence, which uses a different subscript for the first term. Here's an example.

Example 2   *Changing the subscripts used for a sequence*

Consider the sequence given by the closed form

$$a_n = n(n+2) \quad (n = 1, 2, 3, \dots).$$

For the same sequence, find a closed form

$$b_n = \dots \quad (n = 0, 1, 2, \dots).$$

Solution

🔍 The value of n corresponding to each term is reduced by 1 in moving from (a_n) to (b_n), so you need to replace each occurrence of n in the formula for the term by $n + 1$, to leave the term unchanged. 💬

The required closed form is

$$b_n = (n+1)(n+1+2) \quad (n = 0, 1, 2, \dots);$$

that is,

$$b_n = (n+1)(n+3) \quad (n = 0, 1, 2, \dots).$$

🔍 As a check, the closed form for (a_n) gives

$$a_1 = 1 \times 3, \quad a_2 = 2 \times 4, \quad a_3 = 3 \times 5, \quad \dots.$$

The closed form obtained for (b_n) gives

$$b_0 = 1 \times 3, \quad b_1 = 2 \times 4, \quad b_2 = 3 \times 5, \quad \dots.$$

which is the same sequence. 💬

Activity 5   *Changing the subscripts used for sequences*

(a) For each of the sequences (a_n) given by the following closed forms, write down a closed form $b_n = \dots$ $(n = 0, 1, 2, \dots)$ that specifies the same sequence.

(i) $a_n = 2n \quad (n = 1, 2, 3, \dots)$

(ii) $a_n = 3^{n-1} \quad (n = 1, 2, 3, \dots)$

(iii) $a_n = 5 + n \quad (n = 1, 2, 3, \dots)$

(iv) $a_n = 4(n-1) \quad (n = 1, 2, 3, \dots)$

(b) For each of the sequences (a_n) given by the following closed forms, write down a closed form $b_n = \dots$ $(n = 1, 2, 3, \dots)$ that specifies the same sequence.

(i) $a_n = 0.4^n \quad (n = 0, 1, 2, \dots)$

(ii) $a_n = 5n \quad (n = 0, 1, 2, \dots)$

(iii) $a_n = \dfrac{1}{2^n} \quad (n = 0, 1, 2, \dots)$

(iv) $a_n = 2 + 3n \quad (n = 0, 1, 2, \dots)$

(c) For each of the sequences (a_n) given by the following closed forms, write down a closed form $b_n = \dots$ $(n = 2, 3, 4, \dots)$ that specifies the same sequence.

(i) $a_n = \dfrac{3^n}{n+1}$ $(n = 0, 1, 2, \dots)$

(ii) $a_n = \dfrac{1}{(n+1)(n+3)}$ $(n = 0, 1, 2 \dots)$

It's implicit in what we've done so far that where a simple pattern is evident from the first few terms of a sequence, that pattern is assumed to continue unchanged. For example, in Activity 3(d) you were asked to find a closed form for the sequence $1, 8, 27, 64, \dots$. The answer

$$a_n = n^3 \quad (n = 1, 2, 3, \dots)$$

was found by spotting that the first four terms are the cubes of $1, 2, 3, 4$, respectively, and assuming that this pattern continues. However, alternative closed forms can be written down that give the same first four terms; one of these is

$$b_n = n^3 + (n-1)(n-2)(n-3)(n-4) \quad (n = 1, 2, 3, \dots).$$

The terms of the sequence (b_n) differ from those of (a_n) from the fifth term onwards, so these are different sequences. In general, no finite number of terms can describe a sequence without ambiguity, whereas a sequence described by a closed form with a subscript range is unambiguously defined. Where sequences are described by giving the first few terms, we shall always assume that any simple pattern that is evident continues for the remainder of the sequence.

1.3   Recurrence relations for sequences

Some sequences have the property that each term (after the first) can be obtained *from the previous term* by using a formula. For example, consider the sequence with closed form $a_n = 7n$ $(n = 1, 2, 3, \dots)$. Its terms are

$$7, \ 14, \ 21, \ 28, \ 35, \ \dots.$$

Each term (after the first) of this sequence can be obtained from the previous term by adding 7:

$$a_2 = a_1 + 7, \quad a_3 = a_2 + 7, \quad a_4 = a_3 + 7, \quad \dots.$$

If a term (after the first) has subscript n, then the previous term has subscript $n - 1$, so you can write

$$a_n = a_{n-1} + 7 \quad (n = 2, 3, 4, \dots).$$

Note that the range of values of n here begins with 2 rather than 1, because 2 is the first value of n for which the equation $a_n = a_{n-1} + 7$ applies.

In a similar way, the sequence with closed form $b_n = 2^n$ $(n = 0, 1, 2, \ldots)$, whose terms are

$$1, \ 2, \ 4, \ 8, \ 16, \ \ldots,$$

has the property that each term (after the first) is always twice the previous term:

$$b_1 = 2b_0, \quad b_2 = 2b_1, \quad b_3 = 2b_2, \quad \ldots .$$

Hence you can write

$$b_n = 2b_{n-1} \quad (n = 1, 2, 3, \ldots).$$

A formula like $a_n = a_{n-1} + 7$ or $b_n = 2b_{n-1}$, which allows each term of a sequence (after the first) to be obtained from the previous term, is called a **recurrence relation**. It's more specifically a **first-order** recurrence relation because it involves only the immediately preceding term of the sequence. (A second-order recurrence relation would involve the preceding two terms, and so on.) In this module, the words 'recurrence relation' always refer to a first-order recurrence relation, unless otherwise stated.

If you have a recurrence relation for a sequence, and you also know the first term of the sequence, then in principle you can determine any term of the sequence by starting from the first term and repeatedly applying the recurrence relation. For example, from the recurrence relation

$$x_n = x_{n-1}^2 \quad (n = 2, 3, 4, \ldots),$$

and the first term $x_1 = 2$, you can successively calculate

$$x_1 = 2,$$
$$x_2 = x_1^2 = 2^2 = 4,$$
$$x_3 = x_2^2 = 4^2 = 16,$$
$$x_4 = x_3^2 = 16^2 = 256,$$

and so on. Here the expression x_1^2, for example, means $(x_1)^2$, the square of x_1.

Notice that if you keep the same recurrence relation but change the first term, x_1, then you obtain a different sequence; for example, with $x_1 = 1$, the recurrence relation above gives $x_2 = 1$, $x_3 = 1$, $x_4 = 1$, $\ldots$.

Taken together, the specification of a first term, a recurrence relation and the range of values of n for which the recurrence relation applies is called a **recurrence system**, and the resulting sequence is called a **recurrence sequence**. We display the three parts of a recurrence system as follows:

$$x_1 = 2, \qquad x_n = x_{n-1}^2 \quad (n = 2, 3, 4, \ldots);$$

the first term of the sequence is on the left, and the recurrence relation and the range of values of n are on the right. If the first term of the sequence is labelled not as x_1 but as x_0, say, then the range of values of n has to begin with 1 rather than 2, as follows:

$$x_0 = 2, \qquad x_n = x_{n-1}^2 \quad (n = 1, 2, 3, \ldots).$$

Recurrence system for a sequence

A **recurrence relation** for a sequence is an equation that defines each term other than the first as an expression involving the previous term. To specify a sequence using a **recurrence system**, three pieces of information are needed:

- the value of the first term
- the recurrence relation
- the range of values for the subscript n.

Example 3 *Using recurrence systems for sequences*

For each of the following recurrence systems, find the first five terms of the sequence specified.

(a) $a_1 = 1$, $a_n = 5a_{n-1} - 2$ $(n = 2, 3, 4, \ldots)$

(b) $b_1 = 2$, $b_n = \dfrac{1}{b_{n-1}}$ $(n = 2, 3, 4, \ldots)$

(c) $c_0 = 1$, $c_n = nc_{n-1}$ $(n = 1, 2, 3, \ldots)$

Solution

Apply the recurrence relation for each value of n in turn.

(a) $a_1 = 1$

$a_2 = 5 \times a_1 - 2 = 3$

$a_3 = 5 \times a_2 - 2 = 13$

$a_4 = 5 \times a_3 - 2 = 63$

$a_5 = 5 \times a_4 - 2 = 313$

(b) $b_1 = 2$

$b_2 = 1/b_1 = \frac{1}{2}$

$b_3 = 1/b_2 = 2$

$b_4 = 1/b_3 = \frac{1}{2}$

$b_5 = 1/b_4 = 2$

(c) $c_0 = 1$

$c_1 = 1 \times c_0 = 1$

$c_2 = 2 \times c_1 = 2$

$c_3 = 3 \times c_2 = 6$

$c_4 = 4 \times c_3 = 24$

Activity 6   *Using recurrence systems*

For each of the following recurrence systems, find the first five terms of the sequence specified.

(a) $a_1 = 0$, $a_n = 2a_{n-1} + 1$ $(n = 2, 3, 4, \ldots)$

(b) $b_1 = 1$, $b_n = b_{n-1}^2 - 1$ $(n = 2, 3, 4, \ldots)$

(c) $c_0 = 2$, $c_n = \frac{1}{2}\left(c_{n-1} + 2/c_{n-1}\right)$ $(n = 1, 2, 3, \ldots)$

In part (c), round the terms to six decimal places when writing them down, but maintain full calculator precision when calculating each term.

The sequence in Activity 6(c) has the property that it very rapidly gives good approximations to $\sqrt{2}$, as you can check by finding $\sqrt{2}$ on your calculator. A proof of this property is outside the scope of this module, but it illustrates an important use for recurrence systems, namely, that sequences defined by using recurrence systems can sometimes be used to calculate approximations to certain irrational numbers to as many decimal places as may be required.

The next box summarises what you have seen in this section.

Three ways to specify a sequence

A sequence (a_n) can be specified by giving one of the following.

- The values of the first few terms, if we assume that any simple pattern that is apparent continues.

- A closed form,

    $a_n =$ expression in n,

    and a subscript range. This permits the value of a_n to be found directly for any value of n in the subscript range.

- A recurrence system, consisting of the value of the first term, a recurrence relation,

    $a_n =$ expression involving a_{n-1},

    and a range of values of the subscript n. This permits the value of a_n to be found from the value of a_{n-1} for any value of n in the subscript range.

It's often (though not always) convenient to take the first subscript of a sequence to be 1, so to avoid constant repetition we adopt the following convention.

In the next section, you'll study two particular types of recurrence system, and investigate whether closed forms can be found for the corresponding sequences. Many sequences defined by recurrence systems do have closed forms, but not all.

2 Arithmetic and geometric sequences

In this section, we consider two types of sequence that occur frequently in practice.

2.1 Arithmetic sequences

We begin with two sequences that arise in different ways but are of a similar mathematical type.

First, consider the finite sequence

$$7.15, \ 10.50, \ 13.85, \ 17.20, \ \ldots, \ 245.00.$$

This sequence could represent the heights in metres above ground level of successive floors in a very tall building, from the first floor upwards. (The terms are similar to the heights in metres of the habitable floors of the Shard, in London.) We'll call this sequence (h_n), so $h_1 = 7.15$, $h_2 = 10.50$, $h_3 = 13.85$, and so on.

To get from any term in this sequence to the next, we *add* the same number each time:

$$7.15 + 3.35 = 10.50,$$

$$10.50 + 3.35 = 13.85,$$

$$13.85 + 3.35 = 17.20,$$

The Shard, with St Paul's Cathedral on the left

and so on. The number 3.35 occurs here because it is the height difference in metres between successive floors. Thus this sequence can be defined by the recurrence system

$$h_1 = 7.15, \qquad h_n = h_{n-1} + 3.35 \quad (n = 2, 3, 4, \ldots, 72).$$

The last value in the range of n here is 72 because, as will be confirmed later in this subsection, the last term in the sequence is h_{72}. (The 72nd floor of the Shard is about 245 metres above ground level. The total height of the building is 310 metres.)

Next, consider the finite sequence

$$1000, \ 950, \ 900, \ 850, \ \ldots, \ 0.$$

This sequence could represent the volume, measured in litres on successive Saturdays, of oil in a tank supplying a boiler that uses 50 litres of oil per week. We'll call this sequence (v_n), so $v_1 = 1000$, $v_2 = 950$, $v_3 = 900$, and so on.

Once again, to get from any term in this sequence to the next, we *add* the same number each time:

$$1000 + (-50) = 950,$$
$$950 + (-50) = 900,$$
$$900 + (-50) = 850,$$

and so on. The negative number -50 occurs here because each week the volume in the tank is *reduced* by 50 litres. Thus this sequence can be defined by the recurrence system

$$v_1 = 1000, \qquad v_n = v_{n-1} - 50 \quad (n = 2, 3, 4, \ldots, 21).$$

The last value in the range of n here is 21 because 1000 litres at 50 litres per week lasts 20 weeks, so the last term in the sequence is $v_{21} = 0$.

Any sequence with the structure demonstrated above – the addition of a fixed number to obtain the next term – is called an **arithmetic sequence**, or alternatively an **arithmetic progression**. (In this context, 'arithmetic' is pronounced with emphasis on the syllable 'met'.) Thus a general arithmetic sequence is given by the recurrence system

$$x_1 = a, \qquad x_n = x_{n-1} + d \quad (n = 2, 3, 4, \ldots),$$

where a is the first term and d is the number that's added to each term to give the next term. That is, d is the difference $x_n - x_{n-1}$ between any pair of successive terms, usually called the **common difference** of the sequence. Choosing the values of the first term a and the common difference d determines a particular arithmetic sequence; we call a and d the **parameters** of the arithmetic sequence. For example, the floor heights sequence has parameters $a = 7.15$ and $d = 3.35$, and the oil volumes sequence has parameters $a = 1000$ and $d = -50$.

An arithmetic sequence (x_n) can be finite, as for the floor heights sequence and the oil volumes sequence, or infinite. Also, the first term can be x_0 rather than x_1, in which case the sequence is given by

$$x_0 = a, \qquad x_n = x_{n-1} + d \quad (n = 1, 2, 3, \ldots).$$

Activity 7   *Recognising arithmetic sequences*

Which of the following recurrence systems define arithmetic sequences? For each arithmetic sequence, write down the values of the first term a and common difference d.

(a) $x_1 = -1, \qquad x_n = x_{n-1} + 1 \quad (n = 2, 3, 4, \ldots, 100)$

(b) $y_1 = 2, \qquad y_n = -y_{n-1} + 1 \quad (n = 2, 3, 4, \ldots)$

(c) $z_0 = 1, \qquad z_n = z_{n-1} - 1.5 \quad (n = 1, 2, 3, \ldots)$

Suppose now that you have been given the first few terms of an arithmetic sequence (x_n). How can you find its parameters a and d? Well, a is just the first term, and d is the difference $x_n - x_{n-1}$ between any two successive terms x_n and x_{n-1} in the sequence, as illustrated in the following example.

Example 4 *Finding parameters of arithmetic sequences*

(a) For the infinite arithmetic sequence (x_n) whose first four terms are

100, 95, 90, 85,

find the values of the first term a and common difference d, and write down the corresponding recurrence system. Calculate also the next two terms of the sequence.

(b) Repeat part (a) for the infinite arithmetic sequence (y_n) whose first four terms are

$\frac{1}{4}, \frac{1}{2}, \frac{3}{4}, 1$.

Solution

By the convention stated on page 15, take the first term of each sequence to have subscript 1.

Remember that to specify a recurrence system, you have to write down three things: the first term, the recurrence relation and the subscript range.

(a) The first term is $a = 100$, and the common difference is $d = 95 - 100 = -5$. So a suitable recurrence system is

$$x_1 = 100, \qquad x_n = x_{n-1} - 5 \quad (n = 2, 3, 4, \ldots).$$

The next two terms are

$$x_5 = x_4 - 5 = 85 - 5 = 80,$$
$$x_6 = x_5 - 5 = 80 - 5 = 75.$$

(b) The first term is $a = \frac{1}{4}$, and the common difference is $d = \frac{1}{2} - \frac{1}{4} = \frac{1}{4}$. So a suitable recurrence system is

$$y_1 = \frac{1}{4}, \qquad y_n = y_{n-1} + \frac{1}{4} \quad (n = 2, 3, 4, \ldots).$$

The next two terms are

$$y_5 = y_4 + \frac{1}{4} = 1 + \frac{1}{4} = \frac{5}{4},$$
$$y_6 = y_5 + \frac{1}{4} = \frac{5}{4} + \frac{1}{4} = \frac{3}{2}.$$

Activity 8 *Finding parameters of arithmetic sequences*

(a) For the infinite arithmetic sequence (x_n) whose first four terms are

$$1,\ 4,\ 7,\ 10,$$

find the values of the first term a and common difference d, and write down the corresponding recurrence system. Calculate also the next two terms of the sequence.

(b) Repeat part (a) for the infinite arithmetic sequence (y_n) whose first four terms are

$$2.1,\ 3.2,\ 4.3,\ 5.4.$$

(c) Repeat part (a) for the finite arithmetic sequence (z_n) with eleven terms, whose first four terms are

$$1,\ 0.9,\ 0.8,\ 0.7.$$

A special type of arithmetic sequence arises when the common difference d is zero. In this case, each term of the sequence is equal to the first term. Such a sequence is called a **constant sequence**. For example,

$$3,\ 3,\ 3,\ \ldots$$

is a constant sequence.

Finite arithmetic sequences

As you've seen, the method of finding the values of the parameters a and d is the same for any arithmetic sequence, whether it's finite or infinite. For an infinite sequence, the recurrence system has the form

$$x_1 = a, \qquad x_n = x_{n-1} + d \quad (n = 2, 3, 4, \ldots),$$

whereas for a finite sequence, with N terms say, the recurrence system has the form

$$x_1 = a, \qquad x_n = x_{n-1} + d \quad (n = 2, 3, 4, \ldots, N).$$

Here the final number in the range of values of n is N because the final term x_N is obtained by applying the recurrence relation with $n = N$.

If you have the first few terms and the last term of a particular finite arithmetic sequence, and you want to find a recurrence system that specifies the sequence, then you need to find not only the values of the parameters a and d, but also the subscript of the last term. To see how to do this, consider the floor heights sequence,

$$7.15,\ 10.50,\ 13.85,\ 17.20,\ \ldots,\ 245.00.$$

To find how many terms there are in the sequence, you need to work out how many times the common difference 3.35 has been added to the first

term 7.15 to produce the last term 245.00. The total amount added is
$245.00 - 7.15$, so the number of times that 3.35 has been added is

$$\frac{245.00 - 7.15}{3.35} = 71.$$

So there are 71 terms of the sequence after the first term, and hence there
are 72 terms altogether. The corresponding recurrence system for the floor
heights sequence is therefore

$$h_1 = 7.15, \qquad h_n = h_{n-1} + 3.35 \quad (n = 2, 3, 4, \ldots, 72),$$

as stated earlier. In general, the number of terms of a finite non-constant
arithmetic sequence is given by

$$\text{number of terms} = \frac{\text{last term} - \text{first term}}{\text{common difference}} + 1.$$

That is, if a finite arithmetic sequence has N terms, with first term x_1, last
term x_N and common difference d, then

$$N = \frac{x_N - x_1}{d} + 1. \tag{1}$$

You'll meet this equation in a slightly different form in the next subsection.

Activity 9 *Finding the number of terms in a finite arithmetic
sequence*

(a) Find the number of terms in the finite arithmetic sequence

$$1000, \ 970, \ 940, \ 910, \ \ldots, \ 10.$$

(b) Hence write down a recurrence system for this sequence, denoting the
nth term by x_n.

2.2 Closed forms for arithmetic sequences

Arithmetic sequences have a particularly simple form: to get from one
term to the next, you add the same number each time. This pattern allows
you to obtain closed forms for such sequences, which makes them easier to
handle mathematically.

To see how to do this, consider the sequence

$$5, \ 8, \ 11, \ 14, \ \ldots, \ 38.$$

This is a finite arithmetic sequence with parameters $a = 5$, $d = 3$ and
12 terms, which can be described by the recurrence system

$$b_1 = 5, \qquad b_n = b_{n-1} + 3 \quad (n = 2, 3, 4, \ldots, 12).$$

So $b_1 = 5$, $b_2 = 8$, and so on, up to $b_{12} = 38$. The way in which the terms
of this sequence are obtained from the recurrence relation can be pictured
as follows.

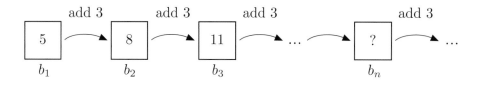

Figure 1   Obtaining the terms of an arithmetic sequence

Starting from $b_1 = 5$,

> to obtain b_2, we add 3,

> to obtain b_3, we add 3 twice,

> to obtain b_4, we add 3 three times,

and so on. In each case the number of added 3s is one fewer than the subscript on the left. Thus, to obtain the general term b_n, you have to add 3 exactly $n - 1$ times; that is, you add $3(n - 1)$. This gives the value of the general term as

$$b_n = 5 + 3(n - 1) \quad (n = 1, 2, 3, \ldots, 12),$$

which can be simplified to

$$b_n = 3n + 2 \quad (n = 1, 2, 3, \ldots, 12).$$

(Notice that the first value in this range of n is 1, whereas the first value in the range of the recurrence relation was 2.)

For example, using this closed form we find that $b_4 = 3 \times 4 + 2 = 14$, as expected.

The reasoning above can be applied to a *general* arithmetic sequence, to obtain a formula for the nth term. Consider the arithmetic sequence given by the recurrence system

$$x_1 = a, \qquad x_n = x_{n-1} + d \quad (n = 2, 3, 4, \ldots).$$

Figure 2 shows how each successive term is obtained from the term before.

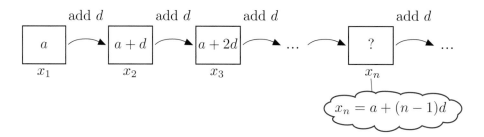

Figure 2   Obtaining the terms of a general arithmetic sequence

To obtain a general term x_n, you start with $x_1 = a$ and add d exactly $n - 1$ times, so $x_n = a + (n - 1)d$.

Closed form for an arithmetic sequence

The arithmetic sequence with recurrence system

$$x_1 = a, \qquad x_n = x_{n-1} + d \quad (n = 2, 3, 4, \ldots)$$

has the closed form and subscript range

$$x_n = a + (n-1)d \quad (n = 1, 2, 3, \ldots).$$

If you have a finite arithmetic sequence, with N terms say, then it has the closed form stated in the box above, but a finite subscript range:

$$x_n = a + (n-1)d \quad (n = 1, 2, 3, \ldots, N).$$

It's easy to check that the formula in the box above gives the correct answers for the first few terms. For example, when $n = 1$ and $n = 2$, the formula gives the correct values $x_1 = a$ and $x_2 = a + d$.

You can simplify the expression $a + (n-1)d$ in the closed form for an arithmetic sequence when a and d have particular values. For example,

$$5 + 3(n-1) = 3n + 2.$$

The next example and activity are about applying the closed form in the box above to particular sequences.

Example 5 *Finding a closed form for an arithmetic sequence*

Find a closed form for the arithmetic sequence $5, 9, 13, 17, \ldots$, given by the recurrence system

$$x_1 = 5, \qquad x_n = x_{n-1} + 4 \quad (n = 2, 3, 4, \ldots).$$

Check that your answer gives the correct value for the fourth term, and also calculate the 10th term of the sequence.

Solution

🔍 Apply the closed-form formula $x_n = a + (n-1)d$ $(n = 1, 2, 3, \ldots)$. 💬

Since $a = 5$ and $d = 4$, the closed form is

$$x_n = 5 + 4(n-1)$$
$$= 4n + 1 \quad (n = 1, 2, 3, \ldots).$$

This gives $x_4 = 4 \times 4 + 1 = 17$, as expected, and also

$$x_{10} = 4 \times 10 + 1 = 41.$$

Activity 10   *Finding a closed form for an arithmetic sequence*

(a) Find a closed form for the arithmetic sequence $1, 4, 7, 10, \ldots$, given by the recurrence system

$$x_1 = 1, \qquad x_n = x_{n-1} + 3 \quad (n = 2, 3, 4, \ldots).$$

Check that your answer gives the correct value for the fourth term, and also calculate the 10th term of the sequence.

(b) Repeat part (a) for the arithmetic sequence $2.1, 3.2, 4.3, 5.4, \ldots$, given by the recurrence system

$$y_1 = 2.1, \qquad y_n = y_{n-1} + 1.1 \quad (n = 2, 3, 4, \ldots).$$

(c) Repeat part (a) for the arithmetic sequence $1, 0.9, 0.8, 0.7, \ldots, 0$, given by the recurrence system

$$z_1 = 1, \qquad z_n = z_{n-1} - 0.1 \quad (n = 2, 3, 4, \ldots, 11).$$

(You were asked to write down the recurrence systems for these sequences in Activity 8.)

Note that if a finite arithmetic sequence has last term x_N, then the closed form that you've met gives

$$x_N = a + (N - 1)d,$$

which can be written as

$$x_N = x_1 + (N - 1)d.$$

This is a rearrangement of equation (1) on page 19, so the two formulas are really just saying the same thing.

Finally, note that an arithmetic sequence with first term a and common difference d has an alternative closed form that's sometimes useful. The closed form that you've met,

$$x_n = a + (n - 1)d \quad (n = 1, 2, 3, \ldots),$$

holds when the subscript n takes values starting from 1. If instead you choose to have the subscript n start from 0, then the closed form is

$$y_n = a + nd \quad (n = 0, 1, 2, \ldots).$$

2.3 Geometric sequences

Next we investigate a different type of sequence. We begin once again with two sequences from real-world contexts.

First, consider the savings account sequence,

1000.00, 1050.00, 1102.50, 1157.63, 1215.51.

This represents the amount of money (in £) in a savings account on each successive 1 January over a five-year period. As pointed out in Subsection 1.1, the terms of this sequence after the third term have been rounded to two decimal places, since they are amounts of money and hence need to be expressed to the nearest penny. The corresponding sequence with unrounded values is

1000, 1050, 1102.5, 1157.625, 1215.506 25.

We shall call this unrounded sequence (s_n), so $s_1 = 1000$, $s_2 = 1050$, $s_3 = 1102.50$, and so on.

To get from any term in this sequence to the next, we *multiply* by the same number each time:

$1.05 \times 1000 = 1050,$

$1.05 \times 1050 = 1102.50,$

$1.05 \times 1102.50 = 1157.625,$

and so on. The number 1.05 occurs here because the interest added at the end of each year is 0.05 times (that is, 5% of) the amount in the account at the *beginning* of the year. Thus this sequence can be defined by the recurrence system

$s_1 = 1000, \qquad s_n = 1.05 s_{n-1} \quad (n = 2, 3, 4, 5).$

Here the range of values of n stops at 5, since the last term in the sequence is s_5. Note that, where rounding is required, you should carry out the complete calculation for each term using exact arithmetic first and round only at the end, rather than rounding at each application of the recurrence relation.

Next, consider the sequence

2000, 1400, 980, 686, 480.2, ...

This could represent the heights, measured in millimetres, of successive bounces of a ball that is assumed to rebound to 70% of the height from which it falls. We shall call this sequence (h_n), so $h_1 = 2000$, $h_2 = 1400$, $h_3 = 980$, and so on.

Once again, to get from any term in this sequence to the next, we *multiply* by the same number each time:

$0.7 \times 2000 = 1400,$

$0.7 \times 1400 = 980,$

$0.7 \times 980 = 686,$

and so on. The number 0.7 occurs here because each successive height is 70% of the previous one. Thus this sequence can be defined by the recurrence system

$$h_1 = 2000, \qquad h_n = 0.7h_{n-1} \quad (n = 2, 3, 4, \ldots),$$

where we have assumed (unrealistically) that the ball will bounce infinitely many times.

Any sequence with the structure demonstrated above – multiplication by a fixed number to obtain the next term – is called a **geometric sequence**, or alternatively a **geometric progression**. Thus a general geometric sequence is given by the recurrence system

$$x_1 = a, \qquad x_n = rx_{n-1} \quad (n = 2, 3, 4, \ldots),$$

where a is the first term and r is the number by which you multiply each term to obtain the next term. That is, r is the constant ratio x_n/x_{n-1} of any two successive terms, often called the **common ratio** of the sequence. Choosing the values of the first term a and common ratio r determines a particular geometric sequence; we call a and r the **parameters** of the geometric sequence. For example, the savings account sequence (s_n) has parameters $a = 1000$ and $r = 1.05$, and the bouncing ball sequence (h_n) has parameters $a = 2000$ and $r = 0.7$.

Geometric sequins

A geometric sequence (x_n) can be finite, as for the savings account sequence, or infinite, as for the bouncing ball sequence. The first term can be x_0 rather than x_1, in which case the sequence is given by the recurrence system

$$x_0 = a, \qquad x_n = rx_{n-1} \quad (n = 1, 2, 3, \ldots).$$

Notice that when $r = 1$ we obtain the constant sequence $a, a, a, \ldots$, so constant sequences are not only a special type of arithmetic sequence, as you saw earlier, but also a special type of geometric sequence.

Activity 11   *Recognising geometric sequences*

Which of the following recurrence systems define geometric sequences? For each geometric sequence, write down the values of the first term a and common ratio r.

(a) $x_1 = -1, \qquad x_n = 3x_{n-1} \quad (n = 2, 3, 4, \ldots)$

(b) $y_0 = 1, \qquad y_n = -0.9y_{n-1} \quad (n = 1, 2, 3, \ldots)$

(c) $z_1 = 2, \qquad z_n = -z_{n-1} + 1 \quad (n = 2, 3, 4, \ldots)$

Suppose now that you know the first few terms of a geometric sequence (x_n) and you want to find its parameters. As with arithmetic sequences, the parameter a is just the first term. The other parameter, r, is the ratio of any pair of successive terms.

The next example and activity are about finding the parameters for some geometric sequences, and so obtaining recurrence systems for these sequences.

Example 6   *Finding parameters of geometric sequences*

(a) For the infinite geometric sequence (x_n) whose first four terms are

$$2, \ -3, \ 4.5, \ -6.75,$$

find the values of the first term a and common ratio r, and write down the corresponding recurrence system. Hence calculate the next two terms of the sequence, to three decimal places.

(b) Repeat part (a) for the infinite geometric sequence (y_n) whose first four terms are

$$100, \ 99, \ 98.01, \ 97.0299,$$

calculating the next two terms to three significant figures.

Solution

🗨 Using the convention stated on page 15, take the first term of each sequence to have subscript 1.

Remember that to specify a recurrence system, you have to write down three things: the first term, the recurrence relation and the subscript range. 💬

(a) The first term is $a = 2$, and the common ratio is $r = (-3)/2 = -1.5$. So the recurrence system is

$$x_1 = 2, \qquad x_n = -1.5x_{n-1} \quad (n = 2, 3, 4, \ldots).$$

The next two terms are

$$x_5 = -1.5x_4 = -1.5 \times (-6.75) = 10.125$$
$$x_6 = -1.5x_5 = -1.5 \times 10.125 = -15.1875 = -15.188 \text{ (to 3 d.p.)}.$$

(b) The first term is $a = 100$, and the common ratio is $r = 99/100 = 0.99$. So the recurrence system is

$$y_1 = 100, \quad y_n = 0.99y_{n-1} \quad (n = 2, 3, 4, \ldots).$$

The next two terms are

$$y_5 = 0.99y_4$$
$$= 0.99 \times 97.0299$$
$$= 96.059\,601 = 96.1 \text{ (to 3 s.f.)},$$

$$y_6 = 0.99y_5$$
$$= 0.99 \times 96.059\,601$$
$$= 95.099\,004\ldots = 95.1 \text{ (to 3 s.f.)}.$$

Activity 12   *Finding parameters of geometric sequences*

(a) For the infinite geometric sequence (x_n) whose first four terms are

$$1, \tfrac{1}{2}, \tfrac{1}{4}, \tfrac{1}{8},$$

find the values of the first term a and common ratio r, and write down the corresponding recurrence system. Calculate also the next two terms of the sequence.

(b) Repeat part (a) for the infinite geometric sequence (y_n) whose first four terms are

$$4.2, \ 7.14, \ 12.138, \ 20.6346.$$

Give the next two terms to three decimal places.

(c) Repeat part (a) for the infinite geometric sequence (z_n) whose first four terms are

$$2, \ -2, \ 2, \ -2.$$

Finite geometric sequences

The method of finding values for the parameters a and r is the same for any geometric sequence, whether it is finite or infinite. However, for a finite sequence you may need to find how many terms there are, as you did for finite arithmetic sequences.

For example, suppose that the savings account sequence is changed by lengthening the period over which the account balance accumulates, giving this sequence of annual balances:

$$1000.00, \ 1050.00, \ 1102.50, \ 1157.63, \ \ldots, \ 2078.93.$$

Here, as before, the amounts are rounded, after their calculation, to two decimal places (that is, to the nearest penny, since the amounts are measured in £). As before, the interest rate is 5% per year, and hence each term (before rounding) is 1.05 times the previous term. How can you find the number of years for which the money is kept in the account? In other words, how many terms are there in the sequence?

Apart from the rounding that takes place, this is a finite geometric sequence with first term 1000, last term 2078.93 and common ratio 1.05. In order to determine how many terms there are in the sequence, N say, you need to find how many times $s_1 = 1000$ has to be multiplied by 1.05 in order to obtain $s_N = 2078.93$. Since progressing from s_1 to s_N involves $N - 1$ multiplications by 1.05, we have

$$1000 \times 1.05^{N-1} = 2078.93.$$

This is an exponential equation of a type that you saw how to solve in Subsection 4.4 of Unit 3. Dividing through by 1000 and taking the natural logarithm of both sides gives

$$1.05^{N-1} = \frac{2078.93}{1000} = 2.078\,93$$
$$(N-1)\ln 1.05 = \ln 2.078\,93$$
$$N = 1 + \frac{\ln 2.078\,93}{\ln 1.05} = 16.0000 \quad (\text{to } 4\,\text{d.p.}).$$

(Recall that the value of s_N has been rounded to two decimal places, so it is not surprising that the outcome for N is not exactly an integer.)

Hence there are 16 terms in the sequence, and the corresponding recurrence system is

$$s_1 = 1000, \qquad s_n = 1.05 s_{n-1} \quad (n = 2, 3, 4, \dots, 16).$$

The same argument can be applied in the general case. If the finite geometric sequence $x_1, x_2, x_3, \dots, x_N$ has common ratio r, then you obtain x_N from x_1 by multiplying by r exactly $N-1$ times. That is,

$$x_N = x_1 r^{N-1}.$$

So you can find the number of terms, N, in the sequence by solving the following equation for N:

$$r^{N-1} = \frac{x_N}{x_1}.$$

You can always do this by using logarithms, as above (except in the simple special cases where $x_1 = 0$, $r = 0$ or $r = \pm 1$). However, care is needed if $r < 0$. In this case, you can find N by solving the equation $|r|^{N-1} = |x_N/x_1|$ by using logarithms.

Here is an example for you to try.

Activity 13   *Finding the number of terms in a finite geometric sequence*

(a) Find the number of terms in the finite geometric sequence (z_n) whose terms are

$$7,\ 35,\ 175,\ 875,\ \dots,\ 2\,734\,375.$$

(b) Hence write down a recurrence system for this sequence.

The situation posed above for the savings account, in which $s_N = 2078.93$ is known but N is unknown, is somewhat artificial. A more realistic question is: how many years will it take for an initial sum of £1000, placed in a savings account paying 5% interest per year, to double in value? In other words, what is the smallest value of N for which $s_N \geq 2000$?

This question can be answered with a similar approach to that above, by solving the equation

$$1000 \times 1.05^{N-1} = 2000.$$

The solution is given by

$$N = 1 + \frac{\ln 2}{\ln 1.05} = 15.2067 \quad \text{(to 4 d.p.).}$$

This shows that when $N = 15$ the account balance has not yet reached twice its initial value, whereas when $N = 16$ it has more than doubled.

2.4 Closed forms for geometric sequences

Geometric sequences, like arithmetic sequences, have a particularly simple form: to get from one term to the next, you multiply by the same number each time. This pattern allows you to obtain a closed form for such sequences.

To see how to do this, consider the bouncing ball sequence,

$$2000, \ 1400, \ 980, \ 686, \ 480.2, \ \ldots.$$

This is a geometric sequence with parameters $a = 2000$ and $r = 0.7$, which can be defined as

$$h_1 = 2000, \qquad h_n = 0.7 h_{n-1} \quad (n = 2, 3, 4, \ldots).$$

The way in which the terms of this sequence are obtained from the recurrence relation can be pictured as follows.

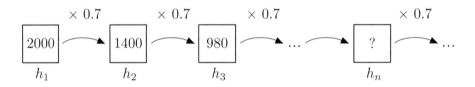

Figure 3   Obtaining the terms of the bouncing ball sequence

Starting from $h_1 = 2000$,

to obtain h_2, you multiply by 0.7,

to obtain h_3, you multiply by 0.7 twice, i.e. by 0.7^2,

to obtain h_4, you multiply by 0.7 three times, i.e. by 0.7^3,

and so on. To obtain the general term h_n, you have to multiply by 0.7 exactly $n - 1$ times; that is, you multiply by 0.7^{n-1}. This gives the value of the general term as $2000 \times 0.7^{n-1}$, so the closed form is

$$h_n = 2000 \times 0.7^{n-1} \quad (n = 1, 2, 3, \ldots).$$

For example, using this closed form you find that $h_4 = 2000 \times 0.7^3 = 686$, as expected.

The reasoning above can be applied to a *general* geometric sequence to obtain a formula for the nth term. Consider the geometric sequence given by the recurrence system

$$x_1 = a, \qquad x_n = r x_{n-1} \quad (n = 2, 3, 4, \ldots).$$

Figure 4 shows how each successive term is obtained from the term before.

Figure 4   Obtaining the terms of a general geometric sequence

To obtain a general term x_n, you start with $x_1 = a$ and multiply by r exactly $n-1$ times, so $x_n = ar^{n-1}$.

> **Closed form for a geometric sequence**
>
> The geometric sequence with recurrence system
> $$x_1 = a, \qquad x_n = rx_{n-1} \quad (n = 2, 3, 4, \ldots)$$
> has the closed form and subscript range
> $$x_n = ar^{n-1} \quad (n = 1, 2, 3, \ldots).$$

If you have a finite geometric sequence, with N terms say, then it has the closed form stated in the box above, but a finite subscript range:
$$x_n = ar^{n-1} \quad (n = 1, 2, 3, \ldots, N).$$

Once again, you can check that this formula gives the correct answers for the first few terms. For example, in the cases $n = 1$ and $n = 2$, the formula gives the correct values $x_1 = a$ and $x_2 = ar$. Also, if the ratio is $r = 1$, then you obtain the constant sequence $x_n = a$ $(n = 1, 2, 3, \ldots)$, as expected.

The next example and activity are about applying the closed form in the box above to particular sequences.

Example 7   *Finding a closed form for a geometric sequence*

Find a closed form for the geometric sequence $2, 6, 18, 54, \ldots$, given by the recurrence system
$$x_1 = 2, \qquad x_n = 3x_{n-1} \quad (n = 2, 3, 4, \ldots).$$

Check that your answer gives the correct value for the fourth term, and also calculate the 10th term of the sequence.

Solution

🗨 Apply the closed-form formula $x_n = ar^{n-1}$ $(n = 1, 2, 3, \ldots)$. 🗨

Since $a = 2$ and $r = 3$, the closed form is

$$x_n = 2 \times 3^{n-1} \quad (n = 1, 2, 3, \ldots).$$

This gives $x_4 = 2 \times 3^{4-1} = 54$, as expected, and also

$$x_{10} = 2 \times 3^{10-1} = 2 \times 3^9 = 39\,366.$$

Activity 14   *Finding a closed form for a geometric sequence*

(a) Find a closed form for the geometric sequence $1, \frac{1}{2}, \frac{1}{4}, \frac{1}{8}, \ldots$, given by the recurrence system

$$x_1 = 1, \qquad x_n = \tfrac{1}{2}x_{n-1} \quad (n = 2, 3, 4, \ldots).$$

Check that your answer gives the correct value for the fourth term, and also calculate the 10th term of the sequence (correct to four significant figures).

(b) Repeat part (a) for the geometric sequence
4.2, 7.14, 12.138, 20.6346, $\ldots$, given by the recurrence system

$$y_1 = 4.2, \qquad y_n = 1.7y_{n-1} \quad (n = 2, 3, 4, \ldots).$$

(c) Repeat part (a) for the geometric sequence $2, -2, 2, -2, \ldots$, given by the recurrence system

$$z_1 = 2, \qquad z_n = -z_{n-1} \quad (n = 2, 3, 4, \ldots).$$

(You were asked to write down the recurrence systems for these sequences in Activity 12.)

Finally, note that the geometric sequence with first term a and common ratio r has an alternative closed form that's sometimes useful. The closed form that you've met,

$$x_n = ar^{n-1} \quad (n = 1, 2, 3, \ldots),$$

holds when the subscript n takes values starting from 1. If instead you choose to have the subscript n start from 0, then the closed form is

$$y_n = ar^n \quad (n = 0, 1, 2, \ldots).$$

3 Graphs and long-term behaviour

In this section you'll see how the information contained in a sequence can be plotted on a graph. You'll then look at what can be said about the behaviour of a sequence after a large number of terms.

3.1   Graphs of sequences

In Unit 3 you were introduced to the idea of a function. You can think of any sequence as a function whose domain is the set of natural numbers $\{1, 2, 3, \ldots\}$. For example, you can think of the sequence

1, 4, 7, 10, 13, ...

as the function for which the input 1 gives the output 1, the input 2 gives the output 4, the input 3 gives the output 7, and so on, as shown in the mapping diagram in Figure 5.

In general, the sequence $(x_n)_{n=1}^{\infty}$ defines a function for which each input number n gives the output x_n, as shown in Figure 6. If you want the subscript of the first term of the sequence to be 0 rather than 1, then you should take the domain of the function to be $\{0, 1, 2, \ldots\}$ rather than $\{1, 2, 3, \ldots\}$. You can make similar adjustments for other possible ranges of subscripts.

Functions can be represented by graphs, and this is in particular true of sequences. Each term x_n corresponds to a point (n, x_n) on the graph. The next example demonstrates how to plot a graph for a sequence.

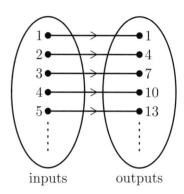

Figure 5   A sequence viewed as a function

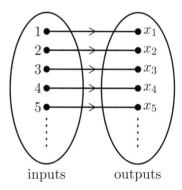

Figure 6   A general sequence viewed as a function

Example 8   *Plotting the graph of an arithmetic sequence*

Plot a graph for the first six terms of the arithmetic sequence given by the closed form

$$x_n = 3n - 2 \quad (n = 1, 2, 3, \ldots).$$

Solution

The sequence is $1, 4, 7, 10, 13, 16, \ldots$.

🗨 Plot the points (n, x_n) for $n = 1, 2, 3, \ldots, 6$. 🗨

The points to be plotted are

$$(1, 1), \ (2, 4), \ (3, 7), \ (4, 10), \ (5, 13), \ (6, 16).$$

The graph for the first six terms is as follows.

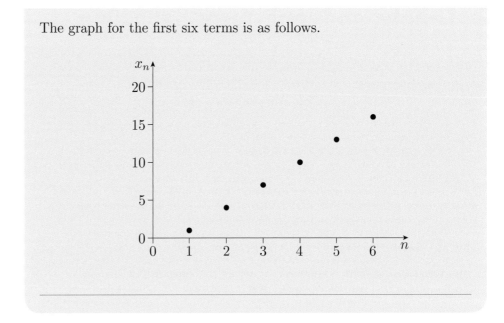

Activity 15   *Plotting the graph of an arithmetic sequence*

Plot a graph for the first six terms of the arithmetic sequence given by the recurrence system

$$z_1 = 1, \qquad z_n = z_{n-1} - 0.1 \quad (n = 2, 3, 4, \dots).$$

Notice that, in each of Example 8 and Activity 15, the graph of the sequence consists of points that lie on a straight line. This happens for every arithmetic sequence. To see why, consider the arithmetic sequence in Example 8, which is given by

$$x_n = 3n - 2 \quad (n = 1, 2, 3, \dots).$$

This equation defines x_n as a *linear* function of n, as introduced in Subsection 1.6 of Unit 3. So it is the equation of a straight line, with n and x_n in place of the usual variables x and y, respectively. You can read off the gradient, 3, in the usual way. (You can also read off the vertical intercept, but it has no relevance here since 0 is not in the domain of the function.) However, the graph of the arithmetic sequence consists only of those isolated points on the line that have first coordinate $n = 1, 2, 3, \dots$, rather than the whole straight line. This graph and the straight line on which it lies are shown in Figure 7.

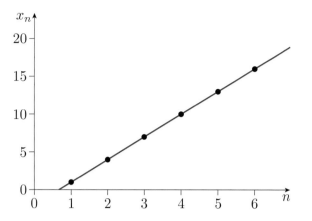

Figure 7   The graph of an arithmetic sequence lying on a straight line

In general, the arithmetic sequence with first term a and common difference d has the closed form

$$x_n = a + (n-1)d \quad (n = 1, 2, 3, \ldots),$$

which can be rearranged as

$$x_n = dn + (a - d) \quad (n = 1, 2, 3, \ldots).$$

So its graph consists of points that lie on a straight line with gradient d.

Note that in the particular case $d = 0$, the straight line has gradient zero and so is horizontal. Correspondingly, the arithmetic sequence is a constant sequence, $a, a, a, \ldots$.

We turn next to the graphs of geometric sequences.

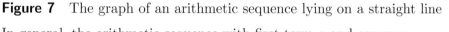

Example 9   *Plotting the graph of a geometric sequence*

Plot a graph for the first six terms of the geometric sequence

$$x_n = \left(\tfrac{1}{2}\right)^{n-1} \quad (n = 1, 2, 3, \ldots).$$

Solution

The sequence is $1, \tfrac{1}{2}, \tfrac{1}{4}, \tfrac{1}{8}, \tfrac{1}{16}, \tfrac{1}{32}, \ldots$.

Plot the points (n, x_n) for $n = 1, 2, 3, \ldots, 6$.

The points to be plotted are

$$(1, 1), \ (2, \tfrac{1}{2}), \ (3, \tfrac{1}{4}), \ (4, \tfrac{1}{8}), \ (5, \tfrac{1}{16}), \ (6, \tfrac{1}{32}).$$

The graph showing the first six terms is as follows.

In each part of the next activity, your first task is to calculate the terms for which the corresponding points are to be plotted.

Activity 16   *Plotting the graphs of geometric sequences*

(a) Plot a graph for the first six terms of the sequence given by the recurrence system

$$y_1 = 4.2, \qquad y_n = 1.7 y_{n-1} \quad (n = 2, 3, 4, \dots).$$

(b) Repeat part (a) for the first five terms of the sequence given by the closed form

$$c_n = (-1)^{n+1} \quad (n = 1, 2, 3, \dots).$$

In Example 9 the common ratio of the geometric sequence is $r = \frac{1}{2}$ and the graph is decreasing, whereas in Activity 16(a) the common ratio is $r = 1.7$ and the graph is increasing. In each case, the graph consists of points that lie on the graph of an exponential growth or decay function. You saw in Subsection 4.6 of Unit 3 that an *exponential growth* or *decay function* is a function of the form $f(x) = ae^{kx}$, where a and k are non-zero constants. Such a function can also be written in the form $f(x) = ab^x$, where a and b are constants with $a \neq 0$, $b > 0$ and $b \neq 1$. If $b > 1$, then f is an exponential growth function, whereas if $0 < b < 1$, then f is an exponential decay function.

For example, consider the sequence from Example 9. It has the closed form

$$x_n = \left(\tfrac{1}{2}\right)^{n-1} \quad (n = 1, 2, 3, \dots),$$

which can be rearranged as $x_n = 2\left(\tfrac{1}{2}\right)^n$, and this is the formula for an exponential decay function, with n and x_n in place of the usual variables x and y, respectively. (Comparing this equation with the general form of an exponential decay function, from above, we have $a = 2$ and $b = \frac{1}{2}$.)

However, the graph of the geometric sequence consists only of those isolated points on the exponential decay curve that have first coordinate $n = 1, 2, 3, \ldots$, rather than the whole curve. The graph and the exponential decay curve on which it lies are shown in Figure 8.

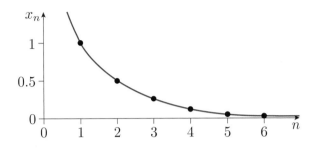

Figure 8   The graph of a geometric sequence lying on the graph of an exponential decay function

As another example, consider the sequence (y_n) from Activity 16(a). It has the closed form $y_n = 4.2 \times 1.7^{n-1}$, which can also be written as $y_n = (4.2/1.7) \times 1.7^n$; that is, $y_n = \frac{42}{17} \times 1.7^n$. So the points of this graph lie on the graph of the exponential growth function $f(x) = ab^x$ with $a = \frac{42}{17}$ and $b = 1.7$.

In general, the geometric sequence with first term a and common ratio r has the closed form

$$x_n = ar^{n-1} \quad (n = 1, 2, 3, \ldots),$$

which can be rearranged as

$$x_n = \left(\frac{a}{r}\right) r^n \quad (n = 1, 2, 3, \ldots),$$

provided that $r \neq 0$. If $r > 0$ and $r \neq 1$, then the graph of this geometric sequence consists of points that lie on the graph of an exponential growth or decay function.

Plotting graphs of sequences with a computer

When you plot the graphs of sequences by hand, you can usually plot only a small number of points. In the next activity you can find out how to use a computer to plot graphs of sequences showing many points. This work will prepare you for studying the long-term behaviour of sequences in the next subsection.

Activity 17   *Plotting graphs of sequences with a computer*

Work through Subsection 11.1 of the *Computer algebra guide*.

3.2　Long-term behaviour of sequences

A graph of a sequence can show information about the sequence only for a limited number of terms. We now investigate what can be said about the **long-term behaviour** of infinite sequences, that is, how each sequence will develop as more and more terms are considered. To start with, here's some terminology that's useful for describing the long-term behaviour of sequences.

Terminology for long-term behaviour

First, we use the words *increasing* and *decreasing* for sequences in much the same way as was introduced for functions in Subsection 1.4 of Unit 3. A sequence (x_n) is **increasing** if $x_{n-1} < x_n$ for each pair of sucessive terms x_{n-1} and x_n, and **decreasing** if $x_{n-1} > x_n$ for each pair of successive terms x_{n-1} and x_n. The graphs in Figure 9 illustrate how this terminology applies. The sequences in (e) and (f) are neither increasing nor decreasing.

Next, suppose that all the terms of a sequence (x_n) lie within some interval $[-A, A]$, where A is a fixed positive number, as illustrated in Figure 9(e), for example. Then we say that the sequence (x_n) is **bounded**. If there is no fixed value of A, however large, for which all the terms of the sequence (x_n) lie within the interval $[-A, A]$, then we say that the sequence (x_n) is **unbounded**, and also that the terms of the sequence become **arbitrarily large**. Again, the graphs in Figure 9 illustrate how this terminology applies.

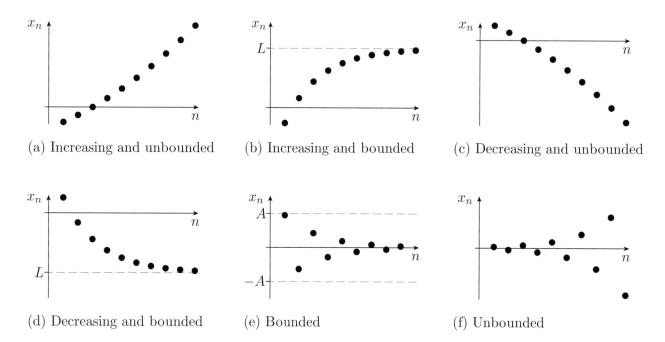

(a) Increasing and unbounded　　(b) Increasing and bounded　　(c) Decreasing and unbounded

(d) Decreasing and bounded　　(e) Bounded　　(f) Unbounded

Figure 9　Sequences with various long-term behaviours

If the terms of a sequence (x_n) approach 0 more and more closely, in such a way that they eventually lie within any interval $[-h, h]$, no matter how small the positive number h is taken to be, then we say that the terms of the sequence (x_n) become **arbitrarily small**. More formally, we say that x_n **tends to 0 as n tends to infinity**, and we write

$$x_n \to 0 \text{ as } n \to \infty. \tag{2}$$

Three sequences with this property are illustrated in Figure 10.

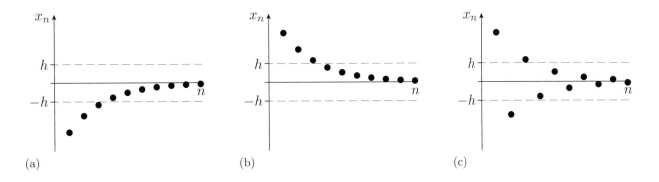

(a)   (b)   (c)

Figure 10   Sequences that tend to 0

More generally, suppose that the terms of a sequence (x_n) approach a particular number L more and more closely, so they eventually lie within any interval $[L - h, L + h]$, no matter how small the positive number h is taken to be. Then we say that x_n **tends to L as n tends to infinity**, and we write

$$x_n \to L \text{ as } n \to \infty. \tag{3}$$

Three sequences with this property are illustrated in Figure 11.

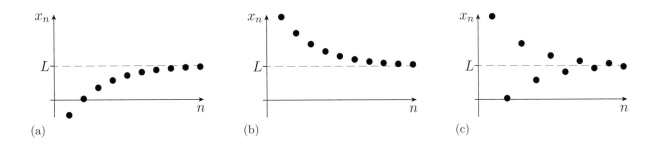

(a)   (b)   (c)

Figure 11   Sequences that tend to L

We also say in such a case that the **limit** of the sequence (x_n) is L, and that the sequence (x_n) **converges** or is **convergent** to the limit L. An alternative way to write statement (3) is

$$\lim_{n \to \infty} x_n = L,$$

which is read as 'the limit as n tends to infinity of x-sub-n is L'. In particular, statement (2) above can be written as

$$\lim_{n \to \infty} x_n = 0.$$

You saw a similar notation for other types of limits in Subsection 1.4 of Unit 6, and in Subsection 1.2 of Unit 8.

We also use arrows to denote 'tends to' in some cases where the sequence is unbounded. If a sequence (x_n) has the property that, whatever positive number A you take, no matter how large, the terms of (x_n) eventually lie in the interval $[A, \infty)$, then we say that x_n **tends to infinity as n tends to infinity**, and we write

$$x_n \to \infty \text{ as } n \to \infty.$$

Similarly, if a sequence (x_n) has the property that, whatever positive number A you take, the terms of (x_n) eventually lie in the interval $(-\infty, -A]$, then we say that x_n **tends to minus infinity as n tends to infinity**, and we write

$$x_n \to -\infty \text{ as } n \to \infty.$$

These definitions are illustrated in Figure 12.

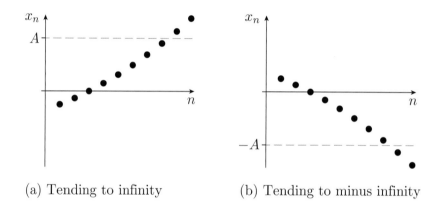

(a) Tending to infinity   (b) Tending to minus infinity

Figure 12   Sequences that tend to infinity or minus infinity

Example 10   *Using the notation for long-term behaviour*

Assuming that the patterns of behaviour suggested by the graphs in Figure 9 (on page 36) continue unchanged as n increases, complete the statement

$$x_n \to \ldots \text{ as } n \to \infty,$$

for each of the sequences (x_n) shown in Figure 9(a) and (d).

Solution

The graph in Figure 9(a) shows that, for this sequence,

$x_n \to \infty$ as $n \to \infty$.

The graph in Figure 9(d) shows that, for this sequence,

$x_n \to L$ as $n \to \infty$ $\left(\text{or } \lim_{n\to\infty} x_n = L\right).$

Activity 18   *Using the notation for long-term behaviour*

Assuming that the patterns of behaviour suggested by the graphs in Figure 9 continue unchanged as n increases, complete the statement

$x_n \to \ldots$ as $n \to \infty$,

for each of the sequences (x_n) shown in Figure 9(b), (c) and (e).

Long-term behaviour of arithmetic sequences

You've seen that the closed form of an arithmetic sequence (x_n) with first term a and common difference d is

$x_n = a + (n-1)d \quad (n = 1, 2, 3, \ldots).$

This closed form can be rearranged as

$x_n = (a - d) + nd \quad (n = 1, 2, 3, \ldots),$

which is the same as

$x_n = b + nd \quad (n = 1, 2, 3, \ldots),$

where $b = a - d$. This last formula is a little simpler than the first one since it involves n rather than $n - 1$. So, when studying the long-term behaviour of arithmetic sequences, we'll consider sequences with the closed form $x_n = b + nd$, where b and d are constants, with $d \neq 0$, and where the range of values of n is $1, 2, 3, \ldots$. These are arithmetic sequences with first term $b + d$ and common difference d.

Since the points that form the graph of an arithmetic sequence lie on a straight line, the long-term behaviour of arithmetic sequences is straightforward to describe.

> **Long-term behaviour of arithmetic sequences**
>
> Suppose that (x_n) is an arithmetic sequence with common difference d.
>
> - If $d > 0$, then (x_n) is increasing and $x_n \to \infty$ as $n \to \infty$.
> - If $d < 0$, then (x_n) is decreasing and $x_n \to -\infty$ as $n \to \infty$.
> - If $d = 0$, then (x_n) is constant.

The three cases are illustrated in Figure 13.

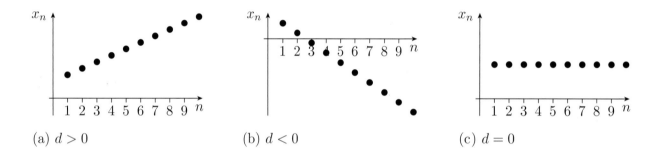

(a) $d > 0$ (b) $d < 0$ (c) $d = 0$

Figure 13   Graphs of arithmetic sequences

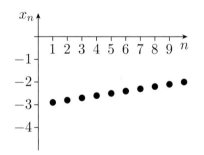

Figure 14   The graph of the sequence in Example 11

Example 11   *Finding the long-term behaviour of an arithmetic sequence*

Describe the long-term behaviour of the sequence (x_n) given by

$$x_n = \tfrac{1}{10}n - 3 \quad (n = 1, 2, 3, \ldots).$$

Solution

🔍 Recognise that (x_n) is an arithmetic sequence, find the common difference and use the facts in the box above. 💬

The sequence (x_n) with closed form $x_n = \tfrac{1}{10}n - 3$ is arithmetic, with common difference $d = \tfrac{1}{10}$.

Since $d > 0$, the sequence (x_n) is increasing and $x_n \to \infty$ as $n \to \infty$.

The graph of the sequence in Example 11 is shown in Figure 14.

Activity 19   *Finding the long-term behaviour of an arithmetic sequence*

Describe the long-term behaviour of the sequence (x_n) given by

$$x_n = 3 - \tfrac{4}{5}n \quad (n = 1, 2, 3, \dots).$$

Long-term behaviour of geometric sequences

You've seen that the closed form of a geometric sequence (x_n) with first term a and common ratio r is

$$x_n = ar^{n-1} \quad (n = 1, 2, 3, \dots).$$

This closed form can be rearranged as

$$x_n = \left(\frac{a}{r}\right) r^n \quad (n = 1, 2, 3, \dots),$$

which is the same as

$$x_n = cr^n \quad (n = 1, 2, 3, \dots),$$

where $c = a/r$. This last formula is a little simpler than the original formula since it involves n rather than $n - 1$. So, when studying the long-term behaviour of geometric sequences, we'll consider sequences with closed form cr^n, where c and r are constants, with $r \neq 0$, and where the range of values of n is $1, 2, 3, \dots$. These are geometric sequences with first term cr and common ratio r.

The long-term behaviour of geometric sequences is much more varied than that of arithmetic sequences. However, you can determine the long-term behaviour of any particular geometric sequence if you know the long-term behaviour of sequences of the form (r^n), for all the different possible values of r. So let's start by looking at that. (The notation (r^n) means the sequence (x_n), where $x_n = r^n$ for $n = 1, 2, 3, \dots$, as you'd expect.)

First, there are three special cases.

  If $r = 0$, then (r^n) is the sequence $0, 0, 0, 0, \dots$.

  If $r = 1$, then (r^n) is the sequence $1, 1, 1, 1, \dots$.

  If $r = -1$, then (r^n) is the sequence $-1, 1, -1, 1, \dots$.

So the sequences for $r = 0$ and $r = 1$ are constant sequences, and the sequence for $r = -1$ alternates indefinitely between -1 and 1.

Let's now look at the cases where r is *positive*, but not equal to 1. You can see what happens in these cases by using facts about exponential functions that you saw in Subsection 4.1 of Unit 3. Recall that the graph of the exponential function $f(x) = b^x$, where b is positive but not equal to 1, is

- increasing if $b > 1$, becoming steeper as x increases;
- decreasing if $0 < b < 1$, becoming less steep as x increases.

These two cases are shown in Figure 15.

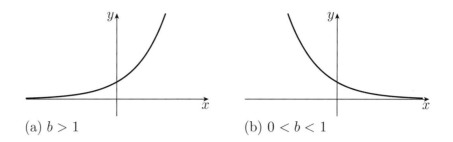

(a) $b > 1$ (b) $0 < b < 1$

Figure 15   Graphs of $y = b^x$

Remember also from Unit 3 that the x-axis is an asymptote of the graph of the exponential function $f(x) = b^x$. When $0 < b < 1$, this means that the graph gets closer and closer to the positive x-axis as x increases, as illustrated in Figure 15(b), so the value of b^x approaches 0 more and more closely as x increases.

The only difference between the sequence (r^n) and the exponential function $y = r^x$ is that the domain of (r^n) consists of all the natural numbers, whereas the domain of $y = r^x$ consists of all the real numbers. Hence the graph of the sequence (r^n) is made up of isolated points, all lying on the graph of the function $y = r^x$, which is a continuous curve. So the long-term behaviour of the sequence (r^n), in the cases where r is positive but not equal to 1, is as follows.

- If $r > 1$, then (r^n) is increasing and $r^n \to \infty$ as $n \to \infty$.

- If $0 < r < 1$, then (r^n) is decreasing and $r^n \to 0$ as $n \to \infty$.

These two cases are illustrated in Figure 16.

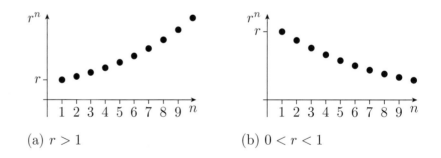

(a) $r > 1$ (b) $0 < r < 1$

Figure 16   Graphs of sequences of the form (r^n)

For example,

- the sequence (2^n) is increasing and $2^n \to \infty$ as $n \to \infty$

- the sequence (0.5^n) is decreasing and $0.5^n \to 0$ as $n \to \infty$,

as illustrated in Figure 17.

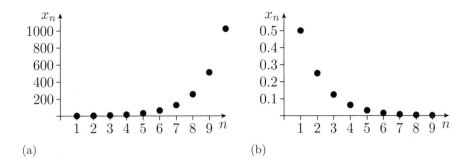

Figure 17   The graphs of the sequences (a) (2^n) (b) (0.5^n)

Now let's consider the long-term behaviour of sequences of the form (r^n) where r is *negative* but not equal to -1.

For example, consider the sequence $((-2)^n)$. The nth term of this sequence, $(-2)^n$, can also be written as $(-1)^n \times 2^n$, so the terms of the sequence have the same magnitude as the terms of the sequence (2^n), but alternate in sign, as illustrated in Figure 18(a). Hence the sequence $((-2)^n)$ is neither increasing nor decreasing, but is unbounded.

Similarly, the terms of the sequence $((-0.5)^n)$ have the same magnitude as the terms of the sequence (0.5^n), but alternate in sign, as illustrated in Figure 18(b). So the sequence $((-0.5)^n)$ is neither increasing nor decreasing, but $(-0.5)^n \to 0$ as $n \to \infty$.

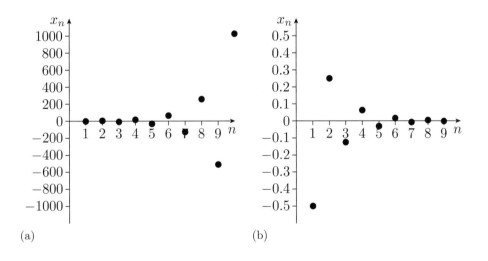

Figure 18   The graphs of the sequences (a) $((-2)^n)$ (b) $((-0.5)^n)$

In general, the long-term behaviour of the sequence (r^n), where r is negative but not equal to -1, is as follows.

- If $r < -1$, then r^n alternates between positive and negative values, and (r^n) is unbounded.

- If $-1 < r < 0$, then r^n alternates between positive and negative values, and $r^n \to 0$ as $n \to \infty$.

Here's a summary of the facts that you've seen about the behaviour of the sequence (r^n), for all possible values of r. All the cases except $r = 0$ are illustrated in Figure 19.

Long-term behaviour of the sequence (r^n)

Value of r	Behaviour of (r^n)
$r > 1$	Increasing, $r^n \to \infty$ as $n \to \infty$
$r = 1$	Constant: $1, 1, 1, \ldots$
$0 < r < 1$	Decreasing, $r^n \to 0$ as $n \to \infty$
$r = 0$	Constant: $0, 0, 0, \ldots$
$-1 < r < 0$	Alternates in sign, $r^n \to 0$ as $n \to \infty$
$r = -1$	Alternates between -1 and 1
$r < -1$	Alternates in sign, unbounded

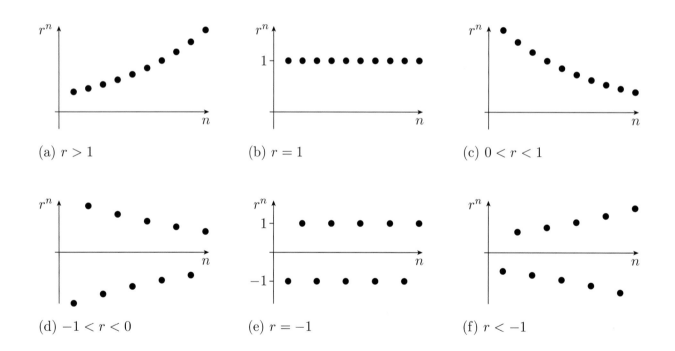

(a) $r > 1$ (b) $r = 1$ (c) $0 < r < 1$

(d) $-1 < r < 0$ (e) $r = -1$ (f) $r < -1$

Figure 19   Sequences of the form (r^n) for all non-zero values of r

Now remember that any geometric sequence has the form (cr^n). You can work out the long-term behaviour of any sequence of this form by thinking about the long-term behaviour of the sequence (r^n) and using the fact that the terms of (cr^n) are obtained by multiplying the terms of (r^n) by c.

For example, since the sequence (2^n) is increasing and tends to infinity, as illustrated in Figure 20(a), it follows that the sequence $\left(\frac{2}{3} \times 2^n\right)$ is also increasing and tends to infinity, as illustrated in Figure 20(b). It also follows that the sequence $\left(-\frac{2}{3} \times 2^n\right)$ is decreasing and tends to minus infinity, as illustrated in Figure 20(c).

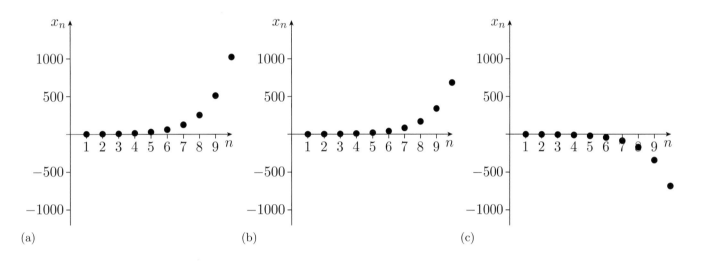

(a)   (b)   (c)

Figure 20   The sequences (a) (2^n) (b) $\left(\frac{2}{3} \times 2^n\right)$ (c) $\left(-\frac{2}{3} \times 2^n\right)$

When you're working out conclusions like these, it's helpful to use the ideas about scalings of graphs that you met in Unit 3. For example, it follows from what you saw there that the graph of the sequence $\left(\frac{2}{3} \times 2^n\right)$ is obtained from the graph of the sequence (2^n) by scaling it vertically by a factor of $\frac{2}{3}$. This squashes the graph vertically. Similarly, the graph of the sequence $\left(-\frac{2}{3} \times 2^n\right)$ is obtained from the graph of the sequence (2^n) by scaling it vertically by a factor of $-\frac{2}{3}$. This squashes the graph vertically, and reflects it in the horizontal axis.

The following box summarises some useful facts about multiplying the terms of a general sequence by a constant. However, when you need to use these facts you may find it easier just to think about the graph of the sequence, as in the paragraph above, rather than apply the facts directly. Try to check the facts in the box by thinking about the graphs of sequences in this way.

Multiplying each term of a sequence by a constant

Suppose that (x_n) is an infinite sequence and c is a constant.

If $c \neq 0$ and (x_n) $\left\{\begin{array}{l} \text{is constant} \\ \text{alternates in sign} \\ \text{is bounded} \\ \text{is unbounded} \\ \text{tends to } 0 \end{array}\right\}$, then so is/does (cx_n).

If $c > 0$ and (x_n) $\left\{\begin{array}{l} \text{is increasing} \\ \text{is decreasing} \\ \text{tends to } \infty \\ \text{tends to } -\infty \end{array}\right\}$, then so is/does (cx_n).

If $c < 0$ and (x_n) $\left\{\begin{array}{l} \text{is increasing} \\ \text{is decreasing} \\ \text{tends to } \infty \\ \text{tends to } -\infty \end{array}\right\}$, then (cx_n) $\left\{\begin{array}{l} \text{is decreasing} \\ \text{is increasing} \\ \text{tends to } -\infty \\ \text{tends to } \infty \end{array}\right\}$.

You might find the tutorial clip for the example below particularly helpful.

Example 12   *Finding the long-term behaviour of geometric sequences*

Describe the long-term behaviour of each of the sequences given by the following closed forms.

(a) $x_n = -20 \times 0.7^n \quad (n = 1, 2, 3, \ldots)$

(b) $y_n = \frac{1}{5} \times 1.5^n \quad (n = 1, 2, 3, \ldots)$

(c) $z_n = 2(-1.1)^n \quad (n = 1, 2, 3, \ldots)$

Solution

🔍 Use the facts in the box on page 44 and in the box above, and think about the graphs of the sequences involved. 💬

(a) Since $0 < 0.7 < 1$, the sequence (0.7^n) is decreasing and $0.7^n \to 0$ as $n \to \infty$.

   To obtain (x_n) we multiply each term by the negative constant -20. Hence (x_n) is increasing and $x_n \to 0$ as $n \to \infty$.

(b) Since $1.5 > 1$, the sequence (1.5^n) is increasing and $1.5^n \to \infty$ as $n \to \infty$.

   To obtain (y_n) we multiply each term by the positive constant $\frac{1}{5}$. Hence (y_n) is increasing and $y_n \to \infty$ as $n \to \infty$.

(c) Since $-1.1 < -1$, the sequence $((-1.1)^n)$ alternates in sign and is unbounded.

To obtain (z_n) we multiply each term by the non-zero constant 2. Hence (z_n) also alternates in sign and is unbounded.

The graphs of the sequences in Example 12 are shown in Figure 21. You can see that the long-term behaviour of the sequences appears to be as determined in the solution to Example 12.

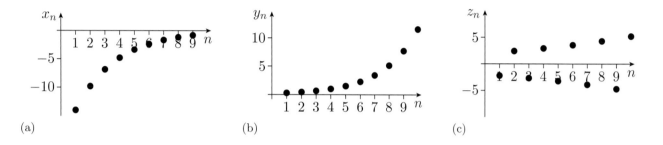

Figure 21 The graphs of the sequences in Example 12

Activity 20 *Finding the long-term behaviour of geometric sequences*

Describe the long-term behaviour of each of the sequences given by the following closed forms.

(a) $x_n = -\frac{1}{3} \times 1.2^n \quad (n = 1, 2, 3, \dots)$

(b) $y_n = 5(-0.9)^n \quad (n = 1, 2, 3, \dots)$

(c) $z_n = -\frac{1}{10}(-2.5)^n \quad (n = 1, 2, 3, \dots)$

You can check your answers to this question by using the computer algebra system to plot the graphs of the sequences.

Long-term behaviour of further sequences

You can find the long-term behaviour of slightly more complicated sequences by using the following facts.

Suppose that a, c and L are constants.

- If $x_n \to L$ as $n \to \infty$, then $x_n + a \to L + a$ as $n \to \infty$.

- If $x_n \to \infty$ as $n \to \infty$, then $x_n + a \to \infty$ as $n \to \infty$.

- If $x_n \to -\infty$ as $n \to \infty$, then $x_n + a \to -\infty$ as $n \to \infty$.

- If $x_n \to L$ as $n \to \infty$, then $cx_n \to cL$ as $n \to \infty$.

To understand why these facts hold, you can again use the ideas about scalings and translations of graphs that you met in Unit 3. For example, since the sequence (0.5^n) has limit 0, as illustrated in Figure 22(a), it follows that the sequence $(0.5^n + 0.1)$ has limit 0.1, as illustrated in Figure 22(b).

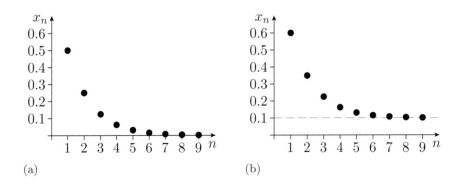

(a)   (b)

Figure 22 The sequences (a) (0.5^n) (b) $(0.5^n + 0.1)$

The following example shows how you can use the facts above, together with the facts that you met earlier in this subsection.

Example 13 *Finding the long-term behaviour of more sequences*

Describe the long-term behaviour of each of the sequences with the following closed forms.

(a) $x_n = -30 \times 0.9^n + 80 \quad (n = 1, 2, 3, \dots)$

(b) $y_n = 5 \times 2^n - 7 \quad (n = 1, 2, 3, \dots)$

Solution

💬 Deal first with the term that involves r^n. 💬

(a) Since $0 < 0.9 < 1$, the sequence (0.9^n) is decreasing and has limit 0. Hence the sequence (-30×0.9^n) is increasing and also has limit 0. Adding 80 to each term gives another increasing sequence, with limit 80. Hence the sequence (x_n) is increasing and $x_n \to 80$ as $n \to \infty$.

(b) Since $2 > 1$, the sequence (2^n) is increasing, and $2^n \to \infty$ as $n \to \infty$. Since the constant 5 is positive, the sequence (5×2^n) is also increasing and $5 \times 2^n \to \infty$ as $n \to \infty$. Subtracting 7 from each term gives another increasing sequence that tends to infinity. Hence the sequence (y_n) is increasing and $y_n \to \infty$ as $n \to \infty$.

The graphs of the sequences in Example 13 are shown in Figure 23.

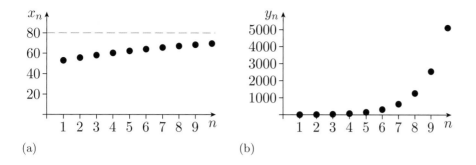

(a)   (b)

Figure 23   The graphs of the sequences in Example 13

Activity 21   *Finding the long-term behaviour of more sequences*

Describe the long-term behaviour of each of the sequences with the following closed forms. (These sequences are closely related to the sequences in Activity 20.)

(a) $a_n = 17 - \frac{1}{3} \times 1.2^n$ $(n = 1, 2, 3, \dots)$

(b) $b_n = 5(-0.9)^n + 45$ $(n = 1, 2, 3, \dots)$

You can check your answers to this question by using the computer algebra system to plot the graphs of the sequences.

---

4 Series

In this section you'll investigate the sums of terms of sequences, and meet a useful notation for such sums.

4.1 Summing finite series

It's sometimes useful or interesting to add up consecutive terms of a sequence. For example, consider the following sums:

$$2 + 2^2 + 2^3 + 2^4 + 2^5,$$
$$(3 \times 4) + (3 \times 5) + (3 \times 6) + \cdots + (3 \times 20).$$

The first expression here is the sum of the first five terms of the geometric sequence (2^n), and the second expression is the sum of the terms, from the fourth to the twentieth, of the arithmetic sequence $(3n)$. Expressions like these are called *series*. That is, a **series** is an expression obtained by adding consecutive terms of a sequence. (The singular and plural forms of the word 'series' are the same.)

The series above are *finite* series, since they have only a finite number of terms. By contrast, an *infinite* series has an infinite number of terms. We'll consider finite series in this subsection and infinite series in the next.

Series are important in calculus, as you'll see in the next unit, and are also used frequently in statistics. They can be of interest too in their own right. For example, look at the series below, whose terms come from the sequence of odd integers:

$$1 = 1$$
$$1 + 3 = 4$$
$$1 + 3 + 5 = 9$$
$$1 + 3 + 5 + 7 = 16.$$

An obvious question is whether this pattern of adding up consecutive odd integers to obtain square numbers continues. You'll be able to answer that question later in the subsection.

The number that you obtain when you add up all the terms of a series is called the **sum** of the series, and the process of finding this sum is called **summing** the series, or **evaluating** the series. For example, the sum of the series $1 + 3 + 5 + 7$ is 16. You may think that this terminology is a little strange, because a series is *already* a sum, but it's standard terminology, and is convenient in practice.

In the rest of this subsection we'll look at summing some particular types of finite series.

Finite arithmetic series

Let's start by looking at sums of finite *arithmetic* series. As you'd expect, an **arithmetic series** is one whose terms come from an arithmetic sequence. Here's an example:

$$5 + 8 + 11 + 14 + 17 + 20 + 23 + 26 + 29 + 32 + 35 + 38 + 41 + 44.$$

The terms of this series are the terms of an arithmetic sequence with first term 5 and common difference 3. One way to find the sum of this series is simply to add up all 14 terms. However, there's another and more illuminating way of finding the sum. First reverse the order of the terms of the series, and then write the result under the original series, with the terms aligned:

$$5 \; + 8 + 11 + 14 + 17 + 20 + 23 + 26 + 29 + 32 + 35 + 38 + 41 + 44$$
$$44 + 41 + 38 + 35 + 32 + 29 + 26 + 23 + 20 + 17 + 14 + 11 \; + 8 \; + 5.$$

Then add the two copies of the series together, starting by adding each term to the one below. This gives

$$49 + 49 + 49 + 49 + 49 + 49 + 49 + 49 + 49 + 49 + 49 + 49 + 49 + 49$$
$$= 14 \times 49 = 686.$$

This number is twice the sum of the original series (since we added two copies of the series together). So the sum of the original series is

$$\tfrac{1}{2} \times 686 = 343.$$

The reason for all the 49s above is that each term in the original series is 3 *more* than the one before, whereas each term in the reverse series is 3 *less* than the one before. When you add each term to the one below, these increases and decreases cancel out, and you obtain a new series all of whose terms are equal to its first term. The first term of this new series is the sum of the first and last terms of the original series, that is, $5 + 44 = 49$.

You can see that you could use the same approach to find the sum of any finite arithmetic series. So, in general, the sum of any finite arithmetic series is

$$\tfrac{1}{2} \times (\text{number of terms}) \times (\text{first term} + \text{last term}). \qquad (4)$$

If you don't know the number of terms then you can work it out by using the equation

$$\text{number of terms} = \frac{\text{last term} - \text{first term}}{\text{common difference}} + 1,$$

which you saw on page 19.

Example 14 *Finding the sum of an arithmetic series*

Find the sum of the arithmetic series

$$517 + 527 + 537 + \cdots + 1007.$$

Solution

🗨 First find the number of terms. 🗨

The first term is 517, the last term is 1007, and the common difference is $527 - 517 = 10$, so the number of terms is

$$\frac{1007 - 517}{10} + 1 = 50.$$

Hence the sum is

$$\tfrac{1}{2} \times (\text{number of terms}) \times (\text{first term} + \text{last term})$$
$$= \tfrac{1}{2} \times 50 \times (517 + 1007)$$
$$= 25 \times 1524$$
$$= 38\,100.$$

Activity 22 *Finding the sum of an arithmetic series*

Find the sum of the arithmetic series

$$6 + 13 + 20 + \cdots + 90.$$

As you saw in Subsection 2.2, the nth term of the arithmetic sequence (x_n) with first term a and common difference d is given by

$$x_n = a + (n-1)d.$$

It follows from this formula and expression (4) that the sum of an arithmetic series with n terms is

$\frac{1}{2} \times$ (number of terms) $\times$ (first term $+$ last term)

$= \frac{1}{2}n(x_1 + x_n)$

$= \frac{1}{2}n(a + a + (n-1)d)$

$= \frac{1}{2}n(2a + (n-1)d)$.

This useful formula is summarised in the box below.

> **Sum of a finite arithmetic series**
>
> The arithmetic series with first term a, common difference d and n terms has sum
>
> $\frac{1}{2} \times$ (number of terms) $\times$ (first term $+$ last term);
>
> that is,
>
> $$\frac{1}{2}n(2a + (n-1)d). \tag{5}$$

Activity 23   *Finding the sums of more arithmetic series*

Use formula (5) to find the sums of the following arithmetic series.

(a) $1 + 2 + 3 + \cdots + 100$

(b) $12 + 15 + 18 + \cdots + 60$

(c) $1 + 3 + 5 + \cdots + 19$

As you'll see shortly, the result of Activity 23(a) can be generalised to a useful formula for the sum of the first n natural numbers. Also, you can generalise the result of Activity 23(c) to prove that adding up consecutive odd numbers, starting at 1, always gives a square number – see the solution to the activity.

Finite geometric series

Now let's look at sums of *geometric* series: a **geometric series** is a series whose terms come from a geometric sequence. Again there's a particular approach that can be used to evaluate the sum of such a series. We'll apply it to find a general formula for the sum of a finite geometric series, after first considering a particular example.

Suppose that you want to evaluate the sum of the finite geometric series

$$1 + 2 + 2^2 + 2^3 + 2^4 + 2^5 + 2^6 + 2^7 + 2^8 + 2^9 + 2^{10} + 2^{11}.$$

One way to find this sum is simply to evaluate all of the 12 terms and then add them together. But there is a quicker and more illuminating way of finding this sum. Suppose that the sum is s. First write down the expressions for s and for $2s$ on successive lines (here $2s$ was chosen because 2 is the common ratio of the series):

$$s = 1 + 2 + 2^2 + 2^3 + 2^4 + 2^5 + 2^6 + 2^7 + 2^8 + 2^9 + 2^{10} + 2^{11},$$
$$2s = \quad\; 2 + 2^2 + 2^3 + 2^4 + 2^5 + 2^6 + 2^7 + 2^8 + 2^9 + 2^{10} + 2^{11} + 2^{12}.$$

The terms in the sums s and $2s$ have been aligned to emphasise that they're the same, except for the appearance of 1 in the expression for s, and 2^{12} in the expression for $2s$. Now subtract the first of these equations from the second. All the common terms cancel on the right-hand side, so

$$s = 2^{12} - 1 = 4096 - 1 = 4095.$$

You can use the same approach to find a general formula for the sum of a finite geometric series.

Consider the finite geometric series with first term a, common ratio r and n terms, and suppose that its sum is s; that is,

$$s = a + ar + ar^2 + ar^3 + \cdots + ar^{n-1}. \tag{6}$$

Then multiply the series by the common ratio r, and write it down below the original series, with like terms aligned. This gives

$$s = a + ar + ar^2 + ar^3 + \cdots + ar^{n-1},$$
$$rs = \quad\; ar + ar^2 + ar^3 + \cdots + ar^{n-1} + ar^n.$$

If you now subtract the bottom series from the top series, then most of the terms cancel each other out, and you obtain

$$s - rs = a - ar^n.$$

Taking out the common factor on each side gives

$$(1 - r)s = a(1 - r^n).$$

So, if $r \neq 1$, then

$$s = \frac{a(1 - r^n)}{1 - r}.$$

If $r = 1$, then it follows directly from equation (6) that

$$s = \underbrace{a + a + \cdots + a}_{n \text{ terms}} = na.$$

Sum of a finite geometric series

The geometric series with first term a, common ratio $r \neq 1$ and n terms has sum

$$\frac{a(1 - r^n)}{1 - r}. \tag{7}$$

As you saw earlier, the common ratio of a geometric sequence can be positive or negative, and when it's negative the terms of the sequence alternate in sign. Expression (7) still applies when the common ratio is negative.

Activity 24   *Finding the sums of geometric series*

(a) Find the sum of the first 10 powers of 3, that is,

$$3 + 3^2 + 3^3 + \cdots + 3^{10}.$$

(b) Find the value of the sum

$$1 - \tfrac{1}{3} + \left(\tfrac{1}{3}\right)^2 - \left(\tfrac{1}{3}\right)^3 + \cdots + \left(\tfrac{1}{3}\right)^8,$$

giving your answer correct to six decimal places.

Other finite series

We now briefly consider some formulas for the sums of other standard finite series.

First, consider the sum of the first n natural numbers:

$$1 + 2 + 3 + \cdots + n.$$

This is a finite arithmetic series with first term 1, last term n and n terms, so its sum is

$$\tfrac{1}{2} \times (\text{number of terms}) \times (\text{first term} + \text{last term}) = \tfrac{1}{2}n(1 + n).$$

Sum of the first n natural numbers

$$1 + 2 + 3 + \cdots + n = \tfrac{1}{2}n(n + 1)$$

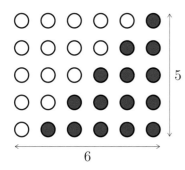

This result has a geometric interpretation, which is illustrated (for the case $n = 5$) in Figure 24. The number of shaded dots, which is $1 + 2 + 3 + 4 + 5$, is equal to half of the total number of dots, which is $\tfrac{1}{2} \times 5 \times 6$.

Figure 24   A geometric interpretation of $1 + 2 + 3 + 4 + 5 = \tfrac{1}{2} \times 5 \times 6$

It is said that the great German mathematician Carl Friedrich Gauss, at the age of ten, was asked along with the rest of his school class to find the sum $1 + 2 + 3 + \cdots + 100$. The teacher intended this to be a lengthy task. However, Gauss came up with the correct answer almost immediately, by applying the approach used earlier to derive expression (4) on page 51.

There are also formulas for the sums of the first n square numbers and the first n cube numbers, as stated in the following box. The proofs of these formulas are beyond the scope of this module, but you'll see the proofs if you go on to study MST125 *Essential mathematics 2*.

Carl Friedrich Gauss
(1777–1855)

> **Sum of the first n square or cube numbers**
>
> $$1^2 + 2^2 + 3^2 + \cdots + n^2 = \tfrac{1}{6}n(n+1)(2n+1)$$
> $$1^3 + 2^3 + 3^3 + \cdots + n^3 = \tfrac{1}{4}n^2(n+1)^2$$

Activity 25   *Using the formulas for the sums of consecutive natural numbers, squares and cubes*

(a) Use the formulas above to find the sums of the following finite series.

    (i) $1 + 2 + 3 + \cdots + 30$

    (ii) $1^2 + 2^2 + 3^2 + \cdots + 10^2$

    (iii) $1^2 + 2^2 + 3^2 + \cdots + 30^2$

    (iv) $1^3 + 2^3 + 3^3 + \cdots + 30^3$

(b) (i)   Use your answers to parts (a)(ii) and (a)(iii) to find the sum of the series

$$11^2 + 12^2 + 13^2 + \cdots + 30^2.$$

    (ii) Use a similar method to find the sum of the series

$$20^3 + 21^3 + 22^3 + \cdots + 40^3.$$

4.2   Summing infinite series

In this subsection we'll look at **infinite series**, which are expressions such as

$$a_1 + a_2 + a_3 + \cdots,$$

where (a_n) is a sequence. So that you can see what it means to add up all the terms in an infinite series, let's start by considering the infinite series

$$\tfrac{1}{2} + \left(\tfrac{1}{2}\right)^2 + \left(\tfrac{1}{2}\right)^3 + \left(\tfrac{1}{2}\right)^4 + \cdots.$$

This is an infinite *geometric* series – its terms are those of the infinite geometric sequence with first term $\tfrac{1}{2}$ and common ratio $\tfrac{1}{2}$. Consider what happens as you add up more and more of the terms of this series:

$$\tfrac{1}{2} = \tfrac{1}{2}$$
$$\tfrac{1}{2} + \left(\tfrac{1}{2}\right)^2 = \tfrac{1}{2} + \tfrac{1}{4} = \tfrac{3}{4}$$
$$\tfrac{1}{2} + \left(\tfrac{1}{2}\right)^2 + \left(\tfrac{1}{2}\right)^3 = \tfrac{1}{2} + \tfrac{1}{4} + \tfrac{1}{8} = \tfrac{7}{8}$$
$$\tfrac{1}{2} + \left(\tfrac{1}{2}\right)^2 + \left(\tfrac{1}{2}\right)^3 + \left(\tfrac{1}{2}\right)^4 = \tfrac{1}{2} + \tfrac{1}{4} + \tfrac{1}{8} + \tfrac{1}{16} = \tfrac{15}{16}$$
$$\tfrac{1}{2} + \left(\tfrac{1}{2}\right)^2 + \left(\tfrac{1}{2}\right)^3 + \left(\tfrac{1}{2}\right)^4 + \left(\tfrac{1}{2}\right)^5 = \tfrac{1}{2} + \tfrac{1}{4} + \tfrac{1}{8} + \tfrac{1}{16} + \tfrac{1}{32} = \tfrac{31}{32}$$
$$\tfrac{1}{2} + \left(\tfrac{1}{2}\right)^2 + \left(\tfrac{1}{2}\right)^3 + \left(\tfrac{1}{2}\right)^4 + \left(\tfrac{1}{2}\right)^5 + \left(\tfrac{1}{2}\right)^6 = \tfrac{1}{2} + \tfrac{1}{4} + \tfrac{1}{8} + \tfrac{1}{16} + \tfrac{1}{32} + \tfrac{1}{64} = \tfrac{63}{64}$$

$$\vdots$$

As you add on more and more terms, the totals get closer and closer to 1. In fact, they get arbitrarily close to 1, but never reach 1, because each time you add on a new term, the difference between the total and 1 halves. You can think of this as meaning that, if you add on *infinitely many* terms, then the total is *exactly* 1. This is illustrated in Figure 25. So in this sense the sum of the infinite series above is 1.

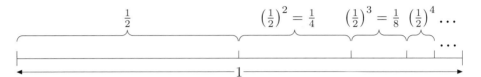

Figure 25   The sum of the infinite series $\frac{1}{2} + \left(\frac{1}{2}\right)^2 + \left(\frac{1}{2}\right)^3 + \cdots$ is 1

One of Zeno's paradoxes

The result illustrated in Figure 25 is related to one of the famous paradoxes attributed to the Greek mathematician Zeno of Elea (*c.* 490–430 BC). It is known as the *dichotomy paradox*, and also as the *race course paradox*. One statement of it is based on the following:

> That which is in locomotion must arrive at the half-way stage before it arrives at the goal.

(Aristotle, *Physics* VI:9, trans. R.P. Hardie and R.K. Gaye (2009), New York, Digireads.com.)

Before covering a fixed distance, half the distance must be covered, but before that, a quarter of the distance must be covered. Before that, an eighth must be covered, and so on. As this involves an infinite number of tasks, it is impossible to achieve.

Many infinite series don't have sums. For example, consider the infinite geometric series with first term 1 and common ratio 2:

$$1 + 2 + 2^2 + 2^3 + \cdots.$$

Consider what happens as you add up more and more of the terms of this series:

$$1 = 1$$
$$1 + 2 = 3$$
$$1 + 2 + 2^2 = 1 + 2 + 4 = 7$$
$$1 + 2 + 2^2 + 2^3 = 1 + 2 + 4 + 8 = 15$$
$$1 + 2 + 2^2 + 2^3 + 2^4 = 1 + 2 + 4 + 8 + 16 = 31$$
$$\vdots$$

With this series, as you add on more and more terms, the total just keeps getting larger and larger, without getting closer and closer to any particular number. So this infinite series doesn't have a sum.

The ideas illustrated above can be applied to any infinite series, to determine whether it has a sum, and to find the value of its sum if it has one. We make the following definitions.

Consider any infinite series

$$a_1 + a_2 + a_3 + \cdots .$$

Let

$$s_1 = a_1,$$
$$s_2 = a_1 + a_2,$$
$$s_3 = a_1 + a_2 + a_3,$$
$$s_4 = a_1 + a_2 + a_3 + a_4,$$

and so on. The numbers $s_1, s_2, s_3, \ldots$ are called the **partial sums** of the series, and the infinite sequence (s_n) that they form is called the **sequence of partial sums** of the series.

If the sequence of partial sums of an infinite series converges to a limit, say s, then we call s the **sum** of the infinite series. On the other hand, if the sequence of partial sums doesn't converge, then the infinite series doesn't have a sum.

For example, you saw at the beginning of this subsection that the infinite series

$$\tfrac{1}{2} + \left(\tfrac{1}{2}\right)^2 + \left(\tfrac{1}{2}\right)^3 + \left(\tfrac{1}{2}\right)^4 + \cdots$$

has the sequence of partial sums

$$\tfrac{1}{2}, \tfrac{3}{4}, \tfrac{7}{8}, \tfrac{15}{16}, \tfrac{31}{32}, \ldots .$$

Since this sequence converges to 1, the infinite series has sum 1, as you saw.

Similarly, you saw that the infinite series

$$1 + 2 + 2^2 + 2^3 + \cdots$$

has the sequence of partial sums

$$1, \ 3, \ 7, \ 15, \ 31, \ \ldots .$$

Since this sequence doesn't converge, the infinite series has no sum.

It's often quite difficult to determine whether the sequence of partial sums of a particular infinite series converges, and if it does converge, what the limit is. However, it's fairly straightforward to deal with infinite arithmetic and geometric series. We'll consider each of these two types of infinite series in turn, starting with geometric series.

Infinite geometric series

Every infinite geometric series has the form

$$a + ar + ar^2 + ar^3 + \cdots,$$

where a is the first term and r is the common ratio. A useful way to determine whether such a series has a sum is to use the fact that each of its partial sums is the sum of a *finite* geometric series, and to apply the formula that you met in the previous subsection for such a sum.

To illustrate this approach, consider once more the infinite geometric series with first term $\frac{1}{2}$ and common ratio $\frac{1}{2}$:

$$\tfrac{1}{2} + \left(\tfrac{1}{2}\right)^2 + \left(\tfrac{1}{2}\right)^3 + \left(\tfrac{1}{2}\right)^4 + \cdots.$$

Its partial sums are

$$s_1 = \tfrac{1}{2}$$
$$s_2 = \tfrac{1}{2} + \left(\tfrac{1}{2}\right)^2$$
$$s_3 = \tfrac{1}{2} + \left(\tfrac{1}{2}\right)^2 + \left(\tfrac{1}{2}\right)^3$$
$$\vdots$$

In general, the nth term of its sequence of partial sums is

$$s_n = \tfrac{1}{2} + \left(\tfrac{1}{2}\right)^2 + \cdots + \left(\tfrac{1}{2}\right)^n.$$

This is the sum of a finite geometric series with first term $a = \frac{1}{2}$, common ratio $r = \frac{1}{2}$ and n terms, so by formula (7) on page 53, we have

$$s_n = \frac{a(1 - r^n)}{1 - r} = \frac{\tfrac{1}{2}\left(1 - \left(\tfrac{1}{2}\right)^n\right)}{1 - \tfrac{1}{2}} = \frac{\tfrac{1}{2}\left(1 - \left(\tfrac{1}{2}\right)^n\right)}{\tfrac{1}{2}} = 1 - \left(\tfrac{1}{2}\right)^n.$$

Since $\left(\tfrac{1}{2}\right)^n \to 0$ as $n \to \infty$, it follows that

$$s_n = 1 - \left(\tfrac{1}{2}\right)^n \to 1 - 0 = 1 \quad \text{as } n \to \infty.$$

So the sequence of partial sums of this series converges to 1, and hence the series has sum 1. This confirms the result found earlier.

You can obtain a general result about the sums of infinite geometric series by applying the same approach. Consider the infinite geometric series with first term $a \neq 0$ and common ratio r:

$$a + ar + ar^2 + ar^3 + \cdots.$$

Its partial sums are

$$s_1 = a$$
$$s_2 = a + ar$$
$$s_3 = a + ar + ar^2$$
$$s_4 = a + ar + ar^2 + ar^3$$
$$\vdots$$

The nth term of its sequence of partial sums is

$$s_n = a + ar + ar^2 + \cdots + ar^{n-1}.$$

This is the sum of a finite geometric series with first term a, common ratio r and n terms. So by formula (7) on page 53, if $r \neq 1$, then

$$s_n = \frac{a(1 - r^n)}{1 - r}.$$

If $-1 < r < 1$, then $r^n \to 0$ as $n \to \infty$, as you saw on page 44, and hence

$$s_n = \frac{a(1 - r^n)}{1 - r} \to \frac{a(1 - 0)}{1 - r} = \frac{a}{1 - r} \quad \text{as } n \to \infty.$$

So if $-1 < r < 1$, then the series has the sum $a/(1 - r)$.

If $r < -1$ or $r > 1$, then r^n is unbounded, as you also saw on page 44, and it follows that $s_n = a(1 - r^n)/(1 - r)$ is also unbounded. So if $r < -1$ or $r > 1$, then the series doesn't have a sum.

The only other possible values of r are $r = -1$ and $r = 1$. When $r = -1$, the series is

$$a - a + a - a + a - a + \cdots.$$

The sequence of partial sums of this series is $a, 0, a, 0, a, \ldots$, which doesn't converge (since $a \neq 0$), so the series doesn't have a sum. When $r = 1$, the series is

$$a + a + a + a + a + \cdots.$$

The sequence of partial sums of this series is $a, 2a, 3a, 4a, \ldots$, which doesn't converge (since $a \neq 0$), so again the series doesn't have a sum.

In summary, the following facts hold.

Sum of an infinite geometric series

The infinite geometric series with first term $a \neq 0$ and common ratio r has

$$\text{sum } \frac{a}{1 - r}, \quad \text{if } -1 < r < 1;$$

$$\text{no sum}, \quad \text{if } r \leq -1 \text{ or } r \geq 1.$$

The only infinite geometric series with first term $a = 0$ is the series $0 + 0 + 0 + \cdots$, which has sum 0.

Example 15   *Summing infinite geometric series*

For each of the following infinite geometric series, determine whether or not it has a sum, and find the value of the sum if it exists.

(a) $\frac{2}{3} + \left(\frac{2}{3}\right)^2 + \left(\frac{2}{3}\right)^3 + \left(\frac{2}{3}\right)^4 + \cdots$

(b) $\frac{5}{2} - \left(\frac{5}{2}\right)^2 + \left(\frac{5}{2}\right)^3 - \left(\frac{5}{2}\right)^4 + \cdots$

Solution

(a) This is an infinite geometric series with first term $a = \frac{2}{3}$ and common ratio $r = \frac{2}{3}$. Since $-1 < r < 1$, the series has a sum, namely

$$\frac{a}{1-r} = \frac{\frac{2}{3}}{1 - \frac{2}{3}} = \frac{\frac{2}{3}}{\frac{1}{3}} = 2.$$

(b) This is an infinite geometric series with first term $a = \frac{5}{2}$ and common ratio $r = -\frac{5}{2}$. Since $r < -1$, the series doesn't have a sum.

Here are some examples for you to try.

Activity 26   *Summing infinite geometric series*

For each of the following infinite geometric series, determine whether or not it has a sum, and find the value of the sum if it exists.

(a) $\frac{3}{4} + \left(\frac{3}{4}\right)^2 + \left(\frac{3}{4}\right)^3 + \left(\frac{3}{4}\right)^4 + \cdots$

(b) $1 - \frac{1}{2} + \left(\frac{1}{2}\right)^2 - \left(\frac{1}{2}\right)^3 + \cdots$

(c) $1 - 2 + 2^2 - 2^3 + 2^4 - 2^5 + \cdots$

(d) $\frac{1}{4} - \frac{1}{4}\left(\frac{2}{3}\right) + \frac{1}{4}\left(\frac{2}{3}\right)^2 - \frac{1}{4}\left(\frac{2}{3}\right)^3 + \cdots$

In fact, you've been dealing with the sums of infinite geometric series since Unit 1 of this module, because any recurring decimal can be thought of as the sum of a terminating decimal (possibly 0) plus an infinite geometric series. For example,

$$0.333\,333\ldots = 3\left(\tfrac{1}{10}\right) + 3\left(\tfrac{1}{10}\right)^2 + 3\left(\tfrac{1}{10}\right)^3 + \cdots,$$

$$5.178\,178\,178\,178\ldots = 5 + 178\left(\tfrac{1}{1000}\right) + 178\left(\tfrac{1}{1000}\right)^2 + 178\left(\tfrac{1}{1000}\right)^3 + \cdots.$$

It follows that one way to find a fraction equivalent to a given recurring decimal is to use the formula $a/(1-r)$ for the sum of a geometric series.

However, there's a neater method, which is equivalent to using this formula. It's illustrated in the next example.

Example 16   *Finding a fraction equivalent to a recurring decimal*

Find a fraction equivalent to $0.123\,123\,123\ldots$.

Solution

Put $s = 0.123\,123\,123\ldots$.

🔍 The repeating group, '123', is 3 digits long, so multiply s by 10^3. 💬

Then

$$1000s = 123.123\,123\,123\ldots = 123 + s.$$

Hence $999s = 123$, so

$$s = \frac{123}{999} = \frac{41}{333}.$$

To find a fraction equivalent to a recurring decimal that has one or more non-zero digits before the recurring part, you can apply the method of Example 16 to find a fraction equivalent to the recurring part, and then add this to the number formed by the other digits. For example, by the solution to Example 16,

$$1.123\,123\,123\ldots = 1 + \frac{41}{333} = \frac{374}{333}.$$

Activity 27   *Finding fractions equivalent to recurring decimals*

Find a fraction equivalent to each of the following numbers.

(a) $0.454\,545\ldots$ (b) $3.729\,729\,729\ldots$

We'll now look at what happens when you try to sum an infinite *arithmetic* series.

Infinite arithmetic series

Every infinite arithmetic series has the form

$$a + (a + d) + (a + 2d) + \cdots,$$

where a is the first term and d is the common difference.

The situation for infinite arithmetic series is much simpler than for infinite geometric series. In summary, the only infinite arithmetic series that has a sum is the infinite series with first term 0 and common difference 0, that is, the series $0 + 0 + 0 + \cdots$, which has sum 0. You can see this by using an approach similar to the one used earlier for infinite geometric series. You use the fact that each partial sum of an infinite arithmetic series is the sum of a *finite* arithmetic series, and apply the formula for the sum of a finite arithmetic series that you met in Subsection 4.1, as follows.

Consider the infinite arithmetic series with first term a and common difference d:

$$a + (a + d) + (a + 2d) + \cdots .$$

The nth term of its sequence of partial sums is

$$s_n = a + (a + d) + (a + 2d) + \cdots + (a + (n - 1)d).$$

This is the sum of a finite arithmetic series with first term a, common difference d and n terms. So, by formula (5) on page 52, we have

$$s_n = \tfrac{1}{2}n(2a + (n - 1)d).$$

If $d \neq 0$, then the expression on the right-hand side of this equation is a quadratic expression in n, so s_n tends to infinity or minus infinity. If $d = 0$, then $s_n = na$, so again s_n tends to infinity or minus infinity, as long as $a \neq 0$. Therefore, provided that a and d are not both zero, the series doesn't have a sum.

4.3 Sigma notation

There's a useful notation for writing series concisely. It can be used for both finite and infinite series, but we'll begin by looking at how it's used for finite series.

For any sequence (x_n), the sum

$$x_p + x_{p+1} + \cdots + x_q$$

(that is, the sum of the terms from the pth term to the qth term) is denoted by

$$\sum_{n=p}^{q} x_n. \tag{8}$$

(This is read as 'the sum from n equals p to q of x-sub-n.) This notation is called **sigma notation** or **summation notation** – the symbol $\sum$ is the upper-case Greek letter sigma. The numbers p and q, which tell you the terms to start and finish at, respectively, are called the **lower** and **upper limits** of the summation, respectively, and the variable n is called an **index variable**. For example, with this notation we can write

$$2 + 2^2 + 2^3 + 2^4 + 2^5 = \sum_{n=1}^{5} 2^n,$$

and

$$(3 \times 4) + (3 \times 5) + (3 \times 6) + \cdots + (3 \times 20) = \sum_{n=4}^{20} 3n.$$

The index variable n in sigma notation is a dummy variable – you can use any other variable name in its place. For example,

$$2 + 2^2 + 2^3 + 2^4 + 2^5 = \sum_{n=1}^{5} 2^n = \sum_{j=1}^{5} 2^j = \sum_{k=1}^{5} 2^k.$$

In this module we'll usually use n or k for the index variable in sigma notation. Sometimes for a finite series it's natural to use n to denote the upper limit, and in that situation we'll use k for the index variable.

When sigma notation is in a line of text, it's sometimes written with the limits to the right of, instead of below and above, the symbol $\sum$. For example, expression (8) can be written as $\sum_{n=p}^{q} x_n$.

Example 17 *Converting from and to sigma notation*

(a) Write each of the following sums without sigma notation, giving the first three terms and the last.

   (i) $\displaystyle\sum_{n=1}^{7} n$ (ii) $\displaystyle\sum_{n=4}^{19} n^2$ (iii) $\displaystyle\sum_{n=1}^{17} (n+3)$

(b) Write each of the following sums in sigma notation.

   (i) $3^3 + 4^3 + 5^3 + \cdots + 9^3$

   (ii) $1 + 2 + 3 + \cdots + n$

   (iii) The finite geometric series $a + ar + ar^2 + \cdots + ar^{n-1}$.

Solution

(a)   In each case, put n equal in turn to each of the integers from the lower to the upper limit of the sum, and add the resulting terms.

The sums are as follows.

   (i) $\displaystyle\sum_{n=1}^{7} n = 1 + 2 + 3 + \cdots + 7$

   (ii) $\displaystyle\sum_{n=4}^{19} n^2 = 4^2 + 5^2 + 6^2 + \cdots + 19^2$

   (iii) $\displaystyle\sum_{n=1}^{17} (n+3) = 4 + 5 + 6 + \cdots + 20$

(b) 🔍 In each case, find an expression for a typical term of the sum, then identify the lower and upper limits. 💬

(i)   The sum is $3^3 + 4^3 + 5^3 + \cdots + 9^3$.

🔍 The terms are of the form n^3, going from $n = 3$ to $n = 9$. 💬

It can be written as $\displaystyle\sum_{n=3}^{9} n^3$.

(ii)   The sum is $1 + 2 + 3 + \cdots + n$.

🔍 The sum already contains the variable name n, so we have to use a different letter for the index variable, say k. The terms are of the form k, going from $k = 1$ to $k = n$. 💬

It can be written as $\displaystyle\sum_{k=1}^{n} k$.

(iii)   The sum is $a + ar + ar^2 + \cdots + ar^{n-1}$.

🔍 Again we have to use a letter other than n for the index variable, say k. The terms are of the form ar^{k-1}, going from $k = 1$ to $k = n$. (Recall that $ar^0 = a \times 1 = a$ and that $ar^1 = ar$.) 💬

It can be written as $\displaystyle\sum_{k=1}^{n} ar^{k-1}$.

This sum can also be written as $\displaystyle\sum_{k=0}^{n-1} ar^k$.

Activity 28   *Converting from and to sigma notation*

(a) Write each of the following sums without sigma notation, giving the first three terms and the last.

(i) $\displaystyle\sum_{n=5}^{20} n^4$ (ii) $\displaystyle\sum_{n=4}^{19} (n+1)^4$ (iii) $\displaystyle\sum_{n=1}^{6} (2n-1)$

(b) Write each of the following sums in sigma notation.

(i) $1 + 2 + 3 + \cdots + 150$

(ii) $5^2 + 6^2 + 7^2 + \cdots + 13^2$

(iii) $2 + 2^2 + 2^3 + \cdots + 2^{12}$

You might have noticed that the series in Activity 28(a)(i) and (ii) are the same, even though they're written differently in sigma notation. The same applies to the two alternative expressions given in the solution to

Example 17(b)(iii). In general, any series can be written in many different ways using sigma notation, even if you use the same index variable.

The formulas that you met earlier for the sums of finite arithmetic and geometric series can be stated concisely using sigma notation, as in the box below. We use k for the index variable since the upper limit is n in each series. In fact we'll use k as the index variable in the rest of this subsection, since the upper limit is sometimes n.

Sums of finite arithmetic and geometric series (in sigma notation)

$$\sum_{k=1}^{n}(a + (k-1)d) = \tfrac{1}{2}n(2a + (n-1)d)$$

$$\sum_{k=1}^{n}ar^{k-1} = \frac{a(1-r^n)}{1-r} \quad (r \neq 1)$$

Similarly, the formulas for the sum of the first n natural numbers, the sum of the first n square numbers and the sum of the first n cube numbers can be stated concisely using sigma notation, as in the box below. The box also includes, at the beginning, the simple formula for adding up n copies of the number 1, which is sometimes useful when you're working with series in sigma notation, as you'll see shortly.

Sums of standard finite series (in sigma notation)

$$\sum_{k=1}^{n}1 = n$$

$$\sum_{k=1}^{n}k = \tfrac{1}{2}n(n+1)$$

$$\sum_{k=1}^{n}k^2 = \tfrac{1}{6}n(n+1)(2n+1)$$

$$\sum_{k=1}^{n}k^3 = \tfrac{1}{4}n^2(n+1)^2$$

Activity 29 *Using formulas in sigma notation*

Use the formulas in the box above to find the sums of the following series.

(a) $\displaystyle\sum_{k=1}^{24}k$ (b) $\displaystyle\sum_{k=1}^{24}k^2$

Sigma notation allows you to work more easily with complicated finite series, and hence find their sums efficiently. To do this, you need to become familiar with a few rules for manipulating finite series in sigma notation. These are stated in the following box, and explained after the box.

Rules for manipulating finite series in sigma notation

$$\sum_{k=p}^{q} cx_k = c \sum_{k=p}^{q} x_k \quad \text{(where } c \text{ is a constant)}$$

$$\sum_{k=p}^{q} (x_k + y_k) = \sum_{k=p}^{q} x_k + \sum_{k=p}^{q} y_k$$

$$\sum_{k=p}^{q} x_k = \sum_{k=1}^{q} x_k - \sum_{k=1}^{p-1} x_k \quad \text{(where } 1 < p \le q)$$

The second rule in the box also holds if you replace the plus signs by minus signs:

$$\sum_{k=p}^{q} (x_k - y_k) = \sum_{k=p}^{q} x_k - \sum_{k=p}^{q} y_k.$$

To see why these rules hold, you can translate them from sigma notation into the usual, longer notation for sums. When you do this, the first rule becomes

$$cx_p + cx_{p+1} + \cdots + cx_q = c(x_p + x_{p+1} + \cdots + x_q).$$

This is just the usual rule for multiplying out brackets.

The second rule becomes

$$(x_p + y_p) + (x_{p+1} + y_{p+1}) + \cdots + (x_q + y_q)$$
$$= (x_p + x_{p+1} + \cdots + x_q) + (y_p + y_{p+1} + \cdots + y_q).$$

This rule holds simply because you can add numbers in any order. A similar argument shows that the version with minus signs holds. (Alternatively, you can deduce the version with minus signs by combining the first two rules in the box, taking $c = -1$.)

Finally, the third rule becomes

$$x_p + x_{p+1} + \cdots + x_q$$
$$= (x_1 + x_2 + \cdots + x_q) - (x_1 + x_2 + \cdots + x_{p-1})$$

This rule says that if you split a series into two parts, then the sum of the second part is equal to the sum of the whole series minus the sum of the first part. You were asked to use this fact in Activity 25(b) on page 55.

The next example illustrates how you can use the rules for manipulating finite series, together with some of the standard formulas for the sums of finite series, to find the sums of some other finite series.

Example 18 *Using series manipulations to find the sums of finite series*

Find the sums of the following finite series.

(a) $\displaystyle\sum_{k=1}^{25}(k^2 + 2k)$ (b) $\displaystyle\sum_{k=50}^{100}(9k - 4)$

Solution

(a) ⚲ Use the rules for manipulating series to express the series in terms of simpler series. 💬

$$\sum_{k=1}^{25}(k^2 + 2k) = \sum_{k=1}^{25}k^2 + \sum_{k=1}^{25}2k$$
$$= \sum_{k=1}^{25}k^2 + 2\sum_{k=1}^{25}k$$

⚲ Use the formulas for the sums of standard series. 💬

$$= \tfrac{1}{6}(25)(25 + 1)(2 \times 25 + 1) + 2 \times \tfrac{1}{2}(25)(25 + 1)$$
$$= \tfrac{1}{6} \times 25 \times 26 \times 51 + 25 \times 26$$
$$= 5525 + 650$$
$$= 6175$$

(b) ⚲ The lower limit isn't 1, so start by applying the third rule for manipulating series. 💬

$$\sum_{k=50}^{100}(9k - 4) = \sum_{k=1}^{100}(9k - 4) - \sum_{k=1}^{49}(9k - 4)$$

⚲ Now use the other rules to express each of the series on the right-hand side in terms of simpler series. 💬

Now

$$\sum_{k=1}^{100}(9k - 4) = \sum_{k=1}^{100}9k - \sum_{k=1}^{100}4$$
$$= 9\sum_{k=1}^{100}k - 4\sum_{k=1}^{100}1$$
$$= 9 \times \tfrac{1}{2} \times 100 \times (100 + 1) - 4 \times 100$$
$$= 45\,450 - 400$$
$$= 45\,050.$$

Similarly,

$$\sum_{k=1}^{49}(9k-4) = \sum_{k=1}^{49}9k - \sum_{k=1}^{49}4$$

$$= 9\sum_{k=1}^{49}k - 4\sum_{k=1}^{49}1$$

$$= 9 \times \tfrac{1}{2} \times 49 \times (49+1) - 4 \times 49$$

$$= 11\,025 - 196$$

$$= 10\,829.$$

Hence

$$\sum_{k=50}^{100}(9k-4) = 45\,050 - 10\,829 = 34\,221.$$

Activity 30 *Using series manipulations to find the sums of finite series*

Find the sums of the following finite series.

(a) $\displaystyle\sum_{k=1}^{30}(2k^3 - k)$ (b) $\displaystyle\sum_{k=1}^{40}(\tfrac{1}{4}k^2 - 1)$ (c) $\displaystyle\sum_{k=65}^{125}(6k + 7)$

Sigma notation for infinite series

To write an infinite series in sigma notation, you write the symbol ∞ in place of the upper limit. For example,

$$\tfrac{1}{2} + \left(\tfrac{1}{2}\right)^2 + \left(\tfrac{1}{2}\right)^3 + \left(\tfrac{1}{2}\right)^4 + \cdots = \sum_{n=1}^{\infty}\left(\tfrac{1}{2}\right)^n .$$

Activity 31 *Using sigma notation for infinite series*

Write the following infinite series in sigma notation.

(a) $\tfrac{1}{5} + \left(\tfrac{1}{5}\right)^2 + \left(\tfrac{1}{5}\right)^3 + \cdots$

(b) $\left(\tfrac{1}{2}\right)^3 + \left(\tfrac{1}{2}\right)^4 + \left(\tfrac{1}{2}\right)^5 + \cdots$

(c) $1 + \left(\tfrac{1}{2}\right)^2 + \left(\tfrac{1}{3}\right)^2 + \left(\tfrac{1}{4}\right)^2 + \cdots$

The formula that you met earlier (on page 59) for the sum of an infinite geometric series can be stated concisely using sigma notation, as follows.

Sum of an infinite geometric series (in sigma notation)

If $-1 < r < 1$, then

$$\sum_{n=1}^{\infty} ar^{n-1} = \frac{a}{1-r}.$$

The rules for manipulating finite series in sigma notation, given in the box on page 66, apply also for infinite series once the upper limit q is replaced everywhere by ∞, provided that each series involved has a sum. Thus, for example, we have

$$\sum_{n=1}^{\infty} \left(\left(\tfrac{1}{2}\right)^n + \left(\tfrac{1}{3}\right)^n\right) = \sum_{n=1}^{\infty} \left(\tfrac{1}{2}\right)^n + \sum_{n=1}^{\infty} \left(\tfrac{1}{3}\right)^n$$

$$= \frac{\tfrac{1}{2}}{1 - \tfrac{1}{2}} + \frac{\tfrac{1}{3}}{1 - \tfrac{1}{3}}$$

$$= 1 + \frac{1}{2} = \frac{3}{2}.$$

4.4   Summing series using a computer

In the following activity you can learn how to use the module computer algebra system to work with series.

Activity 32   *Summing series on a computer*

Work through Subsection 11.2 of the *Computer algebra guide*.

5 The binomial theorem

In this final section you'll meet an important result, called the *binomial theorem*, which will help you to multiply out expressions such as

$$(1+x)^4, \quad (a+b)^7 \quad \text{and} \quad (2y-3)^5.$$

5.1 Expanding powers of binomials

In Subsection 2.3 of Unit 1, you saw how to expand squared brackets, such as

$$(x-5)^2, \quad (x+1)^2 \quad \text{and} \quad (2p-3q)^2. \tag{9}$$

For example,

$$\begin{aligned}(x-5)^2 &= (x-5)(x-5) \\ &= x^2 - 5x - 5x + 25 \\ &= x^2 - 10x + 25.\end{aligned}$$

Each of expressions (9) is of the form

$$(a+b)^2,$$

where a and b represent terms. For example, in the first expression $a = x$ and $b = -5$, and in the third one $a = 2p$ and $b = -3q$.

You saw in Unit 1 that the following general formula holds for multiplying out squared brackets:

$$(a+b)^2 = a^2 + 2ab + b^2. \tag{10}$$

So the square of the sum of two terms is equal to the square of the first term, plus twice the product of the two terms, plus the square of the second term.

The next example reminds you how equation (10) is applied.

Example 19   *Using the formula to expand squared brackets*

Use formula (10) to expand the expression

$$(2x-1)^2.$$

Solution

Substitute $a = 2x$ and $b = -1$ into the formula for $(a+b)^2$.

$$\begin{aligned}(2x-1)^2 &= (2x)^2 + 2(2x)(-1) + (-1)^2 \\ &= 4x^2 - 4x + 1\end{aligned}$$

In Unit 1 you also met the formula

$$(a-b)^2 = a^2 - 2ab + b^2, \tag{11}$$

but in fact formula (10) above is enough alone. For example, you saw in Example 19 that you can expand $(2x-1)^2$ by using formula (10) with $a = 2x$ and $b = -1$, as an alternative to using formula (11) with $a = 2x$ and $b = 1$.

> **Activity 33** *Using the formula to expand squared brackets*
>
> Use formula (10) to expand each of the following squared brackets.
>
> (a) $(c+5)^2$ (b) $(1-3x)^2$ (c) $(p^2-q^2)^2$

In Activity 33 you probably found that using formula (10) to expand the squared brackets is only a little quicker than just writing the expression as two pairs of brackets multiplied together and expanding them in the usual way. However, sometimes you have to expand *cubed* brackets, of the form $(a+b)^3$, or similar brackets raised to an even higher power. It's much quicker to use a formula to expand expressions like these. In this subsection you'll see a general formula for expanding any expression of the form

$$(a+b)^n,$$

where n is a natural number and a and b are terms. This formula is known as the *binomial theorem*. A **binomial** is an expression that is the sum of two terms, so $(a+b)^n$ is a *power of a binomial*.

> The word 'binomial' is derived from a Latin word meaning 'having two names', and is related to the word 'polynomial'.

You've seen and used a formula for $(a+b)^2$, so let's now find a formula for $(a+b)^3$. The easiest way to do this is to take the formula for $(a+b)^2$, and multiply it by $a+b$:

$$
\begin{aligned}
(a+b)^3 &= (a+b)(a+b)^2 \\
&= (a+b)(a^2+2ab+b^2) \\
&= a(a^2+2ab+b^2) + b(a^2+2ab+b^2) \\
&= a^3 + 2a^2b + ab^2 \\
& \quad + a^2b + 2ab^2 + b^3 \\
&= a^3 + 3a^2b + 3ab^2 + b^3.
\end{aligned}
$$

Notice that in the working above, the expression after the fourth equals sign has been written over two lines, with the like terms aligned in columns. This makes it easy to collect the like terms. The working shows that the formula for $(a+b)^3$ is

$$(a+b)^3 = a^3 + 3a^2b + 3ab^2 + b^3. \tag{12}$$

> **Activity 34** *Using the formula to expand cubed brackets*
>
> Use formula (12) to expand the following cubed brackets.
>
> (a) $(5+p)^3$ (b) $(1-2x)^3$ (c) $(2x+3y)^3$

So that you can begin to see what happens for higher powers of binomials, let's work out one more formula, for $(a+b)^4$. We take the formula for $(a+b)^3$ and multiply it by $a+b$:

$$
\begin{aligned}
(a+b)^4 &= (a+b)(a+b)^3 \\
&= (a+b)(a^3 + 3a^2b + 3ab^2 + b^3) \\
&= a(a^3 + 3a^2b + 3ab^2 + b^3) + b(a^3 + 3a^2b + 3ab^2 + b^3) \\
&= a^4 + 3a^3b + 3a^2b^2 + \ ab^3 \\
&\quad\ + \ a^3b + 3a^2b^2 + 3ab^3 + b^4 \\
&= a^4 + 4a^3b + 6a^2b^2 + 4ab^3 + b^4.
\end{aligned}
$$

So the formula for $(a+b)^4$ is

$$
(a+b)^4 = a^4 + 4a^3b + 6a^2b^2 + 4ab^3 + b^4.
$$

You could use the same method to find formulas for $(a+b)^5$, $(a+b)^6$ and so on: you just keep multiplying by $a+b$. The formulas that are obtained by doing this are shown below, along with the three formulas found above. The 'formulas' for $(a+b)^0$ and $(a+b)^1$ are also shown, as it's helpful to consider these as part of the general pattern. Remember that any number raised to the power 0 is 1. The right-hand sides of the formulas have been aligned at their centres, to make it easier to see a particular pattern in them, which will be described shortly.

$$
\begin{aligned}
(a+b)^0 &= 1 \\
(a+b)^1 &= a+b \\
(a+b)^2 &= a^2 + 2ab + b^2 \\
(a+b)^3 &= a^3 + 3a^2b + 3ab^2 + b^3 \\
(a+b)^4 &= a^4 + 4a^3b + 6a^2b^2 + 4ab^3 + b^4 \\
(a+b)^5 &= a^5 + 5a^4b + 10a^3b^2 + 10a^2b^3 + 5ab^4 + b^5 \\
(a+b)^6 &= a^6 + 6a^5b + 15a^4b^2 + 20a^3b^3 + 15a^2b^4 + 6ab^5 + b^6
\end{aligned}
$$

There are two useful things to observe about the formulas above.

First, notice that in each formula on the right-hand side, the powers in each term add up to the power of the brackets on the left-hand side. For example, look at the formula for $(a+b)^4$, and at the second term on the right-hand side, which is $4a^3b$. In this term, a has power 3 and b has power 1, and $3+1=4$, which is the power of the brackets in $(a+b)^4$. You can check that the powers add up to 4 in all the other terms in the formula for $(a+b)^4$.

You can see why this property holds for all the formulas if you look at, and think about, the working that produced the formulas for $(a+b)^2$, $(a+b)^3$ and $(a+b)^4$. Each new formula is produced by multiplying the formula before by $a+b$. When this is done, each term of the old formula is multiplied by a to give terms of the new formula, and separately multiplied by b to give further terms of the new formula (before the like terms are collected). This raises the sum of the powers in each term by 1. So, for example, since the sum of the powers in each term in the formula for

$(a+b)^2$ is 2, it follows that the sum of the powers in each term in the formula for $(a+b)^3$ is 3, and so on.

This property means that the terms on the right-hand side of each formula can be arranged in a standard order, as is done above. In the first term, a is raised to the same power as the brackets on the left-hand side. In each subsequent term, the power of a is decreased by 1 and the power of b is increased by 1 until, in the last term, b is raised to the same power as the brackets.

The second thing to notice about the formulas is that each coefficient on the right-hand side is the sum of the two adjacent coefficients in the line above. For example, the coefficient of a^4b^2 in the formula for $(a+b)^6$ is 15, which is the sum of the two adjacent coefficients 5 and 10 in the formula for $(a+b)^5$, as shown below.

$$(a+b)^5 = a^5 + 5a^4b + 10a^3b^2 + 10a^2b^3 + 5ab^4 + b^5$$

$$(a+b)^6 = a^6 + 6a^5b + 15a^4b^2 + 20a^3b^3 + 15a^2b^4 + 6ab^5 + b^6$$

To see why this always happens, again look at and think about the working for $(a+b)^3$ and $(a+b)^4$, at the steps where the like terms are aligned. You can see that each coefficient in each new formula is obtained by adding two adjacent coefficients from the formula before.

This means that you can find the coefficients for any of the formulas from the triangular array below, which is known as **Pascal's triangle**. The array has 1s down each edge, and each of its other numbers is the sum of the two adjacent numbers in the line above. It can be continued indefinitely.

```
(a + b)⁰                            1
(a + b)¹                        1        1
(a + b)²                    1       2       1
(a + b)³                1       3       3       1
(a + b)⁴            1       4       6       4       1
(a + b)⁵        1       5      10      10       5       1
(a + b)⁶    1       6      15      20      15       6       1
```

Notice that the array is symmetrical – the numbers in each row are the same whether you read them from left to right or from right to left.

Pascal's triangle contains many interesting sequences. For example, look at the diagonal lines of numbers. The first diagonal is $1, 1, 1, 1, 1, \ldots$, and the second diagonal contains the natural numbers $1, 2, 3, 4, 5, \ldots$. The third diagonal contains the numbers $1, 3, 6, 10, 15, \ldots$, which are known as the **triangular numbers**, because they correspond to triangular patterns of dots, as shown in Figure 26. There are many other less obvious patterns in the triangle.

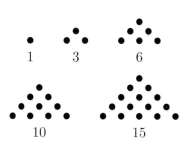

Figure 26 Triangular numbers

Activity 35   *Using Pascal's triangle to find a formula for $(a+b)^7$*

(a) Calculate the row of Pascal's triangle that gives the coefficients for the formula for $(a+b)^7$.

(b) Hence write down the formula for $(a+b)^7$.

Activity 36   *Expanding an expression of the form $(a+b)^n$*

For each of the following expressions, use one of the formulas that you have seen in this subsection to expand the brackets.

(a) $(3x+2)^5$ (b) $(x-4y)^4$

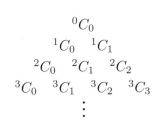

Figure 27   Notation for binomial coefficients

The numbers in Pascal's triangle are called **binomial coefficients**. They can be denoted as follows. If the rows of Pascal's triangle are numbered as row 0, row 1, row 2 and so on, and the coefficients within each row are numbered from left to right as coefficient 0, coefficient 1, coefficient 2 and so on, then coefficient k in row n is denoted by ^nC_k, as illustrated in Figure 27. For example,

$$^3C_0 = 1, \quad ^3C_1 = 3, \quad ^3C_2 = 3 \quad \text{and} \quad ^3C_3 = 1.$$

The letter C in this notation doesn't stand for 'coefficient', as you might expect, but rather for 'choose' or 'combination' – the reason for this is mentioned shortly. The notation ^nC_k is read as 'n choose k' or just as 'n C k'.

A common alternative notation for the binomial coefficients is

$$\binom{n}{k},$$

which is again read as 'n choose k'. (This notation has no connection with the column notation for two-dimensional vectors that you met in Unit 5, though it looks the same.)

With the notation ^nC_k, the general formula for $(a+b)^n$ can be written as follows.

The binomial theorem

For any natural number n,

$$(a+b)^n = {}^nC_0\, a^n + {}^nC_1\, a^{n-1}b + \cdots + {}^nC_{n-1}\, ab^{n-1} + {}^nC_n\, b^n,$$

where ^nC_k is coefficient k in row n of Pascal's triangle (where the rows, and the coefficients within each row, are numbered 0, 1, 2, …).

The right-hand side of the equation in the binomial theorem is known as the **binomial expansion** of $(a+b)^n$.

A good way to remember the terms in the equation in the binomial theorem is to use the fact that the powers of a and b on the right-hand side of the equation follow the pattern described earlier. In the first term a is raised to the same power as the brackets on the left-hand side, and in each subsequent term the power of a is decreased by 1 and the power of b is increased by 1, until in the last term b is raised to the same power as the brackets. To complete the expansion, you just need to include the coefficients of the terms, which are the binomial coefficients $^nC_0, {}^nC_1, {}^nC_2, \ldots, {}^nC_n$.

Intriguingly, the binomial coefficients also occur in a seemingly unrelated area of mathematics, concerned with finding answers to questions such as 'How many different sets of six lottery numbers can be chosen from 49 possible numbers?' This is the context which led to ^nC_k being read as 'n choose k'. You'll learn about it if you go on to study the module MST125 *Essential mathematics 2*.

Pascal's triangle is named after the French mathematician and philosopher Blaise Pascal. He was far from the first person to study this array of numbers, but his work on it in his *Traité du Triangle Arithmétique* was influential. Research on binomial coefficients was also carried out at about the same time by John Wallis (1616–1703) and then by Isaac Newton (1642–1727), who discovered that the binomial theorem can be generalised to negative and fractional powers. You'll learn about this in Unit 11.

Pascal contributed to many other areas of mathematics in his short life. He worked on conic sections and projective geometry, and, together with Pierre de Fermat, laid the foundations for the theory of probability.

Pascal's triangle was studied centuries earlier by the Chinese mathematician Yanghui and the Persian astronomer and poet Omar Khayyám, and is known as the Yanghui triangle in China (see Figure 28).

Blaise Pascal (1623–1662)

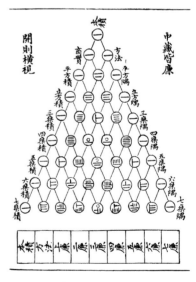

Figure 28 The Yanghui triangle (Pascal's triangle), from a publication of Zhu Shijie, AD 1303

5.2 A formula for binomial coefficients

Pascal's triangle is a convenient way to obtain the binomial coefficients for fairly small values of n. However, it would be tedious to obtain a particular coefficient in the expansion of $(a+b)^{12}$, say, by using Pascal's triangle. It is therefore desirable to have a closed-form formula for ^nC_k, and you'll meet such a formula in this subsection. First you need to learn about *factorials*, which occur in the formula for ^nC_k.

For any natural number n, the product of all the natural numbers up to and including n is called the **factorial** of n, and denoted by $n!$ (this notation is read as 'n factorial' or 'factorial n'). So

$$n! = 1 \times 2 \times 3 \times \cdots \times n.$$

For example,

$$5! = 1 \times 2 \times 3 \times 4 \times 5 = 120.$$

We also define

$$0! = 1,$$

because this interpretation of $0!$ works well with formulas that involve factorials, as you'll see shortly.

The values of $n!$ increase rapidly as n increases. The first few values are shown in Table 1.

Table 1 Values of $n!$

n	0	1	2	3	4	5	6	7	8	9	10
$n!$	1	1	2	6	24	120	720	5040	40 320	362 880	3 628 800

Many calculators can evaluate $n!$, often for values of n up to 69. (The value of 69! is about 1.7×10^{98}, whereas 70! is about 1.2×10^{100}. Typically, calculators don't carry out calculations that involve numbers greater in magnitude than 10^{100}.)

Notice that

$$1! = 1 \times 0!, \quad 2! = 2 \times 1!, \quad 3! = 3 \times 2!, \quad \text{and so on.}$$

In general, $n!$ can be expressed in terms of $(n-1)!$ as follows:

$$n! = n(n-1)! \quad (n = 1, 2, 3, \ldots).$$

So the sequence of factorials, $1, 1, 2, 6, 24, 120, \ldots$, is generated by the recurrence system

$$c_0 = 1, \qquad c_n = nc_{n-1} \quad (n = 1, 2, 3, \ldots).$$

You met this recurrence system, and its first few terms, in Example 3(c) on page 13.

There's a formula for the binomial coefficients that can be stated concisely in terms of factorials, as below. You'll see a justification of this formula at the end of this section.

If n and k are integers with $0 \le k \le n$, then

$$^nC_k = \frac{n!}{k!\,(n-k)!}. \tag{13}$$

For example, this formula gives
$$^5C_2 = \frac{5!}{2!\,3!} = \frac{120}{2\times 6} = 10,$$
which accords with the value of $^5C_2$ in Pascal's triangle.

When you use the formula above to evaluate binomial coefficients by hand, it's generally best *not* to evaluate the three factorials in the formula and then do the division. There's usually an easier and quicker way to proceed. To see this, consider the following calculation of $^7C_3$ using the formula, which is written out in full:
$$^7C_3 = \frac{7!}{3!\,4!} = \frac{7\times 6\times 5\times 4\times 3\times 2\times 1}{(3\times 2\times 1)\times(4\times 3\times 2\times 1)}.$$
The two occurrences of $4\times 3\times 2\times 1$ on the top and bottom cancel out, so
$$^7C_3 = \frac{7\times 6\times 5}{3\times 2\times 1}.$$
We can now do some more cancelling, and hence obtain the value $^7C_3 = 35$.

In general, whenever you use formula (13) to work out a value of ^nC_k, where k is not equal to either 0 or n, the factorial $(n-k)!$ in the denominator cancels with the 'tail' of the factorial $n!$ in the numerator. The numerator then contains the product of all the integers from n down to the integer that's one larger than $n-k$, and the denominator contains just $k!$. So, when k is not equal to 0 or n, formula (13) can be restated in the following form, which is not as neat but usually easier to apply. In fact this form of the formula also applies when $k = n$, but in this case it's just as easy to use the original form.

If n and k are integers with $0 < k \le n$, then
$$^nC_k = \frac{n(n-1)\cdots(n-k+1)}{k(k-1)\cdots 1}.$$

This formula has k factors on the bottom and also k factors on the top. So, to apply it, you start with the integer n on the top and the integer k on the bottom, and for each of these integers you keep multiplying by the next integer down until you have k factors in total.

This is illustrated in the next example, but first here's one more fact to keep in mind when you're evaluating binomial coefficients. Remember that the binomial coefficients in each row of Pascal's triangle are the same no matter whether you read them from left to right or right to left. In other words, we have the following general fact.

$$^nC_k = {}^nC_{n-k}$$

So, for example, if you want to evaluate $^{10}C_7$ using the method described above, then it's better to evaluate $^{10}C_{10-7}$, that is, $^{10}C_3$, instead. You'll get the same answer, but the working will be easier, because you'll have only 3 factors on each of the top and bottom of the fraction, instead of 7.

Example 20 *Evaluating binomial coefficients using the formula*

Evaluate the following binomial coefficients without using a calculator.

(a) $^9C_4$ (b) $^{17}C_{15}$ (c) $^4C_4$

Solution

(a) 🔍 Write down a fraction with 9 on the top and 4 on the bottom. For each of these integers, keep multiplying by the next integer down until you have 4 factors. 💬

$$^9C_4 = \frac{9 \times 8 \times 7 \times 6}{4 \times 3 \times 2 \times 1}$$

🔍 Do all the cancelling that you can do, and hence evaluate the fraction. 💬

$$= 9 \times 2 \times 7 = 126$$

(b) 🔍 Use the fact that $^{17}C_{15} = {}^{17}C_{17-15}$, then proceed as in part (a). 💬

$$^{17}C_{15} = {}^{17}C_2 = \frac{17 \times 16}{2 \times 1} = 17 \times 8 = 136$$

(c) 🔍 Since $n = k$ here, use the original form of formula (13), rather than the alternative form. Remember that $0! = 1$. 💬

$$^4C_4 = \frac{4!}{4!\,0!} = \frac{4!}{4! \times 1} = 1$$

Activity 37 *Evaluating binomial coefficients using the formula*

Evaluate each of the following without using a calculator.

(a) $^8C_4$ (b) $^{12}C_{10}$ (c) $^5C_5$ (d) $^5C_0$ (e) $^{21}C_{20}$

Another way to evaluate binomial coefficients is simply to use your calculator. (You should find that ^nC_r is a function for one of the buttons.)

Activity 38 *Evaluating binomial coefficients using a calculator*

Evaluate each of the following by using a calculator.

(a) $^{25}C_{19}$ (b) $^{32}C_{17}$

The binomial coefficients were known to early Islamic mathematicians. For example, al-Karajī, who flourished early in the 11th century, provided a table of binomial coefficients in a text (now lost but known through a copy in *The Brilliant in Algebra* by al-Samaw'al (1125–1174)), while the formula for them was given by al-Kāshī (d. 1429) in his book *The Calculator's Key*. A proof that this formula is correct was given by Pascal.

5.3   Working with the binomial theorem

In Subsection 5.1 you saw a statement of the binomial theorem, as follows:
For any natural number n,
$$(a+b)^n = {}^nC_0\,a^n + {}^nC_1\,a^{n-1}b + \cdots + {}^nC_{n-1}\,ab^{n-1} + {}^nC_n\,b^n,$$
where ${}^nC_k$ is coefficient k in row n of Pascal's triangle (where the rows, and the coefficients within each row, are numbered $0, 1, 2, \ldots$).

In Subsection 5.2 it was stated that the binomial coefficients are given by
$$\tag{13} {}^nC_k = \frac{n!}{k!\,(n-k)!}.$$

Hence the binomial theorem can now be restated, without direct reference to Pascal's triangle, as follows.

The binomial theorem (restated)

For any natural number n,
$$(a+b)^n = {}^nC_0\,a^n + {}^nC_1\,a^{n-1}b + \cdots + {}^nC_{n-1}\,ab^{n-1} + {}^nC_n\,b^n,$$
where
$$ {}^nC_k = \frac{n!}{k!\,(n-k)!} \quad (k = 0, 1, 2, \ldots, n).$$

The binomial theorem can also be written in sigma notation, as follows.

The binomial theorem (sigma notation)

For any natural number n,
$$(a+b)^n = \sum_{k=0}^{n} {}^nC_k\,a^{n-k}b^k = \sum_{k=0}^{n} \frac{n!}{k!\,(n-k)!}\,a^{n-k}b^k.$$

It's useful to be familiar with the first few binomial coefficients in the expansion of $(a+b)^n$. The formula for ${}^nC_r$ gives
$$ {}^nC_0 = 1, \quad {}^nC_1 = n, \quad {}^nC_2 = \frac{n(n-1)}{2!}, \quad {}^nC_3 = \frac{n(n-1)(n-2)}{3!}.$$

Example 21   *Using the binomial theorem*

Use the binomial theorem to find the first four terms in the expansion of each of the following expressions.

(a) $(x+y)^8$ (b) $(2-x)^7$

Solution

(a) In the binomial theorem, put $n = 8$, $a = x$ and $b = y$.

The first four terms in the binomial expansion of $(x+y)^8$ are

$$x^8 + {}^8C_1 x^7 y + {}^8C_2 x^6 y^2 + {}^8C_3 x^5 y^3$$
$$= x^8 + 8x^7 y + \frac{8 \times 7}{2!} x^6 y^2 + \frac{8 \times 7 \times 6}{3!} x^5 y^3$$
$$= x^8 + 8x^7 y + 28x^6 y^2 + 56x^5 y^3.$$

(b) In the binomial theorem, put $n = 7$, $a = 2$ and $b = -x$.

The first four terms in the binomial expansion of $(2-x)^7$ are

$$2^7 + {}^7C_1 \times 2^6 (-x) + {}^7C_2 \times 2^5 (-x)^2 + {}^7C_3 \times 2^4 (-x)^3$$
$$= 2^7 - 7 \times 2^6 x + \frac{7 \times 6}{2!} \times 2^5 x^2 - \frac{7 \times 6 \times 5}{3!} \times 2^4 x^3$$
$$= 128 - 448x + 672x^2 - 560x^3.$$

Activity 39   *Using the binomial theorem*

Use the binomial theorem to find the first four terms in the expansion of each of the following expressions.

(a) $(1+x)^{10}$ (b) $\left(2 + \tfrac{1}{3}x\right)^{10}$

Sometimes it's useful to find a particular term in a binomial expansion. The next example demonstrates how to do this.

Example 22   *Finding a particular term in a binomial expansion*

Find the coefficient of $x^{12}y^9$ in the expansion of

$$\left(2x - \tfrac{1}{2}y\right)^{21}.$$

Solution

By the binomial theorem, each term in the expansion is of the form

$$^{21}C_k(2x)^{21-k}\left(-\tfrac{1}{2}y\right)^k = {}^{21}C_k \times 2^{21-k}x^{21-k}\left(-\tfrac{1}{2}\right)^k y^k$$

🔍 Write the powers of x and y at the end, and simplify the powers of 2. 💬

$$= {}^{21}C_k(-1)^k 2^{21-k}2^{-k}x^{21-k}y^k$$
$$= {}^{21}C_k(-1)^k 2^{21-2k}x^{21-k}y^k.$$

The term in $x^{12}y^9$ is obtained when $k = 9$. Hence the coefficient of $x^{12}y^9$ is

$$^{21}C_9(-1)^9 2^{21-2\times9} = -{}^{21}C_9 \times 2^3$$

🔍 Use a calculator to evaluate $^{21}C_9$. 💬

$$= -293\,930 \times 8$$
$$= -2351\,440.$$

Activity 40   Finding particular terms in binomial expansions

(a) Find the coefficient of a^6b^5 in the expansion of $(a + b)^{11}$.

(b) Find the coefficient of c^5d^{15} in the expansion of $(3c - d)^{20}$.

Here's a slightly more complicated example.

Example 23   Finding a particular term in another binomial expansion

Find the coefficient of p^4 in the expansion of

$$\left(p^2 + \frac{1}{3p}\right)^{17}.$$

Give your answer as a fraction in its lowest terms.

Solution

By the binomial theorem, each term in the expansion is of the form

$$^{17}C_k\left(p^2\right)^{17-k}\left(\frac{1}{3p}\right)^k = {}^{17}C_k \times p^{2(17-k)}\left(\frac{1}{3}\right)^k\left(\frac{1}{p}\right)^k$$

🗨 Simplify the powers of p. 🗨

$$= {}^{17}C_k \left(\frac{1}{3^k}\right) p^{34-2k} p^{-k}$$

$$= {}^{17}C_k \left(\frac{1}{3^k}\right) p^{34-3k}.$$

For the term in p^4, we need

$$34 - 3k = 4,$$

which gives $30 = 3k$; that is, $k = 10$. Hence the coefficient of p^4 is

$$ {}^{17}C_{10}\left(\frac{1}{3^{10}}\right) = \frac{19\,448}{59\,049}.$$

Activity 41 *Finding particular terms in more binomial expansions*

(a) Find the constant term in the expansion of

$$\left(x - \frac{1}{x}\right)^{12}.$$

(b) Consider the expansion of

$$\left(h - \frac{3}{2h^2}\right)^{15}.$$

   (i) Find the coefficient of h^3.

   (ii) Find the coefficient of h^{-12}.

   (iii) Show that there is no term in h^2.

An important special case of the binomial theorem, which occurs frequently, is obtained by taking $a = 1$ and $b = x$. This gives the following expansion.

For each natural number n,

$$(1+x)^n = 1 + {}^nC_1 x + {}^nC_2 x^2 + \cdots + {}^nC_k x^k + \cdots + x^n$$

$$= 1 + nx + \frac{n(n-1)}{2!}x^2 + \frac{n(n-1)(n-2)}{3!}x^3 + \cdots + x^n.$$

Activity 42   *Applying a special case of the binomial theorem*

Use the form of the binomial theorem in the box above to evaluate the first six terms of the expansion of $(1-x)^{17}$.

Various interesting results can be obtained by choosing particular values for a and b in the statement of the binomial theorem. For example, if $a = b = 1$, we have that

$$1 + {}^nC_1 + {}^nC_2 + {}^nC_3 + \cdots + {}^nC_{n-1} + 1 = 2^n.$$

In sigma notation, this is

$$\sum_{k=0}^{n} {}^nC_k = 2^n.$$

Hence, for each natural number n, the finite series formed from the sequence of binomial coefficients ${}^nC_k$, $k = 0, 1, 2, \ldots, n$, has sum 2^n. In other words, the nth row of Pascal's triangle has sum 2^n.

A proof of the formula for the binomial coefficients

We can prove that the formula

$$ {}^nC_k = \frac{n!}{k!\,(n-k)!} \tag{14}$$

is correct by proving the following two facts.

1.   Formula (14) gives the correct result for each of the 'edge values' of Pascal's triangle – that is, for $n = 0, 1, 2, \ldots$,

$$ {}^nC_0 = 1 \text{ and } {}^nC_n = 1.$$

2.   Formula (14) has the key property of Pascal's triangle described on page 73 – that is, each binomial coefficient (apart from the edge values) in each row is the sum of the two adjacent coefficients in the row above.

Fact 1 holds because, for $n = 0, 1, 2, \ldots$, formula (14) gives

$$ {}^nC_0 = \frac{n!}{n!\,0!} = 1 \quad \text{and} \quad {}^nC_n = \frac{n!}{0!\,n!} = 1.$$

Proving fact 2 takes more work. Consider any binomial coefficient ${}^nC_k$ that isn't an edge value (so $k \neq 0$ and $k \neq n$) in row n of Pascal's triangle. The two adjacent coefficients in the row above (row $n-1$) are

$$ {}^{n-1}C_{k-1} \quad \text{and} \quad {}^{n-1}C_k.$$

Fact 2 can therefore be expressed algebraically as the equation

$$ {}^nC_k = {}^{n-1}C_{k-1} + {}^{n-1}C_k, \tag{15}$$

for $n = 2, 3, 4, \ldots$ and $k = 1, 2, 3, \ldots, n-1$. We now verify that this equation holds.

The formula

$$^nC_k = \frac{n!}{k!\,(n-k)!}$$

gives

$$^{n-1}C_k = \frac{(n-1)!}{k!\,((n-1)-k)!} = \frac{(n-1)!}{k!\,(n-k-1)!}$$

and

$$^{n-1}C_{k-1} = \frac{(n-1)!}{(k-1)!\,((n-1)-(k-1))!} = \frac{(n-1)!}{(k-1)!\,(n-k)!}.$$

Hence the expression on the right-hand side of equation (15) is

$$^{n-1}C_{k-1} + {}^{n-1}C_k = \frac{(n-1)!}{(k-1)!\,(n-k)!} + \frac{(n-1)!}{k!\,(n-k-1)!}.$$

Multiplying the top and bottom of the first fraction by k, and the top and bottom of the second fraction by $n-k$, gives

$$^{n-1}C_{k-1} + {}^{n-1}C_k = \frac{k\,(n-1)!}{k!\,(n-k)!} + \frac{(n-k)\,(n-1)!}{k!\,(n-k)!}$$

$$= \frac{(k+n-k)\,(n-1)!}{k!\,(n-k)!}$$

$$= \frac{n(n-1)!}{k!\,(n-k)!} = \frac{n!}{k!\,(n-k)!} = {}^nC_k,$$

which is the left-hand side of equation (15). This completes the proof.

Learning outcomes

After studying this unit, you should be able to:

- understand and use standard terminology and notation for sequences
- find the parameters of an arithmetic or geometric sequence from the first few terms, and hence write down a recurrence system for the sequence
- find a closed form for an arithmetic or geometric sequence, given the first few terms of the sequence or a recurrence system for it
- draw the graph of the first few terms of a sequence
- determine the long-term behaviour of certain simple sequences
- find the sum of a finite arithmetic or geometric series
- where possible, find the sum of an infinite geometric series
- understand the link between Pascal's triangle and binomial expansions
- find terms in the binomial expansion of an expression of the form $(a+b)^n$, by applying the binomial theorem and evaluating binomial coefficients.

Solutions to activities

Solution to Activity 1

(a) The first term of the sequence

$(b_n)_{n=1}^{\infty}$ with terms 1, 4, 7, 10, 13, 16, 19, ...

is the term with subscript 1; that is, $b_1 = 1$.
The fourth term is $b_4 = 10$.

(b) Counting along the terms of the sequence,
16 is the 6th term. Hence if $b_n = 16$, then $n = 6$.

(c) No, b_0 is not defined, because 0 is not included
in the range of values $n = 1, 2, 3, \ldots$.

Solution to Activity 2

(a) $a_1 = 7$, $a_2 = 14$, $a_3 = 21$, $a_4 = 28$, $a_5 = 35$,
$a_{100} = 700$.

(b) $b_1 = 1$, $b_2 = \frac{1}{2}$, $b_3 = \frac{1}{3}$, $b_4 = \frac{1}{4}$, $b_5 = \frac{1}{5}$,
$b_{100} = \frac{1}{100}$.

(You may have converted these simple fractions
to decimals, but there is no need to do this in
such cases.)

(c) $c_1 = (-1)^{1+1} = (-1)^2 = 1$,
$c_2 = (-1)^{2+1} = (-1)^3 = -1$,
$c_3 = 1$, $c_4 = -1$, $c_5 = 1$, $c_{100} = -1$.

(d) $d_1 = (-1)^1 \times 1 = -1$,
$d_2 = (-1)^2 \times 2 = 2$,
$d_3 = -3$, $d_4 = 4$, $d_5 = -5$, $d_{100} = 100$.

(e) $e_1 = (-2)^1 = -2$,
$e_2 = (-2)^2 = 4$,
$e_3 = -8$, $e_4 = 16$, $e_5 = -32$,
$e_{100} = (-2)^{100} = 1.27 \times 10^{30}$ (to 3 s.f.).

Solution to Activity 3

(a) We have $a_1 = 1$, $a_2 = 2$, $a_3 = 3$, $a_4 = 4$.
A closed form is

$$a_n = n \quad (n = 1, 2, 3, \ldots),$$

and the 10th term is $a_{10} = 10$.

(b) We have $a_1 = 2 = 2^1$, $a_2 = 2^2$, $a_3 = 2^3$, $a_4 = 2^4$.
A closed form is

$$a_n = 2^n \quad (n = 1, 2, 3, \ldots).$$

The 10th term is $a_{10} = 2^{10} = 1024$.

(c) We have $a_1 = -1$, $a_2 = 1$, $a_3 = -1$, $a_4 = 1$.
A closed form is

$$a_n = (-1)^n \quad (n = 1, 2, 3, \ldots),$$

and the 10th term is $a_{10} = (-1)^{10} = 1$.

(d) We have $a_1 = 1^3$, $a_2 = 2^3$, $a_3 = 3^3$, $a_4 = 4^3$.
A closed form is

$$a_n = n^3 \quad (n = 1, 2, 3, \ldots),$$

and the 10th term is $a_{10} = 10^3 = 1000$.

(e) We have $a_1 = 6 \times 1$, $a_2 = 6 \times (-1)$, $a_3 = 6 \times 1$,
$a_4 = 6 \times (-1)$. A closed form is

$$a_n = 6 \times (-1)^{n+1} \quad (n = 1, 2, 3, \ldots).$$

Since $(-1)^{n+1} = (-1)^n(-1)^1 = -(-1)^n$, this
closed form can also be written as

$$a_n = -6 \times (-1)^n \quad (n = 1, 2, 3, \ldots).$$

The 10th term is $a_{10} = 6 \times (-1)^{11} = -6$.

(f) We have $a_1 = \frac{1}{2}$, $a_2 = \frac{2}{3}$, $a_3 = \frac{3}{4}$, $a_4 = \frac{4}{5}$.
A closed form is

$$a_n = \frac{n}{n+1} \quad (n = 1, 2, 3, \ldots).$$

Since $n = (n + 1) - 1$, this closed form can also
be written as

$$a_n = 1 - \frac{1}{n+1} \quad (n = 1, 2, 3, \ldots).$$

The 10th term is $a_{10} = \frac{10}{11}$.

(g) We have $a_1 = 2 \times 1$, $a_2 = -2 \times 2$, $a_3 = 2 \times 3$,
$a_4 = -2 \times 4$. A closed form is

$$a_n = 2n(-1)^{n+1} \quad (n = 1, 2, 3, \ldots).$$

Since $(-1)^{n+1} = (-1)^n(-1)^1 = -(-1)^n$, this
closed form can also be written as

$$a_n = -2n(-1)^n \quad (n = 1, 2, 3, \ldots).$$

The 10th term is $a_{10} = 2 \times 10 \times (-1)^{11} = -20$.

Solution to Activity 4

(a) (i) $a_0 = 3^0 = 1$, $a_1 = 3^1 = 3$, $a_2 = 3^2 = 9$.

(ii) $b_2 = \frac{1}{2}$, $b_3 = \frac{1}{6}$, $b_4 = \frac{1}{12}$.

(iii) $c_1 = \frac{1}{2}$, $c_2 = \frac{1}{6}$, $c_3 = \frac{1}{12}$.

(b) (i)   We have $d_0 = 3^0$, $d_1 = 3^1$, $d_2 = 3^2$, $d_3 = 3^3$.
A closed form is

$$d_n = 3^n \quad (n = 0, 1, 2, \ldots),$$

and the sixth term is $d_5 = 3^5 = 243$.

(ii) We have $e_5 = \frac{1}{5}$, $e_6 = \frac{1}{6}$, $e_7 = \frac{1}{7}$, $e_8 = \frac{1}{8}$.
A closed form is

$$e_n = \frac{1}{n} \quad (n = 5, 6, 7, \ldots),$$

and the sixth term is $e_{10} = \frac{1}{10}$.

(iii) We have $f_2 = \left(-\frac{1}{2}\right)^2$, $f_3 = \left(-\frac{1}{2}\right)^3$,
$f_4 = \left(-\frac{1}{2}\right)^4$, $f_5 = \left(-\frac{1}{2}\right)^5$. A closed form is
$$f_n = \left(-\frac{1}{2}\right)^n \quad (n = 2, 3, 4, \ldots),$$
and the sixth term is $f_7 = \left(-\frac{1}{2}\right)^7 = -\frac{1}{128}$.

Solution to Activity 5

(a) (i) $b_n = 2(n+1) \quad (n = 0, 1, 2, \ldots)$

(ii) $b_n = 3^n \quad (n = 0, 1, 2, \ldots)$

(iii) $b_n = 6 + n \quad (n = 0, 1, 2, \ldots)$

(iv) $b_n = 4n \quad (n = 0, 1, 2, \ldots)$

(b) (i) $b_n = 0.4^{n-1} \quad (n = 1, 2, 3, \ldots)$

(ii) $b_n = 5(n-1) \quad (n = 1, 2, 3, \ldots)$

(iii) $b_n = \dfrac{1}{2^{n-1}} \quad (n = 1, 2, 3, \ldots)$

(iv) $b_n = 2 + 3(n-1) \quad (n = 1, 2, 3, \ldots)$,
which simplifies to
$$b_n = -1 + 3n \quad (n = 1, 2, 3, \ldots).$$

(c) (i) $b_n = \dfrac{3^{n-2}}{n-1} \quad (n = 2, 3, 4, \ldots)$

(ii) $b_n = \dfrac{1}{(n-1)(n+1)} \quad (n = 2, 3, 4, \ldots)$

Solution to Activity 6

(a) $a_1 = 0$, $a_2 = 1$, $a_3 = 3$, $a_4 = 7$, $a_5 = 15$.

(b) $b_1 = 1$, $b_2 = 0$, $b_3 = -1$, $b_4 = 0$, $b_5 = -1$.

(c) $c_0 = 2$, $c_1 = 1.5$,
$c_2 = 17/12 = 1.416\,667$ (to 6 d.p.),
$c_3 = 577/408 = 1.414\,216$ (to 6 d.p.),
$c_4 = 1.414\,214$ (to 6 d.p.).

Solution to Activity 7

(a) The sequence (x_n) is arithmetic, with
parameters $a = -1$ and $d = 1$.

(b) The sequence (y_n) is not arithmetic. The term
y_{n-1} on the right of the recurrence relation is
multiplied by -1.

(c) The sequence (z_n) is arithmetic, with
parameters $a = 1$ and $d = -1.5$.

Solution to Activity 8

(a) The first term is $a = 1$, and the common
difference is $d = 4 - 1 = 3$. So the recurrence
system is
$$x_1 = 1, \qquad x_n = x_{n-1} + 3 \quad (n = 2, 3, 4, \ldots).$$
The next two terms are
$$x_5 = x_4 + 3 = 10 + 3 = 13,$$
$$x_6 = x_5 + 3 = 13 + 3 = 16.$$

(b) The first term is $a = 2.1$, and the common
difference is $d = 3.2 - 2.1 = 1.1$. So the
recurrence system is
$$y_1 = 2.1, \qquad y_n = y_{n-1} + 1.1 \quad (n = 2, 3, 4, \ldots).$$
The next two terms are
$$y_5 = y_4 + 1.1 = 5.4 + 1.1 = 6.5,$$
$$y_6 = y_5 + 1.1 = 6.5 + 1.1 = 7.6.$$

(c) The first term is $a = 1$, and the common
difference is $d = 0.9 - 1 = -0.1$. So the
recurrence system is
$$z_1 = 1, \qquad z_n = z_{n-1} - 0.1 \quad (n = 2, 3, 4, \ldots, 11).$$
The next two terms are
$$z_5 = z_4 - 0.1 = 0.7 - 0.1 = 0.6,$$
$$z_6 = z_5 - 0.1 = 0.6 - 0.1 = 0.5.$$

Solution to Activity 9

(a) The first term is 1000, the last term is 10 and
the common difference is $d = 970 - 1000 = -30$.
Hence the number of terms is
$$\frac{10 - 1000}{-30} + 1 = 34,$$
so there are 34 terms in the sequence.

(b) The corresponding recurrence system is
$$x_1 = 1000, \qquad x_n = x_{n-1} - 30 \quad (n = 2, 3, 4, \ldots, 34).$$

Solution to Activity 10

(a) Since $a = 1$ and $d = 3$, the closed form is
$$x_n = 1 + 3(n-1)$$
$$= 3n - 2 \quad (n = 1, 2, 3, \ldots).$$
This gives $x_4 = 3 \times 4 - 2 = 10$, as expected, and
also
$$x_{10} = 3 \times 10 - 2 = 28.$$

(b) Since $a = 2.1$ and $d = 1.1$, the closed form is
$$y_n = 2.1 + 1.1(n-1)$$
$$= 1.1n + 1 \quad (n = 1, 2, 3, \ldots).$$
This gives $y_4 = 1.1 \times 4 + 1 = 5.4$, as expected, and also
$$y_{10} = 1.1 \times 10 + 1 = 12.$$

(c) Since $a = 1$ and $d = -0.1$, the closed form is
$$z_n = 1 - 0.1(n-1)$$
$$= 1.1 - 0.1n \quad (n = 1, 2, 3, \ldots, 11).$$
This gives $z_4 = 1.1 - 0.1 \times 4 = 0.7$, as expected, and also
$$z_{10} = 1.1 - 0.1 \times 10 = 0.1.$$

Solution to Activity 11

(a) The sequence (x_n) is geometric, with parameters $a = -1$ and $r = 3$.

(b) The sequence (y_n) is geometric, with parameters $a = 1$ and $r = -0.9$.

(c) The sequence (z_n) is not geometric, because the expression on the right of the recurrence relation contains the term $+1$.

Solution to Activity 12

(a) The first term is $a = 1$, and the common ratio is $r = \frac{1}{2}/1 = \frac{1}{2}$. So the recurrence system is
$$x_1 = 1, \qquad x_n = \tfrac{1}{2}x_{n-1} \quad (n = 2, 3, 4, \ldots).$$
The next two terms are
$$x_5 = \tfrac{1}{2}x_4 = \tfrac{1}{2} \times \tfrac{1}{8} = \tfrac{1}{16},$$
$$x_6 = \tfrac{1}{2}x_5 = \tfrac{1}{2} \times \tfrac{1}{16} = \tfrac{1}{32}.$$

(b) The first term is $a = 4.2$, and the common ratio is $r = 7.14/4.2 = 1.7$. So the recurrence system is
$$y_1 = 4.2, \qquad y_n = 1.7y_{n-1} \quad (n = 2, 3, 4, \ldots).$$
The next two terms are
$$y_5 = 1.7y_4 = 1.7 \times 20.6346$$
$$= 35.07882$$
$$= 35.079 \text{ (to 3 d.p.)},$$
$$y_6 = 1.7y_5 = 1.7 \times 35.07882$$
$$= 59.633994$$
$$= 59.634 \text{ (to 3 d.p.)}.$$

(c) The first term is $a = 2$, and the common ratio is $r = (-2)/2 = -1$. So the recurrence system is
$$z_1 = 2, \qquad z_n = -z_{n-1} \quad (n = 2, 3, 4, \ldots).$$
The next two terms are
$$z_5 = -z_4 = -(-2) = 2,$$
$$z_6 = -z_5 = -2.$$

Solution to Activity 13

(a) Suppose that the sequence has N terms, with first term $z_1 = 7$. Then the last term is $z_N = 2734375$. The common ratio is $r = z_2/z_1 = 5$.
Now N is given by
$$r^{N-1} = \frac{z_N}{z_1};$$
that is,
$$5^{N-1} = \frac{2734375}{7} = 390625.$$
Taking the natural logarithm of both sides of this equation gives
$$(N-1)\ln 5 = \ln(390625),$$
from which
$$N = 1 + \frac{\ln(390625)}{\ln 5} = 9.$$
Hence there are nine terms in the sequence.

(b) The corresponding recurrence system is
$$z_1 = 7, \qquad z_n = 5z_{n-1} \quad (n = 2, 3, 4, \ldots, 9).$$

Solution to Activity 14

(a) Since $a = 1$ and $r = \frac{1}{2}$, the closed form is
$$x_n = 1 \times \left(\tfrac{1}{2}\right)^{n-1}$$
$$= \left(\tfrac{1}{2}\right)^{n-1} \quad (n = 1, 2, 3, \ldots).$$
This gives $x_4 = \left(\tfrac{1}{2}\right)^3 = \tfrac{1}{8}$, as expected, and also
$$x_{10} = \left(\tfrac{1}{2}\right)^9 = \tfrac{1}{512}$$
$$= 1.953 \times 10^{-3} \text{ (to 4 s.f.)}.$$

(b) Since $a = 4.2$ and $r = 1.7$, the closed form is
$$y_n = 4.2 \times 1.7^{n-1} \quad (n = 1, 2, 3, \ldots).$$
This gives $y_4 = 4.2 \times 1.7^3 = 20.6346$, as expected, and also
$$y_{10} = 4.2 \times 1.7^9 = 498.1 \text{ (to 4 s.f.)}.$$

(c) Since $a = 2$ and $r = -1$, the closed form is
$$z_n = 2(-1)^{n-1} \quad (n = 1, 2, 3, \ldots).$$
This gives $z_4 = 2(-1)^3 = -2$, as expected, and also
$$z_{10} = 2(-1)^9 = -2.$$

Solution to Activity 15

The first point to be plotted is $(1, z_1) = (1, 1)$. The second point is $(2, z_2) = (2, 0.9)$. The subsequent points are $(3, 0.8)$, $(4, 0.7)$, $(5, 0.6)$ and $(6, 0.5)$. The graph is as follows.

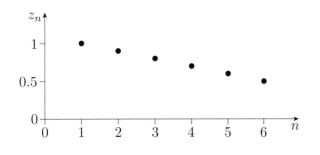

Solution to Activity 16

(a) The first point to be plotted is $(1, y_1) = (1, 4.2)$. The second point is
$$(2, y_2) = (2, 4.2 \times 1.7) \approx (2, 7.1).$$
The subsequent points (to 1 d.p.) are $(3, 12.1)$, $(4, 20.6)$, $(5, 35.1)$ and $(6, 59.6)$. The graph is as follows.

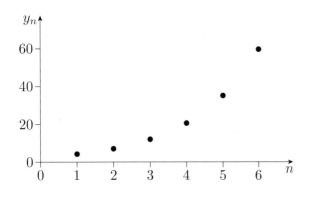

(b) The first point to be plotted is
$$(1, c_1) = (1, (-1)^2) = (1, 1).$$
The second point is
$$(2, c_2) = (2, (-1)^3) = (2, -1).$$
The subsequent points are $(3, 1)$, $(4, -1)$ and $(5, 1)$. The graph is as follows.

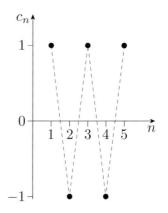

The dashed lines shown above are not part of the graph of the sequence, but draw attention to the fact that the terms of this sequence alternate in sign.

Solution to Activity 18

The graph in Figure 9(b) shows that, for this sequence,
$$x_n \to L \text{ as } n \to \infty \quad \left(\text{or } \lim_{n \to \infty} x_n = L \right).$$
The graph in Figure 9(c) shows that, for this sequence,
$$x_n \to -\infty \text{ as } n \to \infty.$$
The graph in Figure 9(e) shows that, for this sequence,
$$x_n \to 0 \text{ as } n \to \infty \quad \left(\text{or } \lim_{n \to \infty} x_n = 0 \right).$$

Solution to Activity 19

The sequence (x_n) with closed form $x_n = 3 - \frac{4}{5}n$ is arithmetic, with common difference $d = -\frac{4}{5}$. Since $-\frac{4}{5} < 0$, the sequence (x_n) is decreasing and $x_n \to -\infty$ as $n \to \infty$.

Solution to Activity 20

(a) Since $r = 1.2 > 1$, the sequence (1.2^n) is increasing and $1.2^n \to \infty$ as $n \to \infty$. To obtain (x_n) we multiply each term by the negative constant $-\frac{1}{3}$. Hence (x_n) is decreasing and $x_n \to -\infty$ as $n \to \infty$.

(b) Since $-1 < -0.9 < 0$, the sequence $((-0.9)^n)$ alternates in sign and $(-0.9)^n \to 0$ as $n \to \infty$. To obtain (y_n) we multiply each term by the non-zero constant 5. Hence (y_n) alternates in sign and $y_n \to 0$ as $n \to \infty$.

(c) Since $-2.5 < -1$, the sequence $((-2.5)^n)$ alternates in sign and is unbounded. To obtain (z_n) we multiply each term by the negative constant $-\frac{1}{10}$. Hence (z_n) also alternates in sign and is unbounded.

(Details of how to use the CAS to plot graphs of these sequences are given in the *Computer algebra guide*, in the section 'Computer methods for CAS activities in Books A–D'.)

Solution to Activity 21

(a) From Activity 20(a), the sequence with terms $y_n = -\frac{1}{3} \times 1.2^n$ is decreasing and $y_n \to -\infty$ as $n \to \infty$. Since $a_n = y_n + 17$ for each n, it follows that the sequence (a_n) is also decreasing and $a_n \to -\infty$ as $n \to \infty$.

(b) From Activity 20(b), the sequence with terms $z_n = 5(-0.9)^n$ has limit 0 and its terms are of alternating sign. Since $b_n = z_n + 45$ for each n, it follows that $b_n \to 45$ as $n \to \infty$; that is,
$$\lim_{n \to \infty} b_n = 45.$$
Also, the terms of (b_n) alternate either side of 45.

(Details of how to use the CAS to plot graphs of these sequences are given in the *Computer algebra guide*, in the section 'Computer methods for CAS activities in Books A–D'.)

Solution to Activity 22

The sequence is $6, 13, 20, \ldots, 90$. The first term is 6, the last term is 90 and the common difference is $d = 13 - 6 = 7$, so the number of terms is
$$\frac{90 - 6}{7} + 1 = 13.$$
Hence the sum is
$$\tfrac{1}{2} \times 13 \times (6 + 90) = 13 \times 48$$
$$= 624.$$

Solution to Activity 23

Expression (5) is used in each case.

(a) Here $a = 1$, $d = 1$ and $n = 100$. The sum is
$$\tfrac{1}{2} \times 100 \times (2 \times 1 + 99 \times 1) = 50 \times 101$$
$$= 5050.$$

(b) Here $a = 12$, $d = 3$ and
$$n = \frac{60 - 12}{3} + 1 = 17.$$

The sum is
$$\tfrac{1}{2} \times 17 \times (2 \times 12 + 16 \times 3) = \tfrac{1}{2} \times 17 \times 72$$
$$= 612.$$

(c) Here $a = 1$, $d = 2$ and
$$n = \frac{19 - 1}{2} + 1 = 10.$$
The sum is
$$\tfrac{1}{2} \times 10 \times (2 \times 1 + 9 \times 2) = 5 \times 20$$
$$= 100.$$

Each of these answers could also have been obtained using expression (4).

(Notice that the result of part (c) is another example of a pattern observed near the start of this subsection, namely that adding up consecutive odd numbers, starting at 1, always seems to give a square number. Here's how you can prove that this pattern holds in general.

The sum of the first n odd numbers forms an arithmetic series with first term $a = 1$, common difference $d = 2$ and n terms. By the formula in the box above this activity, this series has sum
$$\tfrac{1}{2}n(2 \times 1 + (n - 1) \times 2) = \tfrac{1}{2}n(2 + 2n - 2)$$
$$= \tfrac{1}{2}n \times 2n$$
$$= n^2.)$$

Solution to Activity 24

(a) The numbers added form a geometric sequence whose 10 terms can be expressed as
$$3^n \quad (n = 1, 2, \ldots, 10).$$
The first term is $a = 3$ and the common ratio is $r = 3$. Using expression (7) with $n = 10$, the sum of these terms is
$$\frac{3\left(1 - 3^{10}\right)}{1 - 3} = \tfrac{3}{2}(59\,049 - 1)$$
$$= 88\,572.$$

(b) The numbers added form a geometric sequence with first term 1 and common ratio $-\frac{1}{3}$, and with 9 terms. (Be careful when working out the number of terms of a geometric sequence that has first term 1.) From expression (7) the sum is
$$\frac{1 - \left(-\frac{1}{3}\right)^9}{1 - \left(-\frac{1}{3}\right)} = \tfrac{3}{4}\left(1 + \left(\tfrac{1}{3}\right)^9\right)$$
$$= 0.750\,038 \quad \text{(to 6 d.p.).}$$

Solution to Activity 25

(a) (i) The formula for the first n natural numbers is
$$1 + 2 + 3 + \cdots + n = \tfrac{1}{2}n(n+1).$$
Here $n = 30$, and so
$$1 + 2 + 3 + \cdots + 30 = \tfrac{1}{2} \times 30 \times 31$$
$$= 465.$$

(ii) The formula for the squares of the first n natural numbers is
$$1^2 + 2^2 + 3^2 + \cdots + n^2$$
$$= \tfrac{1}{6}n(n+1)(2n+1).$$
Here $n = 10$, and so
$$1^2 + 2^2 + 3^2 + \cdots + 10^2$$
$$= \tfrac{1}{6} \times 10 \times 11 \times 21$$
$$= 385.$$

(iii) We use the same formula as in part (a)(ii). Here $n = 30$, and so
$$1^2 + 2^2 + 3^2 + \cdots + 30^2$$
$$= \tfrac{1}{6} \times 30 \times 31 \times 61$$
$$= 9455.$$

(iv) The formula for the cubes of the first n natural numbers is
$$1^3 + 2^3 + 3^3 + \cdots + n^3 = \tfrac{1}{4}n^2(n+1)^2.$$
Here $n = 30$, and so
$$1^3 + 2^3 + 3^3 + \cdots + 30^3 = \tfrac{1}{4} \times 30^2 \times 31^2$$
$$= 216\,225.$$

(b) (i) Note that
$$11^2 + 12^2 + 13^2 + \cdots + 30^2$$
$$= (1^2 + 2^2 + 3^2 + \cdots + 30^2)$$
$$\quad - (1^2 + 2^2 + 3^2 + \cdots + 10^2).$$
It follows from the results of parts (a)(ii) and (iii) that
$$11^2 + 12^2 + 13^2 + \cdots + 30^2$$
$$= 9455 - 385$$
$$= 9070.$$

(ii) Note that
$$20^3 + 21^3 + 22^3 + \cdots + 40^3$$
$$= (1^3 + 2^3 + 3^3 + \cdots + 40^3)$$
$$\quad - (1^3 + 2^3 + 3^3 + \cdots + 19^3).$$

Applying the formula from part (a)(iv), we have (with $n = 19$)
$$1^3 + 2^3 + 3^3 + \cdots + 19^3$$
$$= \tfrac{1}{4} \times 19^2 \times 20^2$$
$$= 36\,100$$
and (with $n = 40$)
$$1^3 + 2^3 + 3^3 + \cdots + 40^3$$
$$= \tfrac{1}{4} \times 40^2 \times 41^2$$
$$= 672\,400.$$
It follows that
$$20^3 + 21^3 + 22^3 + \cdots + 40^3$$
$$= 672\,400 - 36\,100$$
$$= 636\,300.$$

Solution to Activity 26

(a) This is an infinite geometric series with first term $a = \tfrac{3}{4}$ and common ratio $r = \tfrac{3}{4}$. Since $-1 < r < 1$, the series has a sum, namely
$$\frac{a}{1-r} = \frac{\tfrac{3}{4}}{1 - \tfrac{3}{4}} = \frac{\tfrac{3}{4}}{\tfrac{1}{4}} = 3.$$

(b) This is an infinite geometric series with first term $a = 1$ and common ratio $r = -\tfrac{1}{2}$. Since $-1 < r < 1$, the series has a sum, namely
$$\frac{a}{1-r} = \frac{1}{1 - \left(-\tfrac{1}{2}\right)} = \frac{1}{\tfrac{3}{2}} = \tfrac{2}{3}.$$

(c) This is an infinite geometric series with first term $a = 1$ and common ratio $r = -2$. Since $r < -1$, the series doesn't have a sum.

(d) This is an infinite geometric series, with first term $a = \tfrac{1}{4}$ and common ratio $r = -\tfrac{2}{3}$. Since $-1 < r < 1$, the series has a sum, namely
$$\frac{a}{1-r} = \frac{\tfrac{1}{4}}{1 - \left(-\tfrac{2}{3}\right)} = \frac{\tfrac{1}{4}}{\tfrac{5}{3}} = \tfrac{3}{20}.$$

Solution to Activity 27

(a) Put $s = 0.454\,545\ldots$. The repeating group, '45', is 2 digits long, so multiply s by 10^2, to obtain
$$100s = 45.454\,545\ldots = 45 + s.$$
Hence we have $s = \tfrac{45}{99} = \tfrac{5}{11}$.

(b) Put $s = 0.729\,729\,729\ldots$. The repeating group, '729', is 3 digits long, so multiply s by 10^3, to obtain

$$1000s = 729.729\,729\,729\ldots = 729 + s.$$

Hence we have $s = \frac{729}{999} = \frac{27}{37}$. It follows that

$$3.729\,729\,729\ldots = 3 + \frac{27}{37} = \frac{138}{37}.$$

Solution to Activity 28

(a) The sums are as follows.

(i) $\displaystyle\sum_{n=5}^{20} n^4 = 5^4 + 6^4 + 7^4 + \cdots + 20^4$

(ii) $\displaystyle\sum_{n=4}^{19} (n+1)^4 = 5^4 + 6^4 + 7^4 + \cdots + 20^4$

(iii) $\displaystyle\sum_{n=1}^{6} (2n-1) = 1 + 3 + 5 + \cdots + 11$

(b) (i) The sum is

$$1 + 2 + 3 + \cdots + 150 = \sum_{n=1}^{150} n.$$

(ii) The sum is

$$5^2 + 6^2 + 7^2 + \cdots + 13^2 = \sum_{n=5}^{13} n^2.$$

(iii) The sum is

$$2 + 2^2 + 2^3 + \cdots + 2^{12} = \sum_{n=1}^{12} 2^n.$$

Solution to Activity 29

(a) $\displaystyle\sum_{k=1}^{24} k = \tfrac{1}{2} \times 24 \times (24+1) = 300$

(b) $\displaystyle\sum_{k=1}^{24} k^2 = \tfrac{1}{6} \times 24 \times (24+1) \times (2 \times 24 + 1)$

$\qquad\quad = \tfrac{1}{6} \times 24 \times 25 \times 49$

$\qquad\quad = 4900$

Solution to Activity 30

The solutions below apply the rules for manipulating finite series using sigma notation, in the box on page 66, and the formulas for the sums of standard finite series in the box on page 65.

(a) $\displaystyle\sum_{k=1}^{30} (2k^3 - k) = \sum_{k=1}^{30} 2k^3 - \sum_{k=1}^{30} k$

$\qquad\qquad = 2\sum_{k=1}^{30} k^3 - \sum_{k=1}^{30} k$

$\qquad\qquad = 2 \times \tfrac{1}{4}(30)^2(31)^2 - \tfrac{1}{2}(30)(31)$

$\qquad\qquad = 432\,450 - 465$

$\qquad\qquad = 431\,985$

(b) $\displaystyle\sum_{k=1}^{40} (\tfrac{1}{4}k^2 - 1) = \sum_{k=1}^{40} \tfrac{1}{4}k^2 - \sum_{k=1}^{40} 1$

$\qquad\qquad = \tfrac{1}{4}\sum_{k=1}^{40} k^2 - \sum_{k=1}^{40} 1$

$\qquad\qquad = \tfrac{1}{4} \times \tfrac{1}{6}(40)(41)(81) - 40$

$\qquad\qquad = 5535 - 40$

$\qquad\qquad = 5495$

(c) We have

$$\sum_{k=65}^{125} (6k+7) = \sum_{k=1}^{125} (6k+7) - \sum_{k=1}^{64} (6k+7).$$

Now

$$\sum_{k=1}^{125} (6k+7) = \sum_{k=1}^{125} 6k + \sum_{k=1}^{125} 7$$

$$= 6\sum_{k=1}^{125} k + 7\sum_{k=1}^{125} 1$$

$$= 6 \times \tfrac{1}{2}(125)(126) + 7 \times 125$$

$$= 47\,250 + 875$$

$$= 48\,125.$$

Similarly,

$$\sum_{k=1}^{64} (6k+7) = \sum_{k=1}^{64} 6k + \sum_{k=1}^{64} 7$$

$$= 6\sum_{k=1}^{64} k + 7\sum_{k=1}^{64} 1$$

$$= 6 \times \tfrac{1}{2}(64)(65) + 7 \times 64$$

$$= 12\,480 + 448$$

$$= 12\,928.$$

Hence

$$\sum_{k=65}^{125} (6k+7) = 48\,125 - 12\,928 = 35\,197.$$

Solution to Activity 31

(a) $\frac{1}{5} + \left(\frac{1}{5}\right)^2 + \left(\frac{1}{5}\right)^3 + \cdots = \sum_{n=1}^{\infty} \left(\frac{1}{5}\right)^n$

(b) $\left(\frac{1}{2}\right)^3 + \left(\frac{1}{2}\right)^4 + \left(\frac{1}{2}\right)^5 + \cdots = \sum_{n=3}^{\infty} \left(\frac{1}{2}\right)^n$

(c) $1 + \left(\frac{1}{2}\right)^2 + \left(\frac{1}{3}\right)^2 + \left(\frac{1}{4}\right)^2 + \cdots = \sum_{n=1}^{\infty} \left(\frac{1}{n}\right)^2$

Solution to Activity 33

(a) $(c+5)^2 = c^2 + 2c \times 5 + 5^2$
$= c^2 + 10c + 25$

(b) $(1-3x)^2 = 1^2 + 2 \times 1 \times (-3x) + (-3x)^2$
$= 1 - 6x + 9x^2$

(c) $(p^2 - q^2)^2 = (p^2)^2 + 2p^2(-q^2) + (-q^2)^2$
$= p^4 - 2p^2q^2 + q^4$

Solution to Activity 34

(a) By formula (12),
$(5+p)^3 = 5^3 + 3 \times 5^2 \times p + 3 \times 5 \times p^2 + p^3$
$= 125 + 75p + 15p^2 + p^3.$

(b) By formula (12),
$(1-2x)^3 = 1^3 + 3 \times 1^2 \times (-2x)$
$+ 3 \times 1 \times (-2x)^2 + (-2x)^3$
$= 1 - 6x + 12x^2 - 8x^3.$

(c) By formula (12),
$(2x+3y)^3 = (2x)^3 + 3 \times (2x)^2 \times 3y$
$+ 3 \times 2x \times (3y)^2 + (3y)^3$
$= 8x^3 + 36x^2y + 54xy^2 + 27y^3.$

Solution to Activity 35

(a) The row is 1, 7, 21, 35, 35, 21, 7, 1.

(b) This gives the formula
$(a+b)^7 = a^7 + 7a^6b + 21a^5b^2 + 35a^4b^3$
$+ 35a^3b^4 + 21a^2b^5 + 7ab^6 + b^7.$

Solution to Activity 36

(a) We use the formula
$(a+b)^5$
$= a^5 + 5a^4b + 10a^3b^2 + 10a^2b^3 + 5ab^4 + b^5.$

Substituting $a = 3x$ and $b = 2$ gives
$(3x+2)^5$
$= (3x)^5 + 5(3x)^4 \times 2 + 10(3x)^3 \times 2^2$
$+ 10(3x)^2 \times 2^3 + 5(3x) \times 2^4 + 2^5$
$= 243x^5 + 810x^4 + 1080x^3 + 720x^2 + 240x + 32.$

(b) We use the formula
$(a+b)^4 = a^4 + 4a^3b + 6a^2b^2 + 4ab^3 + b^4.$
Substituting $a = x$ and $b = -4y$ gives
$(x-4y)^4$
$= x^4 + 4x^3(-4y) + 6x^2(-4y)^2$
$+ 4x(-4y)^3 + (-4y)^4$
$= x^4 - 16x^3y + 96x^2y^2 - 256xy^3 + 256y^4.$

Solution to Activity 37

(a) $^8C_4 = \dfrac{8 \times 7 \times 6 \times 5}{4 \times 3 \times 2 \times 1} = 70$

(b) $^{12}C_{10} = {}^{12}C_2 = \dfrac{12 \times 11}{2 \times 1} = 66$

(c) $^5C_5 = \dfrac{5!}{5!0!} = 1$

(d) $^5C_0 = \dfrac{5!}{0!5!} = 1$

(e) $^{21}C_{20} = {}^{21}C_1 = \dfrac{21}{1} = 21$

Solution to Activity 38

(a) $^{25}C_{19} = 177\,100$

(b) $^{32}C_{17} = 565\,722\,720$

Solution to Activity 39

(a) We put $n = 10$, $a = 1$ and $b = x$ in the binomial theorem. The first four terms in the binomial expansion of $(1+x)^{10}$ are
$1^{10} + {}^{10}C_1 \times 1^9x + {}^{10}C_2 \times 1^8x^2 + {}^{10}C_3 \times 1^7x^3$
$= 1 + 10x + \dfrac{10 \times 9}{2!}x^2 + \dfrac{10 \times 9 \times 8}{3!}x^3$
$= 1 + 10x + 45x^2 + 120x^3.$

(b) Here $n = 10$ (as in part (a)), $a = 2$ and $b = \frac{1}{3}x$. The binomial coefficients needed were obtained in part (a). The first four terms in the binomial expansion of $(2 + \frac{1}{3}x)^{10}$ are
$2^{10} + 10 \times 2^9\left(\frac{1}{3}x\right) + 45 \times 2^8\left(\frac{1}{3}x\right)^2 + 120 \times 2^7\left(\frac{1}{3}x\right)^3$
$= 1024 + \frac{5120}{3}x + 1280x^2 + \frac{5120}{9}x^3.$

Solution to Activity 40

(a) By the binomial theorem, each term in the expansion is of the form
$$^{11}C_k a^{11-k} b^k.$$
The term in $a^6 b^5$ is obtained when $k = 5$. Hence the coefficient of $a^6 b^5$ is
$$^{11}C_5 = \frac{11!}{6!\,5!} = \frac{11 \times 10 \times 9 \times 8 \times 7}{5 \times 4 \times 3 \times 2 \times 1} = 462.$$

(b) By the binomial theorem, each term in the expansion is of the form
$$^{20}C_k (3c)^{20-k}(-d)^k = {}^{20}C_k(-1)^k 3^{20-k} c^{20-k} d^k.$$
The term in $c^5 d^{15}$ is obtained when $k = 15$. Hence the coefficient of $c^5 d^{15}$ is
$$^{20}C_{15}(-1)^{15} 3^5 = -{}^{20}C_{15} \times 3^5$$
$$= -15\,504 \times 243$$
$$= -3\,767\,472.$$

Solution to Activity 41

(a) The constant term arises when the power of x and the power of $-1/x$ in the expansion are the same, namely, 6. By the binomial theorem, this term is
$$^{12}C_6 \times x^6 \left(-\frac{1}{x}\right)^6 = {}^{12}C_6$$
$$= \frac{12 \times 11 \times 10 \times 9 \times 8 \times 7}{6 \times 5 \times 4 \times 3 \times 2 \times 1}$$
$$= 924.$$

(b) By the binomial theorem, each term in the expansion is of the form
$$^{15}C_k \times h^{15-k} \left(-\frac{3}{2h^2}\right)^k$$
$$= {}^{15}C_k \times h^{15-k} \left(-\tfrac{3}{2}\right)^k (h^{-2})^k$$
$$= {}^{15}C_k \left(-\tfrac{3}{2}\right)^k h^{15-k} h^{-2k}$$
$$= {}^{15}C_k \left(-\tfrac{3}{2}\right)^k h^{15-3k}.$$

(i) For the term in h^3, we need
$$15 - 3k = 3,$$
which gives $12 = 3k$; that is, $k = 4$. Hence the coefficient of h^3 is
$$^{15}C_4 \left(-\tfrac{3}{2}\right)^4 = 1365 \times \frac{81}{16} = \frac{110\,565}{16}.$$

(ii) For the term in h^{-12}, we need
$$15 - 3k = -12,$$
which gives $27 = 3k$; that is, $k = 9$. Hence the coefficient of h^{-12} is
$$^{15}C_9 \left(-\tfrac{3}{2}\right)^9 = -5005 \times \frac{19\,683}{512}$$
$$= -\frac{98\,513\,415}{512}.$$

(iii) For a term in h^2, we need
$$15 - 3k = 2,$$
which gives $13 = 3k$. Since there is no integer value of k that satisfies this equation, there is no term in h^2.

Solution to Activity 42

We put $n = 17$ and replace x by $-x$ in the equation in the box. The first six terms of the expansion are
$$1 + {}^{17}C_1(-x) + {}^{17}C_2(-x)^2 + {}^{17}C_3(-x)^3$$
$$+ {}^{17}C_4(-x)^4 + {}^{17}C_5(-x)^5$$
$$= 1 - 17x + \frac{17 \times 16}{2!}x^2 - \frac{17 \times 16 \times 15}{3!}x^3$$
$$+ \frac{17 \times 16 \times 15 \times 14}{4!}x^4$$
$$- \frac{17 \times 16 \times 15 \times 14 \times 13}{5!}x^5$$
$$= 1 - 17x + 136x^2 - 680x^3 + 2380x^4 - 6188x^5.$$

Acknowledgements

Grateful acknowledgement is made to the following sources:

Page 15: Ton Zijlstra / www.flickr.com/photos/tonz/9679968537/. This file is licensed under the Creative Commons Attribution-Noncommercial-ShareAlike Licence http://creativecommons.org/licenses/by-nc-sa/3.0/

Every effort has been made to contact copyright holders. If any have been inadvertently overlooked the publishers will be pleased to make the necessary arrangements at the first opportunity.

Taylor polynomials

Introduction

You may have wondered how a calculator or mathematical software package finds an approximate numerical value for $\ln 3$, $e^{1/2}$ or $\sin(0.2)$, for example. There are various ways in which this can be done, but one common method involves approximating functions such as the natural logarithm function, the exponential function or the sine function by *polynomial functions*.

Recall from Unit 3 that a **polynomial function** has the form

$f(x) =$ a sum of terms, each of the form cx^k, where k is a non-negative integer and c is a constant.

In other words, it has the form

$$f(x) = c_0 + c_1 x + c_2 x^2 + \cdots + c_n x^n,$$

where n is a non-negative integer and $c_0, c_1, c_2, \ldots, c_n$ are constants (possibly 0). The phrase 'polynomial function' is often abbreviated to **polynomial**, and we'll use this abbreviation frequently in this unit. If $c_n \neq 0$, then the polynomial has **degree** n. For example,

$$f(x) = 6 - 3x + 2x^2 + x^3$$

is a polynomial of degree 3.

To find the value of a polynomial function at a particular input value, the only operations that you have to use are addition, subtraction and multiplication. For example, the value of the polynomial function f above when $x = 4$ is

$$f(4) = 6 - 3 \times 4 + 2 \times 4^2 + 4^3$$
$$= 6 - 12 + 32 + 64 = 90.$$

By approximating the natural logarithm function by a polynomial function, a computer can evaluate $\ln 3$, for example, to the accuracy of the computer, using just the operations of addition, subtraction and multiplication. Similarly, by approximating the exponential function and the sine function by polynomial functions, it can evaluate $e^{1/2}$ and $\sin(0.2)$.

In this unit you'll study a particular way of approximating functions by polynomials, called *Taylor polynomials*. By using suitable Taylor polynomials, you can approximate many functions to any required level of accuracy. In fact, calculators and software packages don't use Taylor polynomials to approximate functions, since more efficient (though also more complicated) polynomial methods exist, but by studying Taylor polynomials you'll learn about the basic ideas of polynomial approximation.

In most cases a function can't be approximated by a polynomial function over the whole of its domain. What we'll be interested in throughout the unit is the approximation of a function by a polynomial function close to a particular point (value) in its domain.

Another reason why polynomial approximations are important is that it is straightforward to multiply polynomials together, and to differentiate and integrate them. Also, polynomial approximations allow complex problems to be described by simple mathematical models, making these problems easier to understand and to solve.

Taylor polynomials are also of theoretical importance. They lead naturally to a way of representing functions by infinite series, at least for some points in their domains. Such representations are called *Taylor series*.

In Section 1 you'll study the approximation of functions by linear and quadratic polynomial functions. This is extended to approximation by Taylor polynomials of higher degree in Section 2, and then to Taylor series in Section 3. Finally, in Section 4, you'll see various methods for using known Taylor series to derive Taylor series for further functions.

Taylor series and Taylor polynomials are named after the English mathematician Brook Taylor, who was educated at home and then at St John's College, Cambridge. In 1715 he published *Methodus Incrementorum Directa et Inversa*, which includes the work on which this unit is based, as well as the technique for integration by parts, which you studied in Unit 8. The importance of Taylor polynomials remained largely unrecognised until much later in the eighteenth century. Taylor was elected as a Fellow of the Royal Society in 1712, and was appointed to the committee for adjudicating the claims of Newton and Leibniz to have invented the calculus. He also wrote works on perspective and was a talented musician and artist.

Taylor was not, in fact, the first person to discover Taylor series. The Scottish mathematician James Gregory discovered them more than forty years before Taylor, and several other mathematicians, including Newton and Leibniz, also independently discovered versions of them before Taylor published his work. However, Taylor was the first to appreciate their fundamental significance and applicability.

Brook Taylor (1685–1731)

James Gregory (1638–1675)

1 Taylor polynomials of small degree

In this section you'll look at how you can approximate many functions by polynomial functions of degrees 0, 1 and 2.

Here, and throughout the unit, we'll usually use f to denote a function that is to be approximated, and p to denote an approximating polynomial function. We'll usually use a to denote a point in the domain of f close to which we want to approximate f. Note that we'll usually refer to numbers in the domain of a function f as *points*. You met this use of the word 'point' in Unit 6.

1.1 Constant Taylor polynomials

Let's start by considering how you could approximate a function f, close to a particular point a in its domain, by the simplest type of polynomial function, namely, a *constant* function. Remember from Unit 3 that a **constant function** is a function of the form $p(x) = c$, where c is a constant. Its graph is a horizontal line. Approximating a function by a constant function is rarely useful, but it illustrates the ideas, and it's the first step in obtaining better approximating polynomials, as you'll see.

For example, suppose that you want to approximate the function $f(x) = \sin x$, close to the point $\pi/6$ in its domain, by a constant function p. The best constant function to choose is the one whose graph is the horizontal line through the point with x-coordinate $\pi/6$ on the graph of f, as illustrated in Figure 1. Since $f(\pi/6) = \sin(\pi/6) = \frac{1}{2}$, this constant function is the function $p(x) = \frac{1}{2}$.

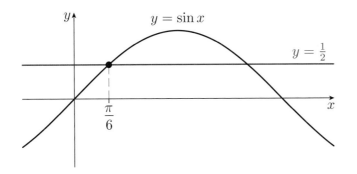

Figure 1   The graph of the function $f(x) = \sin x$ approximated by a constant function near $x = \pi/6$

You can see that, for values of x close to $\pi/6$, the value of $p(x)$ is close to the value of $f(x)$. So the value of $p(x)$ can be used as an approximation to the value of $f(x)$. The approximation is better when x is closer to $\pi/6$ than when it is further away.

For example, the point $\pi/4$ is fairly close to $\pi/6$, and the approximating polynomial $p(x) = \frac{1}{2}$ gives the following approximation for $\sin(\pi/4)$:

$$p\left(\frac{\pi}{4}\right) = \frac{1}{2} = 0.5.$$

The true value of $\sin(\pi/4)$ is

$$\sin\left(\frac{\pi}{4}\right) = \frac{1}{\sqrt{2}} = 0.707 \text{ (to 3 d.p.)}.$$

In general, consider any function f that is **continuous** at a point a in its domain. Informally, this means that you can draw the part of the graph of f that corresponds to values of x slightly less than a to values of x slightly greater than a without taking your pen tip off the paper. Then the constant function p that best approximates f close to a is the constant function whose graph is the horizontal line though the point $(a, f(a))$, as illustrated in Figure 2. In other words, it's the constant function $p(x) = c$ where $c = f(a)$. We say that this function p is the **constant Taylor polynomial about** a **for** f.

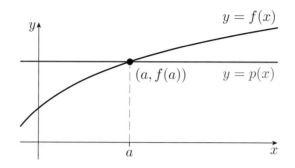

Figure 2   The graph of a function f approximated by a constant function near $x = a$

For example, you have just seen that the constant Taylor polynomial about $\pi/6$ for $f(x) = \sin x$ is $p(x) = \frac{1}{2}$.

If f is any function and p is any approximating polynomial for f, then you can obtain an indication of how good the approximation is at any particular value of x by subtracting the approximating value $p(x)$ from the actual value $f(x)$. The resulting value is known as the **remainder** at x. For example, consider again the function $f(x) = \sin x$ and the approximating polynomial $p(x) = \frac{1}{2}$. If $x = \pi/4$, then the remainder is

$$f(x) - p(x) = \sin\left(\frac{\pi}{4}\right) - \frac{1}{2} = \frac{1}{\sqrt{2}} - \frac{1}{2} = 0.207\ldots.$$

A remainder can be positive, negative or zero, depending on whether $f(x)$ is larger than, smaller than, or equal to $p(x)$. Essentially, the remainder is the size of the vertical gap between $(x, f(x))$ and $(x, p(x))$, with the appropriate sign, as illustrated in Figure 3. The smaller the magnitude of the remainder, the better the approximation.

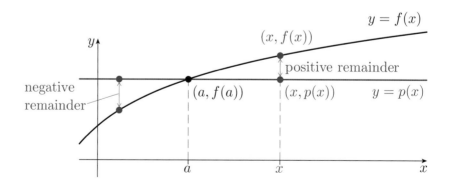

Figure 3   Remainders for a function f and an approximating constant function p

Example 1   *Finding and using a constant Taylor polynomial*

(a) Find the constant Taylor polynomial about 0 for the function $f(x) = e^x$.

(b) Use this constant Taylor polynomial to write down approximations for $e^{0.01}$ and $e^{0.1}$. In each case, use your calculator to find the value of the associated remainder to five decimal places.

Solution

(a) Since $f(0) = e^0 = 1$, the constant Taylor polynomial about 0 for $f(x) = e^x$ is $p(x) = 1$.

(b) The approximation for $e^{0.01}$ given by p is

$$p(0.01) = 1,$$

with remainder

$$f(0.01) - p(0.01) = e^{0.01} - 1 = 0.010\,05 \quad \text{(to 5 d.p.).}$$

Similarly, the approximation for $e^{0.1}$ given by p is

$$p(0.01) = 1,$$

with remainder

$$f(0.1) - p(0.1) = e^{0.1} - 1 = 0.105\,17 \quad \text{(to 5 d.p.).}$$

The constant Taylor polynomial found in part (a) of Example 1 is shown in Figure 4. The results of part (b) of the example illustrate the fact that the approximation provided by the constant Taylor polynomial is better (has a remainder of smaller magnitude) for values of x closer to 0 than for those further from 0. You can also see this from the graph in Figure 4, since the gap between the two graphs decreases in magnitude as the value of x moves towards 0.

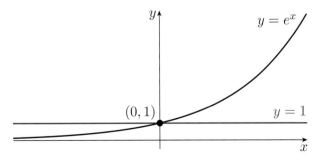

Figure 4   The graph of $f(x) = e^x$ and its constant Taylor polynomial about 0

In the next activity, and in the later activities in this unit, your calculator should be in radian mode when you're calculating the values of trigonometric functions. We'll use radians, rather than degrees, throughout the unit. This is because we'll be working with derivatives, and the standard formulas for the derivatives of trigonometric functions hold only when angles are measured in radians.

Activity 1   *Finding and using constant Taylor polynomials*

(a) Find the constant Taylor polynomial about 0 for the function $f(x) = \cos x$. Use this polynomial to write down approximations for $\cos(0.01)$ and $\cos(0.1)$. In each case, use your calculator to find the value of the associated remainder to five decimal places.

(b) Find the constant Taylor polynomial about 1 for the function $f(x) = \ln x$. Use this polynomial to write down approximations for $\ln(1.01)$ and $\ln(1.1)$. In each case, use your calculator to find the value of the associated remainder to five decimal places.

The constant Taylor polynomials from Activity 1 are shown in Figure 5.

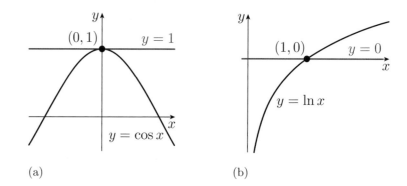

(a)   (b)

Figure 5   The graphs of two constant Taylor polynomials

As mentioned earlier, approximating a function f, close to a point a in its domain, by a constant Taylor polynomial p is usually not very useful. Unless x is extremely close to a, the accuracy of $p(x)$ as an approximation for $f(x)$ is not impressive!

This is illustrated by the fact that none of the approximating constant Taylor polynomials in Figures 1, 4 and 5 look particularly close to the original functions, as the value of x moves away to either side of the point a. However, it could be claimed that the Taylor polynomial in Figure 5(a) appears to be a better approximating polynomial than the others. In this case the function f has a local maximum at $x = a$, and hence the tangent to the graph of f at $(a, f(a))$ is horizontal, and so coincides with the graph of the constant Taylor polynomial, $p(x)$. So in this case the approximating polynomial p not only has the same *value* as the function f at $x = a$, but also its graph has the same *gradient* at $x = a$.

We'll use this idea to obtain better approximating polynomials in the next subsection.

1.2 Linear Taylor polynomials

In this subsection we'll continue to look at how we can approximate a function f, close to a particular point a in its domain, by a simple polynomial function p. In the previous subsection we chose the approximating polynomial p to be a constant function; that is, a function of the form

$$p(x) = c,$$

where c is a constant. We chose the value of c to be $f(a)$, to ensure that the function f and the approximating polynomial p have the same value as each other at $x = a$.

Here we'll choose the approximating polynomial p to be a **linear function**, that is, a function of the form

$$p(x) = mx + c,$$

where m and c are constants. As you know, the graph of such a function is a straight line. We'll choose p to have the property that not only do the function f and the approximating polynomial p have the same value at $x = a$, but also their *first derivatives* have the same value at $x = a$. The second condition ensures that the graphs of f and p have the same gradient at $x = a$.

In order for this to be possible, the function f must not only be continuous at a, but also *differentiable* at a. If you know that f is differentiable at a, then you don't have to check separately that it's continuous at a, as that follows automatically. This is because, as you saw in Unit 6, if a function has a discontinuity at a, then it isn't differentiable at a.

The function p obtained as described above is called the **linear Taylor polynomial** about a for f. Its graph is the tangent to f at a, as illustrated in Figure 6. Usually a linear Taylor polynomial gives better approximations than a constant Taylor polynomial. In some texts, linear Taylor polynomials are called *tangent approximations*.

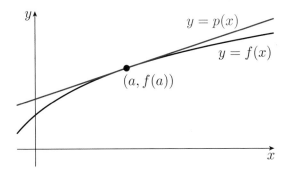

Figure 6   The graph of a function f and its linear Taylor polynomial about a

To illustrate the ideas, let's find the linear Taylor polynomial about 0 for the exponential function $f(x) = e^x$. We'll denote this approximating polynomial by p, as usual.

The graph of p is the straight line that passes through the point with x-coordinate 0 on the graph of the function $f(x) = e^x$, and has the same gradient at that point, as shown in Figure 7.

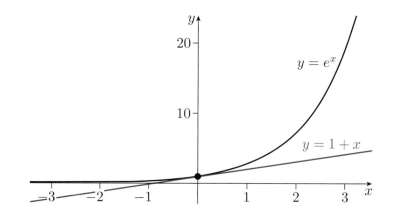

Figure 7   The linear Taylor polynomial about 0 for $f(x) = e^x$

The point with x-coordinate 0 on the graph of $f(x) = e^x$ is $(0, e^0) = (0, 1)$. Also, the derivative of the function $f(x) = e^x$ is $f'(x) = e^x$, so the gradient of the graph of f at the point $(0, 1)$ is $f'(0) = e^0 = 1$. So the graph of the approximating polynomial p is the straight line that passes through the point $(0, 1)$ and has gradient 1. From your work in Section 2 of Unit 2, you know that the straight line with gradient m that passes through the point (x_1, y_1) has equation

$$y - y_1 = m(x - x_1),$$

so the straight line required here has equation

$$(y - 1) = 1(x - 0),$$

which can be simplified to

$$y = 1 + x.$$

Thus the linear Taylor polynomial about 0 for $f(x) = e^x$ is

$$p(x) = 1 + x.$$

You can see from Figure 7 that, as you'd expect, the graph of $p(x) = 1 + x$ approximates that of $f(x) = e^x$ near $x = 0$ more closely than was the case for the graph of the constant Taylor polynomial for $f(x) = e^x$ about 0 in Figure 4.

As for constant Taylor polynomials, the approximation to $f(x)$ provided by $p(x)$ is better for values of x close to 0 than for values of x further away from 0, since the gap between the graphs of f and p increases as the value of x moves away from 0 on either side.

You can use the method above to work out the linear Taylor polynomial for any function f about any point a at which its graph has a gradient. However, a better way to proceed is to apply the method to a *general* function f and a *general* point a. This will give a general formula that you can use to work out a linear Taylor polynomial in any particular case.

To do this, let's suppose that f is a function and a is a point in its domain at which it's differentiable. The point on the graph of f with x-coordinate a is $(a, f(a))$. Also, the gradient of the graph of f at the point $(a, f(a))$ is $f'(a)$. So the graph of p is the straight line that passes through the point $(a, f(a))$ and has gradient $f'(a)$. This straight line has equation

$$y - f(a) = f'(a)(x - a),$$

which can be rearranged as

$$y = f(a) + f'(a)(x - a).$$

So we have the following general formula.

Linear Taylor polynomials

Let f be a function that is differentiable at a. The **linear Taylor polynomial about** a **for** f is

$$p(x) = f(a) + f'(a)(x - a).$$

When $a = 0$, this becomes

$$p(x) = f(0) + f'(0)x.$$

The particular case when $a = 0$ is stated separately in the box because this case occurs commonly and is simpler to work with.

In the next example the linear Taylor polynomial about 0 for the exponential function is worked out again, but this time directly using the formula above. The linear Taylor polynomial is also used to find an approximation for $e^{0.1}$.

Example 2   *Finding a linear Taylor polynomial about 0*

(a) Find the linear Taylor polynomial about 0 for the function $f(x) = e^x$.

(b) Use this polynomial to find an approximation for $e^{0.1}$. Use your calculator to find the value of the associated remainder to five decimal places.

Solution

(a) 🔍 Differentiate f to find f', and hence find the values of $f(0)$ and $f'(0)$. 💬

We have $f(x) = e^x$, so
$$f'(x) = e^x.$$

Hence
$$f(0) = e^0 = 1 \quad \text{and} \quad f'(0) = e^0 = 1.$$

🔍 Apply the second formula in the box above, since in this case $a = 0$. 💬

The linear Taylor polynomial about 0 for $f(x) = e^x$ is
$$p(x) = f(0) + f'(0)x;$$

🔍 Substitute in the values of $f(0)$ and $f'(0)$. 💬

that is,
$$p(x) = 1 + x.$$

(b) The approximation for $e^{0.1}$ given by the linear Taylor polynomial p is
$$p(0.1) = 1 + 0.1 = 1.1.$$

The remainder for this approximation is
$$e^{0.1} - 1.1 = 0.005\,17 \quad \text{(to 5 d.p.)}.$$

The remainder found in Example 2(b) is about 20 times smaller than the remainder 0.105 17 found in Example 1(b), where $e^{0.1}$ was approximated by a constant Taylor polynomial. So the linear Taylor polynomial about 0 for $f(x) = e^x$ provides a much more accurate approximation for the value of $e^{0.1}$ than was obtained using a constant Taylor polynomial. The same applies when you approximate e^x for any other value of x close to 0.

In the next activity you're asked to find a linear Taylor polynomial for the sine function.

Activity 2 *Finding a linear Taylor polynomial about 0*

(a) Find the linear Taylor polynomial about 0 for the function $f(x) = \sin x$.

(b) Use this polynomial to find approximations for $\sin(0.25)$ and $\sin(0.5)$, each to four decimal places. By comparing these approximations with the values obtained from your calculator, show that the magnitude of the remainder at $x = 0.5$ is much larger than that at $x = 0.25$.

Notice from Activity 2(a) that the linear Taylor polynomial about 0 for the sine function contains no constant term; it is $p(x) = x$. This happens because the graph of the sine function passes through the origin. The graphs of $f(x) = \sin x$ and $p(x) = x$ are shown in Figure 8.

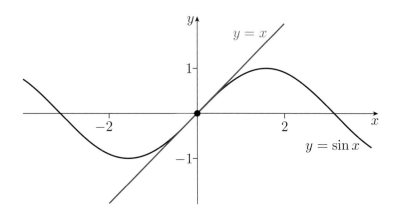

Figure 8 The linear Taylor polynomial about 0 for $f(x) = \sin x$

Activity 3 *Finding another linear Taylor polynomial about 0*

(a) Find the linear Taylor polynomial about 0 for the function $f(x) = \cos x$.

(b) Use this polynomial to find an approximation for $\cos(0.2)$, and use your calculator to find the value of the associated remainder to four decimal places.

Notice from Activity 3(a) that the linear Taylor polynomial about 0 for the cosine function contains no term in x and is therefore a constant function; it is $p(x) = 1$. This happens because the graph of the function $f(x) = \cos x$ has gradient zero at the point where $x = 0$. The graphs of $f(x) = \cos x$ and $p(x) = 1$ are shown in Figure 9.

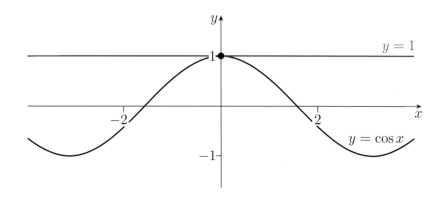

Figure 9 The linear Taylor polynomial about 0 for $f(x) = \cos x$

In fact, the linear Taylor polynomial p in this case is the same as the constant Taylor polynomial about 0 for the cosine function, which you found in Activity 1(a) and whose graph is in Figure 5(a). In Activity 1(a), you started by looking for (and finding) a constant function, whereas in Activity 3(a) you started by looking for a linear function, which turned out to be one in which the coefficient of x is zero.

In the next activity you're asked to use a linear Taylor polynomial to approximate a square root.

Activity 4   *Finding and using another linear Taylor polynomial*

(a) Show that the linear Taylor polynomial about 0 for the function

$$f(x) = (1+x)^{1/2},$$

is

$$p(x) = 1 + \tfrac{1}{2}x.$$

(b) Use the polynomial p from part (a), with $x = 0.01$, to find an approximate value for $\sqrt{1.01}$. Use your calculator to find, to six decimal places, the value of the associated remainder.

Linear Taylor polynomials about $a \neq 0$

All the linear Taylor polynomials that you've seen so far in this subsection have been about 0. The next example and activity relate to linear Taylor polynomials about another point.

Example 3   *Finding a linear Taylor polynomial about a point other than 0*

Find the linear Taylor polynomial about 1 for the function $f(x) = \ln x - 1/x$.

Solution

🔍 Use the first formula in the box on page 105. So start by differentiating f to find f', and then find the values of $f(1)$ and $f'(1)$. 💬

We have $f(x) = \ln x - \dfrac{1}{x}$, so

$$f'(x) = \frac{1}{x} + \frac{1}{x^2}.$$

Hence

$$f(1) = \ln 1 - \frac{1}{1} = -1 \quad \text{and} \quad f'(1) = \frac{1}{1} + \frac{1}{1^2} = 2.$$

🔍 Now apply the formula. Remember that in this case $a = 1$. 💭

Thus the linear Taylor polynomial about 1 for $f(x) = \ln x - 1/x$ is

$$p(x) = f(1) + f'(1)(x - 1);$$

🔍 Substitute in the values of $f(1)$ and $f'(1)$. 💭

that is,

$$p(x) = -1 + 2(x - 1),$$

which can be simplified to

$$p(x) = -3 + 2x.$$

The graphs of the function $f(x) = \ln x - 1/x$ and the linear Taylor polynomial $p(x) = -3 + 2x$ that was found in Example 3 are shown in Figure 10. You can see that $p(x)$ is an approximation to $f(x)$ for values of x close to 1.

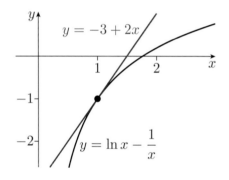

Figure 10   The linear Taylor polynomial about 1 for $f(x) = \ln x - 1/x$

Activity 5   *Finding a linear Taylor polynomial about a point other than 0*

Find the linear Taylor polynomial about 1 for the function $f(x) = e^x$.

In Activity 5 you were asked to obtain the linear Taylor polynomial about 1 for the function $f(x) = e^x$, while in Example 2(a) on page 105 the linear Taylor polynomial about 0 was obtained for the same function. The graphs of these linear Taylor polynomials are shown in Figure 11. As you'd expect, it appears that the first of these polynomials approximates e^x for values of x close to 1, while the second approximates e^x for values of x close to 0. This illustrates that, in general, Taylor polynomials about different points are different polynomials.

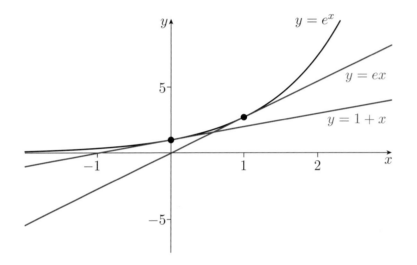

Figure 11   The linear Taylor polynomials about 0 and 1 for $f(x) = e^x$

In Subsection 1.1 we approximated functions by constant Taylor polynomials, and in this subsection we approximated them by linear Taylor polynomials. The linear Taylor polynomials usually provided better approximations than the constant Taylor polynomials. This suggests that we could obtain further improvements by increasing the degree of the approximating polynomial once more, and trying to approximate functions by polynomials of degree 2, which are *quadratic* functions. This is the topic of the next subsection.

1.3 Quadratic Taylor polynomials

We now look at approximating functions by quadratic functions. As you'd expect, this usually gives greater accuracy than approximating functions by linear functions.

Suppose that f is a function that's differentiable at a. In Subsection 1.2 you saw how to approximate f close to a by a linear function p. The particular linear function p was chosen to ensure that the following two conditions hold:

1.   The values of the function and the approximating polynomial are equal at a; that is, $p(a) = f(a)$.

2.   The values of the first derivatives of the function and the approximating polynomial are equal at a; that is, $p'(a) = f'(a)$.

Suppose that we now want to try to approximate f close to a by a *quadratic* function p. As you know, a quadratic function is a function of the form

$$p(x) = c_0 + c_1 x + c_2 x^2,$$

where c_0, c_1 and c_2 are constants. However, in the context of Taylor polynomials, it's more convenient to write the general form of an approximating quadratic function as

$$p(x) = c_0 + c_1(x - a) + c_2(x - a)^2,$$

where c_0, c_1 and c_2 are constants, and a is the point about which we want to find the approximating function. This alternative form is the rule of a quadratic function, since if you multiply out the right-hand side then you obtain powers of x up to and including x^2, but no higher powers. You can see that the form above reduces to the more usual form in the case when $a = 0$.

It seems sensible to choose the approximating quadratic function p to ensure that conditions 1 and 2 above hold. Since there are now three constants to choose, we can also impose a third condition, and a natural one to choose is:

3. The values of the second derivatives of the function and the approximating polynomial are equal at a; that is, $p''(a) = f''(a)$.

We can impose this condition provided that $f''(a)$ exists; that is, provided that f is twice differentiable at a. This is the case for many functions and many points in their domains. In fact, many functions can be differentiated as many times as you wish at all points in their domains. Such functions include all polynomial, rational, trigonometric, exponential and logarithmic functions, and all constant multiples, sums, differences, products, quotients and composites of these.

As you've seen, condition 1 means that the graphs of the function f and the approximating polynomial p both pass through the same point $(a, f(a))$, and condition 2 means that the graphs of the function and the approximating polynomial both have the same gradient at that point. Condition 3 means that the function and the approximating polynomial also have the same rate of change of gradient at that point. Roughly speaking, this means that their graphs have the same 'curvature' at that point.

The polynomial p of the form above that satisfies conditions 1, 2 and 3 is called the **quadratic Taylor polynomial about a for** f. For any point x close to a, the value of $p(x)$ is an approximation for $f(x)$.

In some cases, the polynomial $p(x)$ that satisfies conditions 1, 2 and 3 has $c_2 = 0$ and so is *not* a quadratic polynomial, but has degree 1 or less. If this happens, then we still refer to the approximating polynomial as the *quadratic* Taylor polynomial about 0 for f. This means that a quadratic Taylor polynomial is not necessarily a quadratic polynomial! You'll see an example of this later in this section. You saw in Subsection 1.2 that a similar situation arises with linear Taylor polynomials (a linear Taylor polynomial can be a constant function).

As for linear Taylor polynomials, there's a general formula that you can use to find quadratic Taylor polynomials. It's given in the box on page 114. If you're not interested in knowing where the formula comes from, then you can skip ahead to this box. Otherwise, keep reading!

To illustrate the ideas of how the formula is derived, let's start by finding a particular quadratic Taylor polynomial, namely the quadratic Taylor polynomial about 0 for the exponential function $f(x) = e^x$. As discussed above, we can take it to be of the form

$$p(x) = c_0 + c_1(x - a) + c_2(x - a)^2,$$

where c_0, c_1 and c_2 are constants. In this case, since $a = 0$, it reduces to

$$p(x) = c_0 + c_1 x + c_2 x^2.$$

We have to determine what the values of the constants c_0, c_1 and c_2 must be to ensure that the value of p at 0, and the values of the first and second derivatives of p at 0, are the same as those of f.

The first and second derivatives of the function $f(x) = e^x$ are $f'(x) = e^x$ and $f''(x) = e^x$. Hence

$$f(0) = e^0 = 1, \quad f'(0) = e^0 = 1 \quad \text{and} \quad f''(0) = e^0 = 1.$$

So we have to choose the values of the constants c_0, c_1 and c_2 to ensure that

$$p(0) = 1, \quad p'(0) = 1 \quad \text{and} \quad p''(0) = 1.$$

Here's how we can do that.

First we ensure that $p(0) = 1$. We have

$$p(x) = c_0 + c_1 x + c_2 x^2,$$

so $p(0) = c_0$. Thus to ensure that $p(0) = 1$ we must have $c_0 = 1$.

Next we ensure that $p'(0) = 1$. Differentiating the formula for p gives

$$p'(x) = c_1 + 2c_2 x,$$

so $p'(0) = c_1$. Thus to ensure that $p'(0) = 1$ we must have $c_1 = 1$.

Finally we ensure that $p''(0) = 1$. Differentiating the formula for p' gives

$$p''(x) = 2c_2,$$

so $p''(0) = 2c_2$. Thus to ensure that $p''(0) = 1$ we must have $2c_2 = 1$; that is, $c_2 = \frac{1}{2}$.

So the quadratic Taylor polynomial p for $f(x) = e^x$ about 0 is

$$p(x) = 1 + x + \tfrac{1}{2}x^2.$$

The graphs of $f(x) = e^x$ and the approximating polynomial $p(x) = 1 + x + \frac{1}{2}x^2$ found above are shown in Figure 12. You can see that the quadratic function p appears to be a more accurate approximating polynomial for $f(x) = e^x$ for values of x close to 0 than the linear function found earlier, which is shown in Figure 7 on page 104.

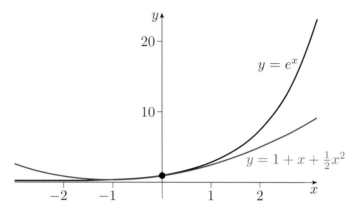

Figure 12 The quadratic Taylor polynomial about 0 for $f(x) = e^x$

As with the constant and linear Taylor polynomials about 0 for $f(x) = e^x$ that you met earlier, which are $p(x) = 1$ and $p(x) = 1 + x$, respectively, the quadratic Taylor polynomial $p(x) = 1 + x + \frac{1}{2}x^2$ provides better approximations for values of x close to 0 than for values of x further away.

You could use the method demonstrated above to work out the quadratic Taylor polynomial for any function f about any point a at which it is twice differentiable. However, let's instead apply the method to a *general* function f and *general* point a. This will give a general formula that we can use to work out a quadratic Taylor polynomial in any particular case.

So let's suppose that f is a function and a is a point in its domain at which it is twice differentiable.

The quadratic Taylor polynomial about a for f is of the form

$$p(x) = c_0 + c_1(x - a) + c_2(x - a)^2,$$

where c_0, c_1 and c_2 are constants. We have to determine what the values of the constants c_0, c_1 and c_2 must be to ensure that the value of p at a, and the values of the first and second derivatives of p at a, are the same as those of f.

To do this, we apply the method demonstrated above, the only difference being that we can't evaluate the quantities $f(a)$, $f'(a)$ and $f''(a)$, so instead we keep them in their general form throughout our working. They'll then appear in the final formula for p, ready to be evaluated for any particular function f and point a.

As before, we have to choose the values of c_0, c_1 and c_2 to ensure that

$$p(a) = f(a), \quad p'(a) = f'(a) \quad \text{and} \quad p''(a) = f''(a).$$

To do that, first we ensure that $p(a) = f(a)$. We have

$$p(x) = c_0 + c_1(x - a) + c_2(x - a)^2,$$

so $p(a) = c_0$. Thus to ensure that $p(a) = f(a)$ we must have $c_0 = f(a)$.

Next we ensure that $p'(a) = f'(a)$. The first step here is to differentiate the formula for p,

$$p(x) = c_0 + c_1(x - a) + c_2(x - a)^2.$$

The first term, c_0, is a constant, so its derivative is 0. To differentiate the second term, $c_1(x - a)$, we use the constant multiple rule, which gives c_1. To differentiate the third term, $c_2(x - a)^2$, we use the constant multiple rule and the chain rule (or the rule for differentiating a function of a linear expression), which gives $2c_2(x - a)$. The final answer is

$$p'(x) = c_1 + 2c_2(x - a).$$

Hence $p'(a) = c_1$. Thus to ensure that $p'(a) = f'(a)$ we must have $c_1 = f'(a)$.

Finally we ensure that $p''(a) = f''(a)$. Differentiating the formula for p', using a method similar to that used to differentiate the formula for p above, gives

$$p''(x) = 2c_2.$$

Hence $p''(a) = 2c_2$. Thus to ensure that $p''(a) = f''(a)$ we must have $2c_2 = f''(a)$; that is, $c_2 = \frac{1}{2}f''(a)$.

So we have the following general formula.

> **Quadratic Taylor polynomials**
>
> Let f be a function that is twice differentiable at a. The **quadratic Taylor polynomial about a for f** is
>
> $$p(x) = f(a) + f'(a)(x - a) + \tfrac{1}{2}f''(a)(x - a)^2.$$
>
> When $a = 0$, this becomes
>
> $$p(x) = f(0) + f'(0)x + \tfrac{1}{2}f''(0)x^2.$$

This formula allows you to find the quadratic Taylor polynomial p about a for any suitable function f. To do this, you calculate the value of f at a, and the values of the first and second derivatives of f at a, and then substitute them into the formula.

In the next example the quadratic Taylor polynomial about 0 for the exponential function is worked out again, this time directly using the formula in the box above.

Example 4   *Finding a quadratic Taylor polynomial about 0*

Find the quadratic Taylor polynomial about 0 for the function $f(x) = e^x$.

Solution

🔍 Differentiate f twice to find f' and f'', and hence find the values of $f(0)$, $f'(0)$ and $f''(0)$. 💬

We have $f(x) = e^x$, so
$$f'(x) = e^x \quad \text{and} \quad f''(x) = e^x.$$

Hence
$$f(0) = e^0 = 1, \quad f'(0) = e^0 = 1 \quad \text{and} \quad f''(0) = e^0 = 1.$$

🔍 Apply the second formula in the box on page 114, since in this case $a = 0$. 💬

The quadratic Taylor polynomial about 0 for $f(x) = e^x$ is
$$p(x) = f(0) + f'(0)x + \tfrac{1}{2}f''(0)x^2;$$

🔍 Substitute in the values of $f(0)$, $f'(0)$ and $f''(0)$. 💬

that is,
$$p(x) = 1 + x + \tfrac{1}{2}x^2.$$

You can see that the quadratic Taylor polynomial about 0 for the function $f(x) = e^x$ found in Example 4 is the same as that found earlier in this subsection, as expected.

In the next two activities you can use the second formula in the box on page 114 to find the quadratic Taylor polynomials about 0 for the cosine and sine functions.

Activity 6   *Finding a quadratic Taylor polynomial about 0*

(a) Find the quadratic Taylor polynomial about 0 for the function
$$f(x) = \cos x.$$

(b) Use this polynomial to find an approximation for $\cos(0.2)$, and use your calculator to find the value of the associated remainder to six decimal places. Compare this approximation for $\cos(0.2)$ with the one found in Activity 3(b). Which is better?

The outcome of Activity 6(b) demonstrates that increasing the degree of the approximating Taylor polynomial from 1 to 2 can significantly increase the accuracy of an approximation at a particular point.

The graphs of $f(x) = \cos x$ and the quadratic Taylor polynomial $p(x) = 1 - \frac{1}{2}x^2$ found in Activity 6(a) are shown in Figure 13. You can see that $p(x)$ appears to be a good approximation for $f(x)$ for values of x in quite a large interval around 0.

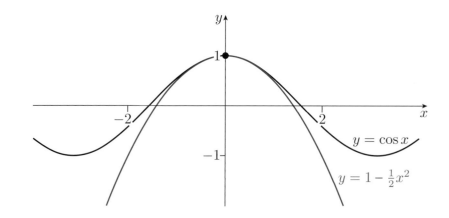

Figure 13   The quadratic Taylor polynomial about 0 for $f(x) = \cos x$

Activity 7   *Finding another quadratic Taylor polynomial about 0*

Find the quadratic Taylor polynomial about 0 for the function

$$f(x) = \sin x.$$

The quadratic Taylor polynomial about 0 for the sine function, $p(x) = x$, is an example of a quadratic Taylor polynomial that is not a quadratic polynomial. The quadratic Taylor polynomial about 0 for the sine function is the same as the linear Taylor polynomial about 0 for the sine function, whose graph is shown in Figure 8 on page 107.

We have now found constant, linear and quadratic Taylor polynomials about 0 for each of the functions $f(x) = e^x$, $f(x) = \sin x$ and $f(x) = \cos x$. These are listed in Table 1.

Table 1   Constant, linear and quadratic Taylor polynomials about 0

Function	Constant	Linear	Quadratic
e^x	1	$1 + x$	$1 + x + \frac{1}{2}x^2$
$\sin x$	0	x	x
$\cos x$	1	1	$1 - \frac{1}{2}x^2$

Notice that, for each of these three functions, the linear Taylor polynomial about 0 can be obtained from the constant Taylor polynomial about 0 by adding the appropriate term in x (this term is $0x$ in the case of cos). Similarly, the quadratic Taylor polynomial about 0 can be obtained from the linear Taylor polynomial about 0 by adding the appropriate term in x^2 (this term is $0x^2$ in the case of sin). You will see in Section 2 that these properties hold for every function f for which these Taylor polynomials can be found, and that similar properties hold for higher-degree Taylor polynomials about 0. When you're calculating Taylor polynomials, this is a very convenient feature.

Quadratic Taylor polynomials about $a \neq 0$

So far in this section, you've seen quadratic Taylor polynomials only about 0. The next example and activity involve quadratic Taylor polynomials about another point.

Example 5   *Finding a quadratic Taylor polynomial about a point other than 0*

Find the quadratic Taylor polynomial about 1 for the function $f(x) = \ln x$.

Solution

🗨 Differentiate f twice to find f' and f'', and find the values of $f(1)$, $f'(1)$ and $f''(1)$. 🗨

We have $f(x) = \ln x$, so

$$f'(x) = \frac{1}{x} \quad \text{and} \quad f''(x) = -\frac{1}{x^2}.$$

Hence

$$f(1) = \ln 1 = 0, \quad f'(1) = \frac{1}{1} = 1 \quad \text{and} \quad f''(1) = -\frac{1}{1^2} = -1.$$

🗨 Apply the first formula in the box on page 114. Remember that in this case $a = 1$. 🗨

The quadratic Taylor polynomial about 1 for $f(x) = \ln x$ is

$$p(x) = f(1) + f'(1)(x-1) + \tfrac{1}{2}f''(1)(x-1)^2;$$

🗨 Substitute in the values of $f(1)$, $f'(1)$ and $f''(1)$. 🗨

that is,

$$p(x) = 0 + 1(x-1) + \tfrac{1}{2}(-1)(x-1)^2,$$

which can be simplified to

$$p(x) = (x-1) - \tfrac{1}{2}(x-1)^2.$$

🗨 Usually, leave the answer in this form, rather than multiplying out. 🗨

You could simplify the quadratic Taylor polynomial found in Example 5 by multiplying out the squared brackets and collecting like terms. This gives

$$p(x) = -\tfrac{3}{2} + 2x - \tfrac{1}{2}x^2.$$

However, normally we don't simplify quadratic Taylor polynomials in this way. Instead, we leave them in the form

$$p(x) = c_0 + c_1(x - a) + c_2(x - a)^2.$$

To understand why, remember that a convenient property of Taylor polynomials about 0 is that you can obtain the linear Taylor polynomial about 0 for a function f by adding the appropriate term in x to the constant Taylor polynomial about 0 for f, and similarly for higher-degree Taylor polynomials. Taylor polynomials about a point a other than 0 have the same property, as long as you use the form above for the Taylor polynomials; that is, as long as you consider terms in powers of $x - a$ rather than terms in powers of x. You'll see in the next section why this is true for any value of a.

The graphs of the function $f(x) = \ln x$ and the quadratic Taylor polynomial $p(x) = (x - 1) - \tfrac{1}{2}(x - 1)^2$ found in Example 5 are shown in Figure 14.

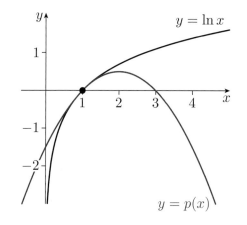

Figure 14   The quadratic Taylor polynomial about 1 for $f(x) = \ln x$

Activity 8   *Finding a quadratic Taylor polynomial about a point other than 0*

Find the quadratic Taylor polynomial about 1 for the function $f(x) = e^x$.

So far you've seen how you can use constant, linear and quadratic Taylor polynomials about a point a for a function f to approximate the values of f close to a. You saw that when we increased the degree of the Taylor polynomial the accuracy of the approximations was usually improved. In the next section you'll see that this fact generalises to approximating polynomials of higher degree.

2   Taylor polynomials of any degree

In this section you'll look at approximating functions by polynomials of any degree, and how you can use such polynomials to find approximate values for functions at particular points.

2.1   Taylor polynomials of degree n

From what you saw in Section 1, you might guess that for any suitable function f and any point a in its domain, you can obtain more and more accurate approximating polynomials for f close to a by taking polynomials of higher and higher degrees, and choosing the coefficients to ensure that the values of higher and higher derivatives of the polynomial at a are the same as those of the corresponding derivatives of f. Here 'suitable function f' means that f must be differentiable at a the required number of times.

For example, to try to improve on the approximations provided by the quadratic Taylor polynomial about a for f, you could attempt to approximate f by a cubic function, of the form

$$p(x) = c_0 + c_1(x - a) + c_2(x - a)^2 + c_3(x - a)^3,$$

whose value is the same as that of f at a, and whose first, second and third derivatives have the same values at a as the corresponding derivatives of f.

More generally, for any chosen value of n, you could try to find a polynomial

$$p(x) = c_0 + c_1(x - a) + c_2(x - a)^2 + c_3(x - a)^3 + \cdots + c_n(x - a)^n, \quad (1)$$

whose value is the same as that of f at a, and whose first, second, third, ..., nth derivatives have the same values at a as the corresponding derivatives of f. The polynomial that satisfies these conditions is called the **Taylor polynomial of degree n about a for f**.

There's a general formula for this Taylor polynomial, for any function f, any degree n, and any point a at which f is differentiable n times. As you'd expect, this formula involves the values of the first, second, third, ..., nth derivatives of f at a. Remember that for $n \geq 3$ the nth derivative of the function f is denoted by $f^{(n)}$, so the value of the nth derivative of f at a is denoted by $f^{(n)}(a)$. (The third derivative $f^{(3)}$ is sometimes denoted by f'''.) The general formula is given in the box on page 121. If you're not interested in knowing how it's derived, then you can skip ahead to it. Otherwise, as before, keep reading.

To find the formula, we'll use the method that was used for quadratic polynomials in the previous section, but we'll continue with derivatives up to the nth, rather than just the second. Similarly to before, we can't evaluate the first, second, third, ..., nth derivatives of f at a, because we don't know what f and a are, so throughout our working we'll denote them by $f'(a)$, $f''(a)$, $f^{(3)}(a)$, ..., $f^{(n)}(a)$. These quantities will then appear in the final formula for p, ready to be evaluated for any particular function f and point a.

Here's how the working goes. We need to determine what the values of the constants c_0, c_1, c_2, ..., c_n in equation (1) must be to ensure that the value of p at a, and the values of the first, second, third, ..., nth derivatives of p at a, are the same as those of f.

First we ensure that $p(a) = f(a)$. We have
$$p(x) = c_0 + c_1(x - a) + c_2(x - a)^2 + c_3(x - a)^3 + c_4(x - a)^4$$
$$+ \cdots + c_n(x - a)^n,$$
so $p(a) = c_0$. Thus to ensure that $p(a) = f(a)$ we must have
$$c_0 = f(a).$$

Next we ensure that $p'(a) = f'(a)$. We have
$$p'(x) = c_1 + 2c_2(x - a) + 3c_3(x - a)^2 + 4c_4(x - a)^3$$
$$+ \cdots + nc_n(x - a)^{n-1},$$
so $p'(a) = c_1$. Thus to ensure that $p'(a) = f'(a)$ we must have
$$c_1 = f'(a).$$

Then we ensure that $p''(a) = f''(a)$. We have
$$p''(x) = 2c_2 + 3 \times 2 \, c_3(x - a) + 4 \times 3 \, c_4(x - a)^2$$
$$+ \cdots + n(n - 1)c_n(x - a)^{n-2},$$
so $p''(a) = 2c_2$. Thus to ensure that $p''(a) = f''(a)$ we must have $2c_2 = f''(a)$; that is,
$$c_2 = \tfrac{1}{2} f''(a).$$

It's useful to write this as
$$c_2 = \frac{f''(a)}{2!},$$
where 2! denotes 2×1, that is, 2 factorial, as you saw in Unit 10. This allows the pattern in the next few calculations to be seen more easily. (Recall that if n is a positive integer, then, by definition,
$$n! = n(n - 1) \times \cdots \times 2 \times 1.)$$

Then we ensure that $p^{(3)}(a) = f^{(3)}(a)$. We have
$$p^{(3)}(x) = 3 \times 2 \, c_3 + 4 \times 3 \times 2 \, c_4(x - a)$$
$$+ \cdots + n(n - 1)(n - 2)c_n(x - a)^{n-3},$$
so $p^{(3)}(a) = 3! \, c_3$. Thus to ensure that $p^3(a) = f^3(a)$ we must have $3! \, c_3 = f^{(3)}(a)$; that is,
$$c_3 = \frac{f^{(3)}(a)}{3!}.$$

Continuing in this way, we find that we must have
$$c_4 = \frac{f^{(4)}(a)}{4!}, \qquad c_5 = \frac{f^{(5)}(a)}{5!}, \qquad \text{and so on,}$$
until finally, to ensure that $p^{(n)}(a) = f^{(n)}(a)$, we must have
$$c_n = \frac{f^{(n)}(a)}{n!}.$$

The resulting formula for the approximating polynomial is stated below. You can see that it generalises the formulas for constant, linear and quadratic Taylor polynomials given earlier. In the case where $a = 0$ the formula reduces to a simpler form, which is also stated below.

Taylor polynomials

Let f be a function that is n-times differentiable at a point a. The **Taylor polynomial of degree n about a for f** is

$$p(x) = f(a) + f'(a)(x - a) + \frac{f''(a)}{2!}(x - a)^2 + \frac{f^{(3)}(a)}{3!}(x - a)^3$$
$$+ \cdots + \frac{f^{(n)}(a)}{n!}(x - a)^n. \tag{2}$$

The point a is called the **centre** of the Taylor polynomial.

When $a = 0$, the Taylor polynomial above becomes

$$p(x) = f(0) + f'(0)x + \frac{f''(0)}{2!}x^2 + \frac{f^{(3)}(0)}{3!}x^3 + \cdots + \frac{f^{(n)}(0)}{n!}x^n. \tag{3}$$

Formula (2) allows you to find the Taylor polynomial p of degree n about a for any suitable function f. To do this, you calculate the value of f at a, and the values of the first, second, third, $\ldots$, nth derivatives of f at a, and substitute them into the formula.

The formula also confirms that any Taylor polynomial about a for a function f can be obtained from a Taylor polynomial of lower degree about a for f by adding the appropriate further terms. For example, the Taylor polynomial of degree 1 about a for f is

$$p(x) = f(a) + f'(a)(x - a),$$

while the Taylor polynomial of degree 2 about 0 for f is

$$p(x) = f(a) + f'(a)(x - a) + \frac{f''(a)}{2!}(x - a)^2.$$

The second polynomial is obtained from the first simply by adding the term in $(x - a)^2$.

For some functions f, the value of $f^{(n)}(a)$ is 0. In such a case, formula (2) gives a polynomial whose degree is less than n. If this happens, then the polynomial is still called the Taylor polynomial of degree n about a for f. This means that a Taylor polynomial of degree n is not necessarily a polynomial of degree n. You've seen examples of this already, in the cases $n = 1$ and $n = 2$, and you'll see more examples later in this section.

You've seen the terms *constant*, *linear* and *quadratic* used to describe Taylor polynomials of degrees 0, 1 and 2, respectively. The terms **cubic**, **quartic** and **quintic** are used to describe Taylor polynomials of degrees 3, 4 and 5, respectively.

The next example and the two activities that follow concern Taylor polynomials about 0. So in these we use formula (3) for a Taylor polynomial about 0, rather than the general formula (2).

Example 6   *Finding a quartic Taylor polynomial about 0*

Find the quartic Taylor polynomial about 0 for the function $f(x) = e^x$.

Solution

🗨 Repeatedly differentiate f to find f', f'', $f^{(3)}$ and $f^{(4)}$, and find the values of $f(0)$, $f'(0)$, $f''(0)$, $f^{(3)}(0)$ and $f^{(4)}(0)$. 🗨

Here $f(0) = e^0 = 1$. Also, for each positive integer n, the nth derivative of the function $f(x) = e^x$ is $f^{(n)}(x) = e^x$, so

$$f^{(n)}(0) = e^0 = 1, \quad \text{for all positive integers } n.$$

🗨 Apply formula (3) in the box above, since in this case $a = 0$. Also, $2! = 2 \times 1 = 2$, $3! = 3 \times 2 \times 1 = 6$ and $4! = 4 \times 3 \times 2 \times 1 = 24$. 🗨

Hence, by formula (3), the Taylor polynomial of degree 4 about 0 for $f(x) = e^x$ is

$$p(x) = 1 + x + \frac{1}{2!}x^2 + \frac{1}{3!}x^3 + \frac{1}{4!}x^4;$$

that is,

$$p(x) = 1 + x + \tfrac{1}{2}x^2 + \tfrac{1}{6}x^3 + \tfrac{1}{24}x^4.$$

Notice that, as you'd expect, the first three terms found in Example 6 agree with those of the quadratic Taylor polynomial about 0 for the exponential function, which was found in Example 4.

The graphs of the function $f(x) = e^x$ and the quartic Taylor polynomial about 0 found in Example 6 are shown in Figure 15. Notice how much better this approximating polynomial is than the quadratic one shown in Figure 12 on page 113.

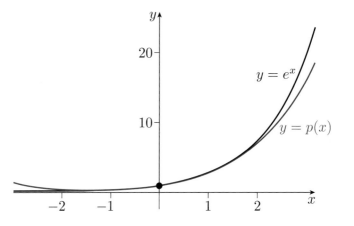

Figure 15   The quartic Taylor polynomial about 0 for $f(x) = e^x$

Since for the function $f(x) = e^x$ we have that $f^{(n)}(0) = 1$ for all positive integers n, it follows from formula (3) that, for any n, the Taylor polynomial of degree n about 0 for $f(x) = e^x$ is

$$p(x) = 1 + x + \frac{1}{2!}x^2 + \frac{1}{3!}x^3 + \cdots + \frac{1}{n!}x^n.$$

In the next activity you're asked to find the quartic Taylor polynomials about 0 for the cosine and sine functions.

Activity 9 *Finding quartic Taylor polynomials about 0*

Find the quartic Taylor polynomial about 0 for each of the following functions.

(a) $f(x) = \cos x$ (b) $f(x) = \sin x$

Notice that the constant term, the term in x and the term in x^2 in the Taylor polynomials that you were asked to find in Activity 9 are the same as those in the quadratic Taylor polynomials about 0 for the cosine and sine functions, which you were asked to find in Activities 6 and 7.

The quartic Taylor polynomial about 0 for the sine function is an example of a Taylor polynomial of degree n whose polynomial degree is less than n.

The graphs of the cosine and sine functions, and the quartic Taylor polynomials for these functions that you were asked to find in Activity 9, are shown in Figure 16(a) and (b), respectively.

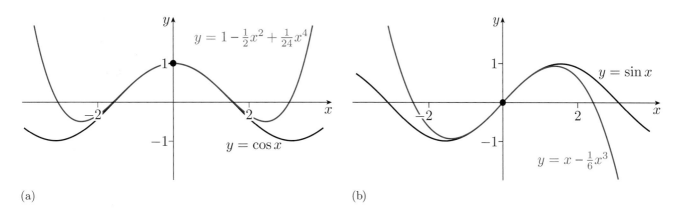

(a)   (b)

Figure 16   The quartic Taylor polynomials about 0 for cosine and sine

In the next activity you're asked to find a general formula for a Taylor polynomial of degree n about 0 for a particular function, by spotting how the pattern of derivatives develops.

Activity 10   *Finding a Taylor polynomial of degree n*

Consider the function

$$f(x) = \frac{1}{1-x}.$$

(a) (i)   Use the chain rule (from Unit 7) to show that, if k is a constant, then

$$\frac{\mathrm{d}}{\mathrm{d}x}\left(\frac{1}{(1-x)^k}\right) = \frac{k}{(1-x)^{k+1}}.$$

   (ii)   Use the result of part (a)(i) to find formulas for f', f'' and $f^{(3)}$, and hence find the values of $f'(0)$, $f''(0)$ and $f^{(3)}(0)$.

   (iii)   Hence find the cubic Taylor polynomial about 0 for f.

(b) (i)   Use the result of part (a)(i) to find successive derivatives of f beyond the third, until the pattern is clear and you can write down a formula for the nth derivative of f, in terms of x and n.

   (ii)   Hence write down a formula in terms of n for $f^{(n)}(0)$, the value of the nth derivative of f at 0.

   (iii)   Hence write down, using the $+\cdots+$ notation, a formula for the Taylor polynomial of degree n about 0 for f.

The graph of the function $f(x) = 1/(1-x)$, and the graph of the cubic Taylor polynomial about 0 for this function from Activity 10(a), are shown in Figure 17.

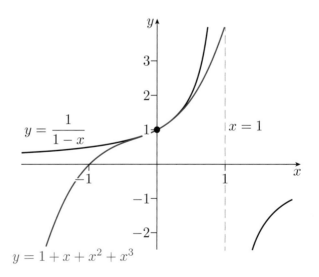

Figure 17   The cubic Taylor polynomial about 0 for $f(x) = 1/(1-x)$

Even and odd functions

In Activity 9 earlier in this subsection you saw that the quartic Taylor polynomials about 0 for the cosine and sine functions are

$$1 - \tfrac{1}{2}x^2 + \tfrac{1}{24}x^4 \quad \text{and} \quad x - \tfrac{1}{6}x^3,$$

respectively.

Notice that the quartic Taylor polynomial about 0 for the cosine function contains terms in even powers of x only, whereas that for the sine function contains terms in odd powers of x only. These observations are explained by the facts that the cosine function is an *even* function and the sine function is an *odd* function, as defined in general below.

A function f is said to be **even** if its graph is unchanged under reflection in the y-axis, as illustrated in Figure 18(a). Thus f is even if

$$f(-x) = f(x), \quad \text{for all } x \text{ in the domain of } f.$$

Similarly, a function f is said to be **odd** if its graph is unchanged by rotation through a half turn about the origin, as illustrated in Figure 18(b). Thus f is odd if

$$f(-x) = -f(x), \quad \text{for all } x \text{ in the domain of } f.$$

A rotation through a half turn about the origin has the same effect as a reflection in the y-axis followed by a reflection in the x-axis. Hence the graph of an odd function is the same as an 'upside down' reflection of itself in the y-axis.

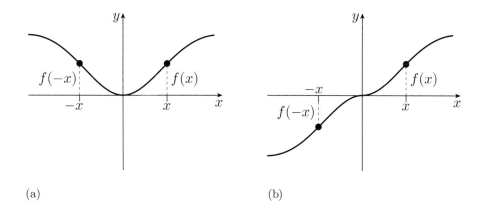

(a)   (b)

Figure 18   (a) An even function   (b) An odd function

These definitions are summarised below.

> ### Even and odd functions
>
> A function f is
>
> - **even** if $f(-x) = f(x)$ for all x in the domain of f
> - **odd** if $f(-x) = -f(x)$ for all x in the domain of f.

Here are some examples.

- $f(x) = x^2$ is an even function, since

$$f(-x) = (-x)^2 = x^2 = f(x), \quad \text{for all } x \in \mathbb{R}.$$

- $f(x) = x^3$ is an odd function, since

$$f(-x) = (-x)^3 = -x^3 = -f(x), \quad \text{for all } x \in \mathbb{R}.$$

- $f(x) = \sin x$ is an odd function, since

$$f(-x) = \sin(-x) = -\sin x = -f(x), \quad \text{for all } x \in \mathbb{R}.$$

- $f(x) = \cos x$ is an even function, since

$$f(-x) = \cos(-x) = \cos x = f(x), \quad \text{for all } x \in \mathbb{R}.$$

- $f(x) = e^x$ is neither even nor odd, since we can find a value of x, say $x = 1$, such that $e^{-x} \neq e^x$ and $e^{-x} \neq -e^x$. (In fact, $e^{-1} \approx 0.368$ and $e^1 \approx 2.718$.)

(Remember that the symbol $\in$ means 'in' or 'belongs to' and that the symbol $\mathbb{R}$ denotes the set of real numbers.)

Taylor polynomials about 0 for even and odd functions have the following properties.

> **Taylor polynomials about 0 for even and odd functions**
>
> A Taylor polynomial about 0 for an even function contains terms in even powers of x only.
>
> A Taylor polynomial about 0 for an odd function contains terms in odd powers of x only.

Here's an explanation of why these facts are true.

By looking at the symmetry of the graph in Figure 18(a), and thinking about even functions in general, you can see that if f is an even function, then for all x in its domain the gradient of the graph of f at $-x$ has the same magnitude as the gradient at x, but the opposite sign (provided that the gradient exists). In other words,

if $f(-x) = f(x)$, for all x in the domain of f,

then $f'(-x) = -f'(x)$, for all x in the domain of f'.

This means that if f is an even function then f' is an odd function.

Similarly, by looking at the symmetry of the graph in Figure 18(b) and thinking about odd functions in general, you can see that if f is an odd function, then for all x in its domain the gradient of f is the same at $-x$ as at x (provided that the gradient exists). In other words,

if $f(-x) = -f(x)$, for all x in the domain of f,

then $f'(-x) = f'(x)$, for all x in the domain of f'.

This means that if f is an odd function then f' is an even function.

So differentiation turns any even function into an odd function, and vice versa.

Notice also that if f is an odd function whose domain contains 0, then, since $f(-x) = -f(x)$ for all x in its domain, we have in particular that $f(0) = -f(0)$, and it follows that $f(0) = 0$. Hence any odd function has the value 0 at 0.

Now let f be any even function that's differentiable infinitely many times at 0. It follows from the discussion above that f'', $f^{(4)}$, $f^{(6)}$, ..., are all even functions, and f', $f^{(3)}$, $f^{(5)}$, ..., are all odd functions. Since any odd function has the value 0 at the point 0, the values of $f'(0)$, $f^{(3)}(0)$, $f^{(5)}(0)$, ..., are all 0. Hence, from the general formula for a Taylor polynomial about 0, any Taylor polynomial about 0 for f contains only terms with even powers of x.

Similar reasoning applies in the case of an odd function.

By the facts in the box above, any Taylor polynomial about 0 for the cosine function contains terms in even powers of x only, and any Taylor polynomial about 0 for the sine function contains terms in odd powers of x only. For example, the Taylor polynomial of degree 9 about 0 for $f(x) = \cos x$ is

$$p(x) = 1 - \frac{1}{2!}x^2 + \frac{1}{4!}x^4 - \frac{1}{6!}x^6 + \frac{1}{8!}x^8.$$

Similarly, the Taylor polynomial of degree 9 about 0 for $f(x) = \sin x$ is

$$p(x) = x - \frac{1}{3!}x^3 + \frac{1}{5!}x^5 - \frac{1}{7!}x^7 + \frac{1}{9!}x^9.$$

You can find these Taylor polynomials by extending the solution to Activity 9, and noting the patterns in the coefficients of the Taylor polynomials. These patterns continue indefinitely for higher-degree Taylor polynomials for the cosine and sine functions. You'll be asked to verify this later in the unit.

Taylor polynomials of degree n about $a \neq 0$

So far in this section, all the examples and activities have involved Taylor polynomials about 0. The next example and activity involve Taylor polynomials about another point a. So here we use the general formula for a Taylor polynomial given by equation (2) on page 121.

Example 7 *Finding a quartic Taylor polynomial about a point other than 0*

Find the quartic Taylor polynomial about 1 for the function $f(x) = \ln x$.

Solution

🗨 Repeatedly differentiate f to find f', f'', $f^{(3)}$ and $f^{(4)}$, and find the values of $f(1)$, $f'(1)$, $f''(1)$, $f^{(3)}(1)$ and $f^{(4)}(1)$. 🗨

The first four derivatives of the function $f(x) = \ln x$ are as follows:

$$f'(x) = \frac{1}{x}, \quad f''(x) = -\frac{1}{x^2}, \quad f^{(3)}(x) = \frac{2}{x^3},$$

$$f^{(4)}(x) = -\frac{3 \times 2}{x^4} = -\frac{3!}{x^4}.$$

🗨 The product 3×2 has been simplified to $3!$ rather than 6 here to highlight the emerging pattern. 🗨

So

$$f(1) = 0, \quad f'(1) = 1, \quad f''(1) = -1, \quad f^{(3)}(1) = 2,$$

$$f^{(4)}(1) = -3!.$$

🗨 Apply formula (2) on page 121. Remember that in this case $a = 1$. 🗨

Hence the quartic Taylor polynomial about 1 for the function $f(x) = \ln x$ is

$$p(x) = 0 + 1 \times (x-1) + \frac{(-1)}{2!}(x-1)^2 + \frac{2}{3!}(x-1)^3$$
$$+ \frac{(-3!)}{4!}(x-1)^4;$$

that is,

$$p(x) = (x-1) - \tfrac{1}{2}(x-1)^2 + \tfrac{1}{3}(x-1)^3 - \tfrac{1}{4}(x-1)^4.$$

As you saw earlier in the case of quadratic Taylor polynomials, we usually leave a Taylor polynomial about a point a as a sum of terms each of which is the product of a constant and a power of $x - a$, rather than multiplying it out. However, we might make an exception for a polynomial of low degree for which the multiplied-out form is simpler.

The graphs of the function $f(x) = \ln x$ and the quartic Taylor polynomial about 1 found in Example 7 are shown in Figure 19. As you'd expect, the quartic Taylor polynomial appears to be a better approximating polynomial than the quadratic Taylor polynomial about 1 for f shown in Figure 14 on page 118.

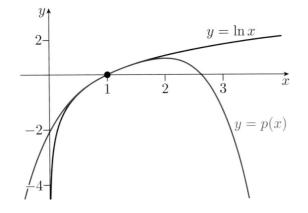

Figure 19   The quartic Taylor polynomial about 1 for $f(x) = \ln x$

If, in the solution to Example 7, you look at the patterns in the formulas for f, f', f'', $f^{(3)}$, ..., and hence in the values of $f(1)$, $f'(1)$, $f''(1)$, $f^{(3)}(1)$, ..., then you can see that the pattern of terms in the Taylor polynomial found in the example continues as the degree of the Taylor polynomial increases. So, for any positive integer n, the Taylor polynomial of degree n about 1 for $f(x) = \ln x$ is

$$p(x) = (x-1) - \tfrac{1}{2}(x-1)^2 + \tfrac{1}{3}(x-1)^3 - \cdots + (-1)^{n-1}\frac{1}{n}(x-1)^n.$$

The expression $(-1)^{n-1}$ in the final term here is, as you saw in Unit 10, a neat way to give the term a negative sign when n is even and a positive sign when n is odd. This expression can also be written as $-(-1)^n$, since

$$(-1)^n = (-1) \times (-1)^{n-1} = -(-1)^{n-1}.$$

Activity 11   *Finding a cubic Taylor polynomial about a point other than 0*

Find the cubic Taylor polynomial about $\pi/6$ for the function $f(x) = \sin x$.

The graphs of the function $f(x) = \sin x$ and the cubic Taylor polynomial about $\pi/6$ found in Activity 11 are shown in Figure 20.

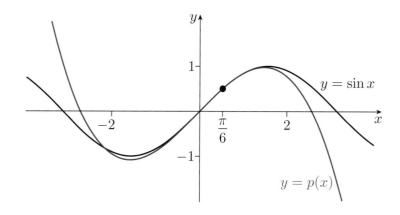

Figure 20 The cubic Taylor polynomial about $\pi/6$ for $f(x) = \sin x$

The cubic Taylor polynomial about $\pi/6$ for the function $f(x) = \sin x$, which you were asked to find in Activity 11, contains terms in $(x - \pi/6)^k$ with k even as well as with k odd. This is not surprising, since the earlier discussion about even and odd functions applies only to Taylor polynomials about 0.

Activity 12 *Investigating graphs of Taylor polynomials*

Open the *Graphs of Taylor polynomials* applet. Initially it shows the graphs of the function $f(x) = e^x$ and its Taylor polynomial of degree 1 about 0.

(a) Increase the degree n of the Taylor polynomial and observe the effect on its graph.

(b) Try changing the function f and then varying n.

(c) Try changing the centre a of the Taylor polynomial and then varying n.

(d) Try some other functions and other centres for the Taylor polynomial.

Using sigma notation for Taylor polynomials

Sigma notation for series, which you met in Unit 10, provides a concise way to write down Taylor polynomials. Formula (3) on page 121, for the Taylor polynomial of degree n about 0 for a function f, is

$$p(x) = f(0) + f'(0)x + \frac{f''(0)}{2!}x^2 + \frac{f^{(3)}(0)}{3!}x^3 + \cdots + \frac{f^{(n)}(0)}{n!}x^n.$$

This polynomial can be written in sigma notation as

$$p(x) = \sum_{k=0}^{n} \frac{f^{(k)}(0)}{k!} x^k.$$

(Here $f^{(0)}$ is interpreted to mean f itself. Also, by convention, 0^0 is taken to have the value 1 in series of this type. Recall also that $0! = 1$.)

For example, the quartic Taylor polynomial about 0 for the function $f(x) = e^x$, which was found in Example 6, is

$$p(x) = 1 + x + \frac{1}{2!}x^2 + \frac{1}{3!}x^3 + \frac{1}{4!}x^4 = \sum_{k=0}^{4} \frac{1}{k!} x^k.$$

You can often express particular Taylor polynomials concisely in this way, once the pattern of terms is clear.

2.2 Taylor polynomials for approximation

In this subsection we'll use Taylor polynomials to calculate approximations for values of functions at particular points. In doing so, we'll compare approximations obtained from Taylor polynomials of different degrees, and for clarity we need a notation that indicates the degree of each Taylor polynomial. The notation that we use is to denote a Taylor polynomial by p_n, where n is its degree, rather than by just p. Thus, for example, the Taylor polynomials of degrees 1 and 2 about 0 for the function $f(x) = e^x$ are $p_1(x) = 1 + x$ and $p_2(x) = 1 + x + \frac{1}{2}x^2$, respectively.

You've seen that usually the greater the degree of a Taylor polynomial p_n about a point a for a function f, the more accurate $p_n(x)$ is as an approximation to $f(x)$ for values of x close to a.

For example, consider the Taylor polynomials about 0 for the function $f(x) = e^x$. You saw earlier that, for any positive integer n, the Taylor polynomial of degree n about 0 for this function is

$$p_n(x) = 1 + x + \frac{1}{2!}x^2 + \frac{1}{3!}x^3 + \cdots + \frac{1}{n!}x^n.$$

Figure 21 shows the graphs of the Taylor polynomials of degrees 0, 1, 2 and 3 about 0 for the function $f(x) = e^x$, together with the graph of $f(x) = e^x$ itself. As you'd expect, it appears that as the degree of the Taylor polynomial increases, its graph approximates the graph of f near 0 more and more closely.

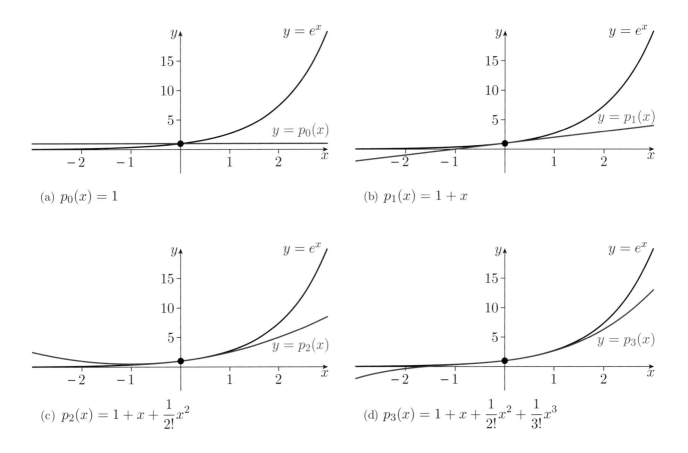

(a) $p_0(x) = 1$

(b) $p_1(x) = 1 + x$

(c) $p_2(x) = 1 + x + \dfrac{1}{2!}x^2$

(d) $p_3(x) = 1 + x + \dfrac{1}{2!}x^2 + \dfrac{1}{3!}x^3$

Figure 21   Taylor polynomials about 0 for $f(x) = e^x$

Table 2 provides a numerical illustration for the same function, $f(x) = e^x$, for a particular value of x near 0, namely $x = 0.25$. The value of $e^{0.25}$ is 1.284 025 4167, to ten decimal places. For values of n from 0 to 8, the table gives the Taylor polynomial $p_n(x)$ about 0 for f, the value of this polynomial when $x = 0.25$, and the associated remainder. All the values are given to ten decimal places. You can see that as the degree n of the Taylor polynomial increases, the accuracy of $p_n(0.25)$ as an approximation for $e^{0.25}$ improves.

Table 2   Successive Taylor polynomial approximations for $e^{0.25}$

n	$p_n(x)$	$p_n(0.25)$	$e^{0.25} - p_n(0.25)$
0	1	1	0.284 025 4167
1	$1 + x$	1.25	0.034 025 4167
2	$1 + x + x^2/2!$	1.281 25	0.002 775 4167
3	$1 + x + x^2/2! + x^3/3!$	1.283 854 1667	0.000 171 2500
4	$1 + x + x^2/2! + \cdots + x^4/4!$	1.284 016 9271	0.000 008 4896
5	$1 + x + x^2/2! + \cdots + x^5/5!$	1.284 025 0651	0.000 000 3516
6	$1 + x + x^2/2! + \cdots + x^6/6!$	1.284 025 4042	0.000 000 0125
7	$1 + x + x^2/2! + \cdots + x^7/7!$	1.284 025 4163	0.000 000 0004
8	$1 + x + x^2/2! + \cdots + x^8/8!$	1.284 025 4167	0.000 000 0000

Table 2 shows that for $f(x) = e^x$ the Taylor polynomial of degree 8 about 0 for f gives a method of calculating the value of $e^{0.25}$ correct to 10 decimal places by using only the standard arithmetical operations of addition, subtraction and multiplication. (Raising to a power is just repeated multiplication.)

In general, Taylor polynomials can often be used to calculate approximations for values of functions to any desired accuracy. If f is a function and x is a particular value in the domain of f, then to find an approximation for $f(x)$ we calculate a Taylor polynomial for f about some suitable point a close to x, and then evaluate it at x using only the standard arithmetical operations.

Unfortunately, there's no easy method for determining a suitable degree for the Taylor polynomial in any individual case. However, there's a 'rule of thumb' that works in many cases, and in particular in most of the cases that you're likely to come across. If you want an approximation accurate to m decimal places, then you calculate approximations using Taylor polynomials of degree 1, 2, 3, and so on, until two successive approximations agree to $m + 2$ decimal places. (You start with degree 1 rather than 0 because constant Taylor polynomials rarely give useful approximations.) This method is illustrated in Example 8 below.

Note that when we say that two numbers agree to a particular number of decimal places, we mean that the values resulting from rounding them to that number of decimal places are equal. Thus, for example, 0.237 and 0.241 agree to two decimal places, since in each case rounding to two decimal places gives 0.24. However, 0.241 and 0.247 don't agree to two decimal places, since rounding to two decimal places gives 0.24 in the first case and 0.25 in the second.

Example 8   *Finding an approximate value of a function*

You saw on page 129 that, for each positive integer n, the Taylor polynomial of degree n about 1 for $f(x) = \ln x$ is

$$p_n(x) = (x - 1) - \tfrac{1}{2}(x - 1)^2 + \tfrac{1}{3}(x - 1)^3 - \cdots + (-1)^{n-1}\frac{1}{n}(x - 1)^n.$$

Use these Taylor polynomials to find the likely value of $\ln(1.1)$ to four decimal places.

Solution

Calculate $p_1(1.1)$, $p_2(1.1)$, $p_3(1.1)$, and so on, by repeatedly adding on extra terms. You want to find two successive values that agree to $4 + 2 = 6$ decimal places, so calculate values to 6 decimal places.

Calculating these values to six decimal places, we obtain
$$p_1(1.1) = 1.1 - 1 = 0.1$$
$$p_2(1.1) = p_1(1.1) - \tfrac{1}{2}(1.1 - 1)^2 = 0.095$$
$$p_3(1.1) = p_2(1.1) + \tfrac{1}{3}(1.1 - 1)^3 = 0.095\,333$$

$$p_4(1.1) = p_3(1.1) - \tfrac{1}{4}(1.1-1)^4 = 0.095\,308$$
$$p_5(1.1) = p_4(1.1) + \tfrac{1}{5}(1.1-1)^5 = 0.095\,310$$
$$p_6(1.1) = p_5(1.1) - \tfrac{1}{6}(1.1-1)^6 = 0.095\,310.$$

The values of $p_5(1.1)$ and $p_6(1.1)$ agree to six decimal places, so it is likely that

$$\ln(1.1) = 0.0953$$

to four decimal places.

You can check using your calculator that it is indeed true that $\ln(1.1) = 0.0953$ to four decimal places, as obtained in Example 8.

In Example 8, each successive approximation $p_n(1.1)$ was calculated by evaluating just the final term of $p_n(x)$ with $x = 1.1$, and then adding this value to $p_{n-1}(1.1)$, the previous approximation. This is an efficient way to proceed, but when working through a similar example yourself, you must make sure that each time you add an evaluated term to the previous approximation, you use the full-calculator-precision version of the previous approximation, rather than the rounded version that you just wrote down. Not doing so will cause errors in some cases.

If you have a modern calculator, then you should be able to carry out this procedure without having to write down the unrounded values. Each time you want to add a new term, you can access the previous answer and calculate and add the new term, all in one step. After each such addition you can round off the approximation and write it down.

Activity 13   *Finding an approximate value of a function*

You saw on page 123 that, for each positive integer n, the Taylor polynomial of degree n about 0 for $f(x) = e^x$ is

$$p_n(x) = 1 + x + \frac{1}{2!}x^2 + \frac{1}{3!}x^3 + \cdots + \frac{1}{n!}x^n.$$

Use these Taylor polynomials to find the likely value of $e^{-0.05}$ to four decimal places.

The next example is similar to Example 8 and Activity 13, but it involves Taylor polynomials about 0 for the sine function. Since this function is odd, its Taylor polynomials about 0 contain no even powers of x, as explained on page 126. Hence each Taylor polynomial of even degree is the same as the Taylor polynomial of degree one less; that is, $p_2(x) = p_1(x)$, $p_4(x) = p_3(x)$, and so on. You would therefore rapidly find two successive approximations that agree to any specified number of decimal places, but this would tell you nothing about the accuracy of the approximation! For this reason it makes sense to consider only the Taylor polynomials of odd degree for this function.

Example 9   *Finding an approximate value of an odd function*

The Taylor polynomials of odd degree about 0 for $f(x) = \sin x$ were discussed on page 127. They are

$$p_1(x) = x, \qquad p_3(x) = x - \frac{1}{3!}x^3, \qquad p_5(x) = x - \frac{1}{3!}x^3 + \frac{1}{5!}x^5$$

$$p_7(x) = x - \frac{1}{3!}x^3 + \frac{1}{5!}x^5 - \frac{1}{7!}x^7, \qquad \text{and so on.}$$

Use these Taylor polynomials to find the likely value of $\sin(0.2)$ to six decimal places.

Solution

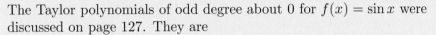 Calculate $p_1(0.2)$, $p_3(0.2)$, $p_5(0.2)$, and so on. You want to find a pair of successive values that agree to $6 + 2 = 8$ decimal places, so calculate values to 8 decimal places. Remember that each successive polynomial is obtained by adding a new term to the previous polynomial.

Calculating values to eight decimal places, we obtain

$$p_1(0.2) = 0.2$$

$$p_3(0.2) = p_1(0.2) - \frac{1}{3!}(0.2)^3 = 0.198\,666\,67$$

$$p_5(0.2) = p_3(0.2) + \frac{1}{5!}(0.2)^5 = 0.198\,669\,33$$

$$p_7(0.2) = p_5(0.2) - \frac{1}{7!}(0.2)^7 = 0.198\,669\,33.$$

The values of $p_5(0.2)$ and $p_7(0.2)$ agree to eight decimal places, so it is likely that

$$\sin(0.2) = 0.198\,669$$

to six decimal places.

You can check using your calculator that it is indeed true that $\sin(0.2) = 0.198\,669$ to six decimal places, as obtained in the solution to Example 8.

Activity 14 *Finding an approximate value of an even function*

The Taylor polynomials of even degree about 0 for $f(x) = \cos x$ were discussed on page 127. They are

$$p_0(x) = 1, \qquad p_2(x) = 1 - \frac{1}{2!}x^2, \qquad p_4(x) = 1 - \frac{1}{2!}x^2 + \frac{1}{4!}x^4$$

$$p_6(x) = 1 - \frac{1}{2!}x^2 + \frac{1}{4!}x^4 - \frac{1}{6!}x^6, \qquad \text{and so on.}$$

Use these Taylor polynomials to find the likely value of $\cos(0.2)$ to six decimal places.

In the final activity of this section you can use an applet to see the graphs of a variety of functions and their Taylor polynomials.

3 Taylor series

In Section 2 you saw that, usually, the greater the degree of a Taylor polynomial about a point a for a function f, the more accurate the Taylor polynomial is as an approximating polynomial for f close to a. But what happens if we take a Taylor polynomial of 'infinite degree'; that is, if we add on all possible terms? We'll look at that in this section.

3.1 What is a Taylor series?

In Activity 10 on page 124 you saw that the Taylor polynomial of degree n about 0 for the function $f(x) = 1/(1-x)$ is

$$p_n(x) = 1 + x + x^2 + x^3 + \cdots + x^n.$$

Let's now consider what happens to this expression if we include all possible terms. The result is an infinite series,

$$1 + x + x^2 + x^3 + \cdots. \tag{4}$$

From what you saw in Section 2, you'd expect that for any value of x close to 0, as you add on more and more terms to the infinite series above, the resulting sums will approach the value of $1/(1-x)$ more and more closely.

As you saw in Unit 10, this is the same as saying that for any value of x close to 0, the infinite series has a *sum*, and the sum is given by $1/(1-x)$.

But how close to 0 does x have to be for this to happen? The answer is that x must be in the range $-1 < x < 1$. For any value of x in this range, the infinite series has sum $1/(1-x)$. For any other value of x the series doesn't have a sum at all.

These facts follow from a result that you met in Unit 10. Consider the infinite geometric series with first term a and common ratio r:

$$a + ar + ar^2 + ar^3 + \cdots .$$

You saw in Subsection 4.2 of Unit 10 that this series has

sum $\dfrac{a}{1-r}$,   if $-1 < r < 1$;

no sum,   if $r \le -1$ or $r \ge 1$.

The infinite series (4) above is an infinite geometric series, with first term 1 and common ratio x. Hence it has

sum $\dfrac{1}{1-x}$,   if $-1 < x < 1$;

no sum,   if $x \le -1$ or $x \ge 1$,

as stated above.

For example, if $x = 0.5$ then series (4) is

$$1 + 0.5 + (0.5)^2 + (0.5)^3 + \cdots = 1 + 0.5 + 0.25 + 0.125 + \cdots ,$$

and it has sum

$$\frac{1}{1 - 0.5} = 2.$$

In other words, for this infinite series, as more and more terms are added the resulting sum approaches $1/(1 - 0.5)$ more and more closely.

By contrast, if $x = 2$ then the function $f(x) = 1/(1-x)$ has value $f(2) = 1/(1-2) = -1$, but series (4) is

$$1 + 2 + 2^2 + 2^3 + 2^4 + \cdots = 1 + 2 + 4 + 8 + 16 + \cdots ,$$

and this infinite series has no sum. As more and more terms are added, the resulting partial sums get larger and larger, without approaching any particular value.

In general, if f is a function that's differentiable infinitely many times at a point a in its domain, then you can form an infinite series in which, for any integer $n \ge 0$, the first $n + 1$ terms form the Taylor polynomial of degree n about a for f. This series is called the **Taylor series about a for f**.

For example, series (4) is the Taylor series about 0 for the function $f(x) = 1/(1-x)$.

You can obtain formulas for Taylor series from those for Taylor polynomials of degree n, by taking infinitely many terms. The following general formulas for Taylor series follow from formulas (2) and (3) on page 121.

They're called Taylor series because they're Taylor-made to fit!

Taylor series about a

Let f be a function that is differentiable infinitely many times at a point a. The **Taylor series about a for f** is

$$f(a) + f'(a)(x-a) + \frac{f''(a)}{2!}(x-a)^2 + \frac{f^{(3)}(a)}{3!}(x-a)^3$$

$$+ \cdots + \frac{f^{(n)}(a)}{n!}(x-a)^n + \cdots . \qquad (5)$$

The point a is called the **centre** of the Taylor series.

When $a = 0$, the Taylor series becomes

$$f(0) + f'(0)x + \frac{f''(0)}{2!}x^2 + \frac{f^{(3)}(0)}{3!}x^3 + \cdots + \frac{f^{(n)}(0)}{n!}x^n + \cdots . \quad (6)$$

This series is also known as the **Maclaurin series** for f.

In this module, we usually refer to Taylor series about 0, rather than Maclaurin series.

Notice that in the box above the general term of each series, involving $(x-a)^n$ (or x^n, in the case $a = 0$), has been written down explicitly as part of the series. This helps to clarify the general pattern.

Colin Maclaurin (1698–1746)

Colin Maclaurin was born in Argyllshire, studied at the University of Glasgow and became professor of mathematics first at Marischal College, Aberdeen and then at the University of Edinburgh. In 1742 he published the two-volume *Treatise of Fluxions*, which was the first systematic exposition of Newton's methods in calculus. He wrote it as a reply to attacks made on calculus for its lack of rigorous foundations. In this treatise Maclaurin uses Taylor series about 0. Although he acknowledged Taylor, Maclaurin's name is now often used to describe these series.

Example 10   *Finding a Taylor series about 0*

Find the Taylor series about 0 for the function $f(x) = e^x$.

Solution

🗨 Repeatedly differentiate f to find f', f'', $f^{(3)}$, ..., and find the values of $f(0)$, $f'(0)$, $f''(0)$, $f^{(3)}(0)$, ... Then apply formula (6). 🗨

Here $f(0) = e^0 = 1$. Also, the nth derivative of the function $f(x) = e^x$ is $f^{(n)}(x) = e^x$, so $f^{(n)}(0) = 1$ for all positive integers n.

Hence, by the formula for a Taylor series about 0, the required Taylor series is

$$1 + x + \frac{1}{2!}\, x^2 + \frac{1}{3!}\, x^3 + \frac{1}{4!}\, x^4 + \cdots .$$

In the next activity you're asked to find the Taylor series about 0 for the cosine and sine functions.

Activity 15   *Finding Taylor series*

Find the Taylor series about 0 for each of the following functions, writing down enough terms to make the general pattern clear.

(a) $f(x) = \cos x$ (b) $f(x) = \sin x$

In each case you should be able to see a pattern in the values $f(0)$, $f'(0)$, $f''(0)$, $f^{(3)}(0)$, ..., from your working for Activity 9.

It follows from what you saw earlier about Taylor polynomials for even and odd functions that the Taylor series about 0 for an even function contains terms in even powers of x only, and the Taylor series about 0 for an odd function contains terms in odd powers of x only. The Taylor series in Activity 15 are examples of this fact. Remember that the cosine function is an even function and the sine function is an odd function.

All the Taylor series that you've seen so far in this section have had centre 0. In the next activity you're asked to find a Taylor series with a different centre. So here you need to use formula (5), for a Taylor series about a point a, rather than formula (6), for a Taylor series about 0.

Activity 16   *Finding a Taylor series about a point other than 0*

Find the Taylor series about $\pi/2$ for the function $f(x) = \sin x$, writing down enough terms to make the general pattern clear.

Validity of Taylor series

You've seen that the Taylor series about a point a for a function f usually has sum $f(x)$ for values of x close to a, but may not have sum $f(x)$ for other values of x. If x is a point for which the Taylor series about a for f has sum $f(x)$, then we say that the Taylor series is **valid** at the point x.

For example, you saw at the beginning of this subsection that the Taylor series about 0 for the function $f(x) = 1/(1-x)$ is valid for all x in the interval $-1 < x < 1$, but isn't valid for values of x outside this interval.

You may be surprised to learn that the Taylor series about 0 for the exponential, sine and cosine functions (found in Example 10 and Activity 15) are all valid for *every* real number x. In other words, the equations

$$e^x = 1 + x + \frac{1}{2!}\,x^2 + \frac{1}{3!}\,x^3 + \frac{1}{4!}\,x^4 + \cdots ,$$

$$\sin x = x - \frac{1}{3!}\,x^3 + \frac{1}{5!}\,x^5 - \frac{1}{7!}\,x^7 + \frac{1}{9!}\,x^9 - \cdots ,$$

$$\cos x = 1 - \frac{1}{2!}\,x^2 + \frac{1}{4!}\,x^4 - \frac{1}{6!}\,x^6 + \frac{1}{8!}\,x^8 - \cdots ,$$

are true for all $x \in \mathbb{R}$.

When you remember that the coefficients of a Taylor series for a function are chosen by taking into account the value of the function and its derivatives at a *single* point a, it may seem amazing that the resulting series can turn out to be equal to the function for *every* real number x!

A Taylor series about a point a is always valid for $x = a$. This is because if we set $x = a$ in formula (5) on page 138, then all the terms except the first are equal to zero, so the sum of the series is just the first term $f(a)$, which is precisely the value of f at a. This is by design, since the first term of a Taylor polynomial is chosen to be $f(a)$ to ensure that the value of the polynomial at a is the same as the value of f at a.

Often, though not always, the largest set of points for which a Taylor series about a point a for a function is valid is either the whole set of real numbers $\mathbb{R}$, or an interval with two endpoints whose midpoint is a. Each endpoint may or may not be included in the interval.

Any interval of values of x for which a Taylor series is valid is called an **interval of validity** for the series, and the series is said to **represent** the function on any interval of validity. For example, $-1 < x < 1$ is an interval of validity for the Taylor series about 0 for the function $f(x) = 1/(1-x)$. Any interval that is contained within the interval $-1 < x < 1$, such as $-\frac{1}{2} < x < \frac{1}{2}$, is also an interval of validity for this series, but $-1 < x < 1$ is the largest such interval. This interval could also be denoted by $(-1, 1)$, using the usual notation for an open interval, but the inequality notation is more usual in the context of Taylor series, and it will be used throughout this unit.

You might wonder how it can be determined that $\mathbb{R}$ is an interval of validity for the Taylor series about 0 for the exponential, sine and cosine functions, and more generally, how the largest interval of validity for a Taylor series can be found. There's a method for doing this, as follows. You first find a formula for the remainder $r_n(x) = f(x) - p_n(x)$, which is the difference between the value of the function f at x and that of the Taylor polynomial of degree n about a for f. Then you have to decide for which values of x this remainder $r_n(x)$ tends to 0 as n tends to ∞. The techniques that you need to do this are taught in more advanced modules on pure mathematics. You won't be expected to find intervals of validity in this module, except in Section 4 where you'll be working from known results.

Using sigma notation for Taylor series

Formula (5) on page 138 for the Taylor series about a for a function f can be written concisely in sigma notation as

$$\sum_{n=0}^{\infty} \frac{f^{(n)}(a)}{n!}(x-a)^n.$$

You can often write Taylor series for particular functions concisely in sigma notation in a similar way. For example, the Taylor series about 0 for the function $f(x) = e^x$, given in Example 10, is

$$1 + x + \frac{1}{2!}x^2 + \frac{1}{3!}x^3 + \frac{1}{4!}x^4 + \cdots = \sum_{n=0}^{\infty} \frac{1}{n!}x^n.$$

In the cases of odd and even functions, it's more awkward to write down the Taylor series about 0 in sigma notation, because for even functions such series contain only even powers of x, and for odd functions they contain only odd powers of x. The Taylor series for the function $f(x) = \sin x$, given on page 140, is usually written as

$$x - \frac{1}{3!}x^3 + \frac{1}{5!}x^5 - \frac{1}{7!}x^7 + \frac{1}{9!}x^9 - \cdots = \sum_{n=0}^{\infty} \frac{(-1)^n}{(2n+1)!}x^{2n+1}.$$

Here, for $n = 0, 1, 2, \ldots$, the expression x^{2n+1} equals x, x^3, x^5, $\ldots$, while the expression $(2n+1)!$ takes the values 1, $3!$, $5!$, $\ldots$, and the expression $(-1)^n$ deals with the alternating signs.

The Taylor series for the function $f(x) = \cos x$, given on page 140, is usually written as

$$1 - \frac{1}{2!}x^2 + \frac{1}{4!}x^4 - \frac{1}{6!}x^6 + \frac{1}{8!}x^8 - \cdots = \sum_{n=0}^{\infty} \frac{(-1)^n}{(2n)!}x^{2n}.$$

Here, for $n = 0, 1, 2, \ldots$, the expression x^{2n} equals 1, x^2, x^4, $\ldots$, while the expression $(2n)!$ takes the values $0! = 1$, $2!$, $4!$, $\ldots$, and again the expression $(-1)^n$ deals with the alternating signs.

Taylor series about 0 for other odd and even functions can be written in sigma notation in a similar way.

3.2   Some standard Taylor series

In Subsection 3.1 we obtained the Taylor series about 0 for the exponential, sine and cosine functions, and for the function $f(x) = 1/(1-x)$. For ease of reference, these series are stated in the following box, along with the Taylor series about 0 for two other standard functions. These Taylor series can be obtained by using the second formula in the box on page 138. The following box also gives intervals of validity for the Taylor series.

Shall we record the whole series?

Standard Taylor series about 0

$$\sin x = x - \frac{1}{3!}x^3 + \frac{1}{5!}x^5 - \frac{1}{7!}x^7 + \frac{1}{9!}x^9 - \cdots, \quad \text{for } x \in \mathbb{R}$$

$$\cos x = 1 - \frac{1}{2!}x^2 + \frac{1}{4!}x^4 - \frac{1}{6!}x^6 + \frac{1}{8!}x^8 - \cdots, \quad \text{for } x \in \mathbb{R}$$

$$e^x = 1 + x + \frac{1}{2!}x^2 + \frac{1}{3!}x^3 + \frac{1}{4!}x^4 + \cdots, \quad \text{for } x \in \mathbb{R}$$

$$\ln(1+x) = x - \tfrac{1}{2}x^2 + \tfrac{1}{3}x^3 - \tfrac{1}{4}x^4 + \tfrac{1}{5}x^5 - \cdots, \quad \text{for } -1 < x < 1$$

$$\frac{1}{1-x} = 1 + x + x^2 + x^3 + x^4 + \cdots, \quad \text{for } -1 < x < 1$$

$$(1+x)^\alpha = 1 + \alpha x + \frac{\alpha(\alpha-1)}{2!}x^2 + \frac{\alpha(\alpha-1)(\alpha-2)}{3!}x^3 + \cdots,$$
$$\text{for } -1 < x < 1 \text{ (where } \alpha \text{ is any real number)}$$

The last series here is called the **binomial series**. You'll see shortly how it's linked to the binomial theorem, which you met in Unit 10.

The binomial series was discovered by Isaac Newton.

Notice that each of the intervals of validity given in the box is an open interval whose midpoint is the centre 0 of the series. These intervals of validity are the largest intervals for which the series are valid, with two exceptions. The series for $\ln(1+x)$ is also valid when $x = 1$, but the box gives the interval $-1 < x < 1$ because it's often convenient to work with open intervals. For example, this is the case when you're differentiating and integrating Taylor series, as you'll see later in the unit.

The other exception involves the binomial series. For $-1 < x < 1$, this series sums to $(1+x)^\alpha$ for any real number α, including negative and fractional numbers. For most values of α, the largest interval of validity is $-1 < x < 1$, but when α is a non-negative integer, the series is valid for *every* real number x. You'll see after the next example why this is so.

The box gives a Taylor series about 0 for the function $\ln(1+x)$, rather than for the standard function $\ln x$. This is because the function $\ln x$ has no Taylor series about 0, since its domain $(0, \infty)$ does not contain 0.

Note that it's often convenient to say 'the function $\ln(1+x)$', as in the paragraph above, as a shorthand for a more precise statement such as 'the function $f(x) = \ln(1+x)$'.

Example 11   *Using the binomial series*

Use the binomial series to find the Taylor series about 0 for each of the following functions. In each case state an interval of validity for the series.

(a) $f(x) = \dfrac{1}{1+x}$ (b) $f(x) = (1+x)^4$

Solution

(a) Since $1/(1+x) = (1+x)^{-1}$, we take $\alpha = -1$ in the binomial series, to give

$$\frac{1}{1+x} = 1 + (-1)x + \frac{(-1)(-2)}{2!}\,x^2 + \frac{(-1)(-2)(-3)}{3!}\,x^3 + \cdots$$

$$= 1 - x + x^2 - x^3 + x^4 - \cdots .$$

🔍 When writing down an infinite series, remember to include either $+\cdots$ or $-\cdots$ at the end, to indicate that there are further terms. 💬

This Taylor series is valid for $-1 < x < 1$.

(b) Taking $\alpha = 4$ in the binomial series gives

$$(1+x)^4 = 1 + 4x + \frac{4 \times 3}{2!}\,x^2 + \frac{4 \times 3 \times 2}{3!}\,x^3$$

$$+ \frac{4 \times 3 \times 2 \times 1}{4!}\,x^4 + \frac{4 \times 3 \times 2 \times 1 \times 0}{5!}\,x^5$$

$$+ \frac{4 \times 3 \times 2 \times 1 \times 0 \times (-1)}{6!}\,x^6 + \cdots$$

$$= 1 + 4x + 6x^2 + 4x^3 + x^4 .$$

This Taylor series is valid for $-1 < x < 1$.

🔍 In fact this Taylor series is valid for $x \in \mathbb{R}$, which would be an equally appropriate answer. (See the discussion below.) 💬

Example 11(b) illustrates that it's possible for a Taylor series to have a *finite* number of terms. This occurs when the coefficients of all terms from some term onwards are zero. The series in this example may also look familiar to you: it is the binomial expansion of $(1+x)^4$.

If α is any positive integer, then all terms after the term in x^α in the binomial Taylor series for $(1+x)^\alpha$ contain the factor $\alpha - \alpha = 0$, and are therefore equal to 0. The series is then the same as the binomial expansion of $(1+x)^\alpha$, which is valid for all $x \in \mathbb{R}$. The binomial series therefore generalises the binomial expansion of $(1+x)^\alpha$ from cases where α is a positive integer to cases where α can be any real number.

Activity 17   *Using the binomial series*

Use the binomial series to find the Taylor series about 0 for the function $f(x) = 1/(1+x)^2$. (Write down enough terms to make the general pattern clear.) State an interval of validity for the series.

Activity 17 involved using the binomial series when the power of $1 + x$ is a negative integer. The next example illustrates using the binomial series when the power of $1 + x$ is a fraction.

Example 12   *Finding a binomial series for a fractional power of $1 + x$*

Use the binomial series to find the Taylor series about 0 for the function $f(x) = (1+x)^{-1/2}$. (Write down enough terms to make the general pattern clear.) State an interval of validity for the series.

Solution

Taking $\alpha = -\frac{1}{2}$ in the binomial series gives

$$(1+x)^{-1/2} = 1 + (-\tfrac{1}{2})x + \frac{(-\tfrac{1}{2})(-\tfrac{3}{2})}{2!}\,x^2 + \frac{(-\tfrac{1}{2})(-\tfrac{3}{2})(-\tfrac{5}{2})}{3!}\,x^3$$

$$+ \frac{(-\tfrac{1}{2})(-\tfrac{3}{2})(-\tfrac{5}{2})(-\tfrac{7}{2})}{4!}\,x^4 + \cdots$$

$$= 1 - \tfrac{1}{2}x + \frac{1\times 3}{2^2 \times 2!}\,x^2 - \frac{1\times 3\times 5}{2^3 \times 3!}\,x^3$$

$$+ \frac{1\times 3\times 5\times 7}{2^4 \times 4!}\,x^4 - \cdots .$$

This Taylor series is valid for $-1 < x < 1$.

In Example 12, the coefficients in the Taylor series have been left in the form shown, rather than completely evaluated, so that the pattern involved is clear. It's usually a good idea to do this, but sometimes you may be asked to evaluate the first few coefficients of a Taylor series explicitly, in which case you should write each coefficient as a single integer or fraction.

Activity 18   *Finding a binomial series for a fractional power of $1 + x$*

Use the binomial series to find the Taylor series about 0 for the function $f(x) = (1+x)^{1/2}$. (Write down enough terms to make the general pattern clear.) State an interval of validity for the series.

Once you know the Taylor series for a function f about a point a, you can find the corresponding Taylor polynomial of any degree n by truncating the series at the appropriate term. (To *truncate* a series at a term is to delete all subsequent terms.)

Activity 19 *Using a Taylor series to find a Taylor polynomial*

You saw earlier that the Taylor series about 0 for the function $f(x) = \ln(1 + x)$ is

$$\ln(1 + x) = x - \tfrac{1}{2}x^2 + \tfrac{1}{3}x^3 - \tfrac{1}{4}x^4 + \tfrac{1}{5}x^5 - \cdots, \quad \text{for } -1 < x < 1.$$

Using this series, write down the cubic Taylor polynomial about 0 for this function f.

The Taylor polynomials obtained by truncating a Taylor series for a function f can, in principle, be used to find approximations for $f(x)$ for all values of x for which the series is valid. For example, you've seen that the Taylor series about 0 for the function $f(x) = \ln(1 + x)$ is valid for all values of x in the interval $-1 < x < 1$. This means that, in principle, you can use Taylor polynomials about 0 to find an approximation for $\ln(1 + x)$ for any value of x in this interval. However, the further x is from the centre 0 of the Taylor series, the greater is the degree of the Taylor polynomial that you need to provide the desired level of accuracy.

For instance, you can find an approximation for $\ln(1.1)$ by putting $x = 0.1$ in a Taylor polynomial about 0 for $\ln(1 + x)$, and you can find an approximation for $\ln(1.5)$ by putting $x = 0.5$ in the same Taylor polynomial. However, to find an approximation for $\ln(1.1)$ correct to four decimal places, by using the method of Subsection 2.2 and obtaining the required Taylor polynomials by truncating the Taylor series at the appropriate terms, you have to evaluate six successive Taylor polynomials, whereas to find an approximation for $\ln(1.5)$ to the same level of accuracy you have to evaluate 17 successive Taylor polynomials. For $\ln(1.9)$ you need 92 successive Taylor polynomials!

In the next activity you're asked to use the method of Subsection 2.2 to find an approximation for a particular value $f(x)$ of a function f, obtaining the required Taylor polynomials by truncating the Taylor series for f about a point a close to x.

Activity 20 *Finding an approximate value for a function*

You saw in Activity 18 that the Taylor series about 0 for the function $f(x) = (1+x)^{1/2}$ is

$$(1+x)^{1/2} = 1 + \tfrac{1}{2}x - \frac{1}{2^2 \times 2!}\,x^2 + \frac{1 \times 3}{2^3 \times 3!}\,x^3 - \frac{1 \times 3 \times 5}{2^4 \times 4!}\,x^4 + \cdots,$$

and that it is valid for $-1 < x < 1$. By writing 1.1 as $1 + 0.1$, use this series to find the value of $\sqrt{1.1}$ to three decimal places.

(Notice that $x = 0.1$ lies within the interval of validity $-1 < x < 1$ for the Taylor series.)

3.3 Using a computer to find Taylor polynomials

In the following activity you'll learn how to use the module computer algebra system to find Taylor polynomials.

Activity 21 *Taylor polynomials on a computer*

Work through Section 12 of the *Computer algebra guide*.

---

4 Manipulating Taylor series

In this final section, you'll see some methods that allow you to obtain Taylor series for many functions from a few known Taylor series such as the standard ones in the box on page 142. This usually involves much less work than obtaining the required Taylor series by using one of the general formulas in the box on page 138.

When finding a Taylor series for a function, you can use any of the standard Taylor series. You're not expected to derive any of the standard series unless explicitly asked to do so.

4.1 Substituting for the variable in a Taylor series

You've seen that the Taylor series about 0 for the function $g(x) = 1/(1-x)$ is given by

$$\frac{1}{1-x} = 1 + x + x^2 + x^3 + \cdots, \quad \text{for } -1 < x < 1.$$

Consider the effect of substituting $x = 2t$ in this equation. This gives

$$\frac{1}{1-2t} = 1 + 2t + (2t)^2 + (2t)^3 + \cdots$$
$$= 1 + 2t + 4t^2 + 8t^3 + \cdots .$$

We have obtained a series equal to $1/(1 - 2t)$. Since the Taylor series for $g(x) = 1/(1 - x)$ is valid for $-1 < x < 1$, the series in t above is equal to $1/(1 - 2t)$ for $-1 < 2t < 1$, that is, for $-\frac{1}{2} < t < \frac{1}{2}$.

Let's now replace t by x, since it's more usual to use x rather than t for the variable. This gives

$$\frac{1}{1-2x} = 1 + 2x + 4x^2 + 8x^3 + \cdots , \quad \text{for } -\tfrac{1}{2} < x < \tfrac{1}{2}. \tag{7}$$

The series in equation (7) is equal to the function $f(x) = 1/(1 - 2x)$ for $-\frac{1}{2} < x < \frac{1}{2}$, but is it a *Taylor series*? It's of the right form to be a Taylor series about 0, since each of its terms is a power of x multiplied by a constant. However, if we were to use formula (6) on page 138 to find the Taylor series about 0 for the function f, would we obtain the same series? The answer to this question is yes. This follows from the following fact, whose proof is beyond the scope of this module.

Uniqueness of Taylor series

Let f be a function. If you can by any means find a series

$$c_0 + c_1(x - a) + c_2(x - a)^2 + c_3(x - a)^3 + \cdots$$

that is equal to $f(x)$ for all x in some open interval containing a, then this series is the Taylor series about a for f, and hence it is the *only* series of this form that is equal to $f(x)$ for all x in that interval.

You can assume this important fact throughout the rest of this unit.

You can find Taylor series for many functions by substituting for the variable in a Taylor series that you already know, and you can often deduce an interval of validity for the new series from an interval of validity for the original Taylor series. When substituting for the variable, it's quicker to avoid introducing a new variable t as was done above, and instead replace x in the original Taylor series by an expression involving x, as illustrated in the next example.

Example 13   *Substituting into a Taylor series*

Find the Taylor series about 0 for the function

$$f(x) = \frac{1}{1 + x^2},$$

and determine an interval of validity for this series.

Solution

🗨 The expression $1/(1+x^2)$ is similar to $1/(1-x)$, for which there's a standard Taylor series (given on page 142). The first expression is obtained from the second expression by replacing x by $-x^2$. 🗨

The Taylor series about 0 for $1/(1-x)$ is

$$\frac{1}{1-x} = 1 + x + x^2 + x^3 + \cdots, \quad \text{for } -1 < x < 1.$$

Replacing each occurrence of x by $-x^2$ gives

$$\frac{1}{1-(-x^2)} = 1 + (-x^2) + (-x^2)^2 + (-x^2)^3 + \cdots; \qquad (8)$$

that is,

$$\frac{1}{1+x^2} = 1 - x^2 + x^4 - x^6 + \cdots.$$

This is the Taylor series about 0 for $1/(1+x^2)$.

🗨 Deduce an interval of validity for the new series from the interval of validity for the original series. 🗨

The Taylor series for $1/(1-x)$ is valid for $-1 < x < 1$, so the series for $1/(1-(-x^2))$ is valid for $-1 < -x^2 < 1$.

🗨 The double inequality $-1 < -x^2 < 1$ is equivalent to the two single inequalities $-1 < -x^2$ and $-x^2 < 1$. 🗨

The left-hand inequality is $-1 < -x^2$, which is equivalent to $1 > x^2$; that is, $-1 < x < 1$.

The right-hand inequality is $-x^2 < 1$, which is equivalent to $x^2 > -1$ and therefore does not place any restriction on x, since the square of any real number is non-negative.

Thus the Taylor series about 0 for $1/(1+x^2)$ is valid for $-1 < x < 1$.

In Example 13, the variable x was replaced by $-x^2$. This is equivalent to making the substitution $x = -t^2$ and then replacing t by x.

As illustrated in Example 13, when you deduce an interval of validity for a Taylor series from an interval of validity for another Taylor series, you usually have to rearrange inequalities. Rules for rearranging inequalities were given in Subsection 5.2 of Unit 3.

When you have to rearrange a double inequality like $-1 < -x^2 < 1$, it's often helpful to split it into two single inequalities and rearrange each independently, as was done in Example 13. With simple double inequalities, such as $-1 < 2x < 1$, you may be able to rearrange both single inequalities together; for example, in this case we simply multiply both inequalities by $\frac{1}{2}$ to obtain $-\frac{1}{2} < x < \frac{1}{2}$.

When you replace each occurrence of x in a Taylor series by an expression involving x, it's helpful to enclose the whole expression in brackets at each replacement, and then simplify the resulting terms, as illustrated in Example 13. Make sure that you enclose the *whole* expression in brackets. For instance, in equation (8) the third term is $(-x^2)^2 = x^4$, not $-(x^2)^2 = -x^4$.

Activity 22   *Substituting into a Taylor series*

By substituting for the variable in a standard Taylor series, find the Taylor series about 0 for each of the following functions. In each case determine an interval of validity for the series.

(a) $f(x) = 1/(1 + 2x)$ (b) $f(x) = \ln(1 - x)$ (c) $f(x) = \ln(1 + 3x)$

(d) $f(x) = e^{x^3}$

You've seen that substituting for the variable in a Taylor series gives a Taylor series for another function. In each case so far, the new series has had the same centre as the original series. However, some substitutions lead to a new Taylor series with a different centre. For example, suppose that the Taylor series about 0 for a function g is

$$g(x) = c_0 + c_1 x + c_2 x^2 + c_3 x^3 + \cdots .$$

If you replace each occurrence of x by $x - a$, then you obtain

$$g(x - a) = c_0 + c_1(x - a) + c_2(x - a)^2 + c_3(x - a)^3 + \cdots .$$

This is the Taylor series about a for the function f given by $f(x) = g(x - a)$. You're asked to use this fact in the following activity.

Activity 23   *Changing the centre of a Taylor series*

In Example 11(a), the binomial series was used to show that the Taylor series about 0 for $1/(1 + x)$ is

$$\frac{1}{1 + x} = 1 - x + x^2 - x^3 + \cdots , \quad \text{for } -1 < x < 1.$$

By replacing x by $x - 1$ in this series, find the Taylor series about 1 for the function $f(x) = 1/x$. Determine an interval of validity for this series.

Remember that you can be sure that the series found in the solution to Activity 23 is indeed the Taylor series about 1 for $1/x$, because of the fact about the uniqueness of Taylor series in the box on page 147.

Sometimes you can find a Taylor series for a particular function by rewriting its rule to make it more similar to a function whose Taylor series you already know, and then replacing the variable x by a suitable expression in x. This is demonstrated in the following activity.

Activity 24   *Rearranging in order to find a Taylor series*

(a) Find the Taylor series about 0 for the function
$$f(x) = \frac{3}{3 + 2x},$$
by writing
$$f(x) = \frac{3}{3 + 2x} = \frac{1}{1 + \frac{2}{3}x}.$$
Determine an interval of validity for this series.

(b) Find the Taylor series about -1 for the function
$$f(x) = \frac{1}{3 + 2x},$$
by writing
$$f(x) = \frac{1}{3 + 2x} = \frac{1}{1 + 2(x + 1)}.$$
Determine an interval of validity for this series.

4.2 Adding, subtracting and multiplying Taylor series

Another way to find Taylor series for some functions is to apply standard arithmetical operations to known Taylor series, doing this term by term, as illustrated in the following example.

Example 14   *Adding Taylor series*

Find the Taylor series about 0 for the function
$$f(x) = e^x + \frac{1}{1 - x},$$
explicitly evaluating the coefficients of the first five terms. Determine an interval of validity for this series.

Solution

🔍 There are standard Taylor series about 0 for e^x and for $1/(1 - x)$ (given on page 142). Adding these two series together term by term will give the required Taylor series. 💬

We have the following standard series:
$$e^x = 1 + x + \frac{1}{2!}x^2 + \frac{1}{3!}x^3 + \frac{1}{4!}x^4 + \cdots, \qquad \text{for } x \in \mathbb{R},$$
$$\frac{1}{1 - x} = 1 + x + x^2 + x^3 + x^4 + \cdots, \qquad \text{for } -1 < x < 1.$$

It follows that

$$e^x + \frac{1}{1-x} = \left(1 + x + \frac{1}{2!}x^2 + \frac{1}{3!}x^3 + \frac{1}{4!}x^4 + \cdots\right)$$
$$+ \left(1 + x + x^2 + x^3 + x^4 + \cdots\right)$$
$$= (1+1) + (1+1)x + \left(\frac{1}{2!}+1\right)x^2$$
$$+ \left(\frac{1}{3!}+1\right)x^3 + \left(\frac{1}{4!}+1\right)x^4 + \cdots$$
$$= 2 + 2x + \tfrac{3}{2}x^2 + \tfrac{7}{6}x^3 + \tfrac{25}{24}x^4 + \cdots.$$

This is the Taylor series about 0 for the function $f(x) = e^x + 1/(1-x)$.

🔍 Deduce an interval of validity for the new Taylor series from the intervals of validity for the original Taylor series. 💬

The series for e^x is valid for $x \in \mathbb{R}$, and the series for $f(x) = 1/(1-x)$ is valid for $-1 < x < 1$. The second interval is contained within the first, so both series are valid for $-1 < x < 1$. Hence $-1 < x < 1$ is an interval of validity for the Taylor series for $f(x) = e^x + 1/(1-x)$.

You can add or subtract any two Taylor series with the same centre term by term in the way demonstrated in Example 14. The resulting Taylor series is valid for all values of x for which *both* original Taylor series are valid, and possibly for a larger interval of values.

Activity 25 *Subtracting Taylor series*

The following standard Taylor series about 0 was stated earlier (page 142):

$$\ln(1+x) = x - \tfrac{1}{2}x^2 + \tfrac{1}{3}x^3 - \tfrac{1}{4}x^4 + \cdots, \quad \text{for } -1 < x < 1.$$

In the solution to Activity 22(b) this series is used to deduce the following Taylor series about 0:

$$\ln(1-x) = -x - \tfrac{1}{2}x^2 - \tfrac{1}{3}x^3 - \tfrac{1}{4}x^4 - \cdots, \quad \text{for } -1 < x < 1.$$

By using the fact that

$$\ln\left(\frac{1+x}{1-x}\right) = \ln(1+x) - \ln(1-x),$$

use the two series above to find the Taylor series about 0 for

$$\ln\left(\frac{1+x}{1-x}\right).$$

Determine an interval of validity for this series.

The result from Activity 25 turns out to be useful for finding an approximation for the natural logarithm of any positive number. Any positive number t can be expressed in the form $t = (1 + x)/(1 - x)$ for some number x in the interval $-1 < x < 1$. For example, $3 = (1 + \frac{1}{2})/(1 - \frac{1}{2})$. You can see that this is possible for every positive number t by rearranging the equation above to make x the subject:

$$t = \frac{1 + x}{1 - x} \qquad (x \neq 1)$$
$$(1 - x)t = 1 + x$$
$$t - xt = 1 + x$$
$$t - 1 = xt + x$$
$$t - 1 = x(t + 1)$$
$$x = \frac{t - 1}{t + 1}.$$

This final equation gives the value of x corresponding to a positive number t. For example, if $t = 3$, then $x = (3 - 1)/(3 + 1) = \frac{1}{2}$.

To see that the value of x always turns out to lie in the interval $-1 < x < 1$, note that the expression on the right-hand side of the final equation above can be rearranged as follows:

$$x = \frac{t - 1}{t + 1} = \frac{(t + 1) - 2}{t + 1} = 1 - \frac{2}{t + 1}.$$

Since t is positive, the value of $2/(t + 1)$ is positive, and hence $x < 1$. Also, again since t is positive, the value of $2/(t + 1)$ is less than 2, and hence $x > -1$.

Thus in principle you can use the Taylor series found in Activity 25 to find an approximation for $\ln t$ for any number t in the domain $(0, \infty)$ of the function $\ln$.

In contrast, you can use the series for $\ln(1 + x)$ to find an approximation for $\ln t$ only for $0 < t \leq 2$, since these are the only values of t that can be expressed in the form $t = 1 + x$ for some x in the interval $-1 < x \leq 1$ (see page 145).

For both series, the further x is from 0, the more terms of the series you have to evaluate to obtain the desired level of accuracy. However, to find the value of $\ln t$ for a number t for which you could use either series, you usually have to evaluate fewer terms of the series found in Activity 25 than of the series for $\ln(1 + x)$ to obtain the desired level of accuracy.

Activity 26　*Finding the value of a particular logarithm*

Find the value of $x = (t - 1)/(t + 1)$ that corresponds to $t = 1.5$. Hence use the Taylor series found in Activity 25, namely

$$\ln\left(\frac{1 + x}{1 - x}\right) = 2x + \tfrac{2}{3}x^3 + \tfrac{2}{5}x^5 + \tfrac{2}{7}x^7 + \cdots,$$

to find the value of $\ln(1.5)$ to four decimal places.

In Activity 26, it was necessary to evaluate five successive Taylor polynomials in order to find the value of $\ln(1.5)$ correct to four decimal places. If you used the series for $\ln(1+x)$ for this task, with $x = 0.5$, then you would need to evaluate 17 successive Taylor polynomials, as mentioned earlier (page 145). This illustrates the comment above that you need to use fewer terms of the series found in Activity 25.

You've seen that you can add and subtract Taylor series. You can also multiply a Taylor series term by term by a non-zero constant. The resulting series is valid for every value of x for which the original Taylor series is valid.

For example, you can multiply the Taylor series

$$e^x = 1 + x + \frac{1}{2!}x^2 + \frac{1}{3!}x^3 + \frac{1}{4!}x^4 + \cdots, \quad \text{for } x \in \mathbb{R},$$

by 3, to deduce that

$$3e^x = 3 + 3x + \frac{3}{2!}x^2 + \frac{3}{3!}x^3 + \frac{3}{4!}x^4 + \cdots, \quad \text{for } x \in \mathbb{R}.$$

In the next activity you're asked to use the technique of multiplying a Taylor series by a constant, together with substitution, to find the Taylor series about 0 for the function $1/(3+x)^2$. Here it's useful to use the rearrangement

$$\frac{1}{(3+x)^2} = \frac{1}{(3(1+\frac{1}{3}x))^2} = \frac{1}{3^2(1+\frac{1}{3}x)^2}.$$

Activity 27   *Finding a Taylor series for* $1/(3+x)^2$

You were asked to show in Activity 17 that the Taylor series about 0 for the function $1/(1+x)^2$ is

$$\frac{1}{(1+x)^2} = 1 - 2x + 3x^2 - 4x^3 + \cdots, \quad \text{for } -1 < x < 1.$$

Use this Taylor series, together with the fact that

$$\frac{1}{(3+x)^2} = \frac{1}{3^2} \times \frac{1}{(1+\frac{1}{3}x)^2},$$

to find the Taylor series about 0 for $1/(3+x)^2$, and determine an interval of validity for this series.

You can find the Taylor series about 0 for any function of the form $(c+x)^\alpha$, where c is any positive constant and α is any real number, by deducing it from the series for $(1+x)^\alpha$ using the method of Activity 27. That is, you first express $(c+x)^\alpha$ as $c^\alpha(1+x/c)^\alpha$.

The next example and activity involve using the techniques that you've met in this section to find the Taylor series about 0 for two further standard mathematical functions. The function sinh (usually pronounced as 'shine' or 'sine-sh') is the **hyperbolic sine function**, and is given by

$$\sinh x = \tfrac{1}{2}(e^x - e^{-x}).$$

The function cosh (pronounced just as 'cosh') is the **hyperbolic cosine function**, and is given by

$$\cosh x = \tfrac{1}{2}(e^x + e^{-x}).$$

The graphs of these two functions are shown in Figure 22.

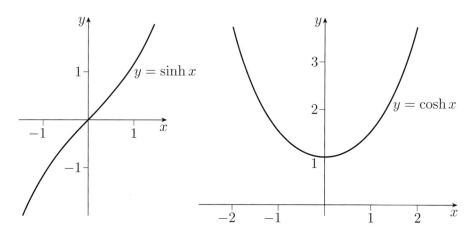

Figure 22   The graphs of the functions sinh and cosh

Although you might not expect it from their definitions or their graphs, the hyperbolic functions sinh and cosh have many properties analogous to those of the trigonometric functions sin and cos. For example, cosh, like cos, is an even function and sinh, like sin, is an odd function. Also, the derivative of sinh is cosh and

$$\sinh(x + y) = \sinh x \cosh y + \cosh x \sinh y.$$

The two properties immediately above are exact analogues of properties of trigonometric functions. Some properties of sinh and cosh are similar to, but not exactly analogous to, those of sin and cos. For example, for sin and cos we have the trigonometric identity $\sin^2 x + \cos^2 x = 1$, whereas for sinh and cosh we have the identity $\cosh^2 x - \sinh^2 x = 1$. Also, the derivative of cos is $- \sin$, whereas the derivative of cosh is sinh.

You'll learn more about the functions sinh and cosh if you study the module MST125 *Essential mathematics 2*.

You can find the Taylor series about 0 for the functions sinh and cosh by using their definitions, together with the standard Taylor series about 0 for the exponential function. You have to use the techniques of adding and multiplying by a constant, and the technique of substitution. The series for cosh is found in the next example, and you're asked to find the series for sinh in the activity that follows.

Example 15   *Finding the Taylor series about 0 for* $\cosh x$

Find the Taylor series about 0 for the function $f(x) = \cosh x$ and determine an interval of validity for this series.

Solution

We use the formula
$$\cosh x = \tfrac{1}{2}(e^x + e^{-x}).$$
The Taylor series about 0 for e^x is
$$e^x = 1 + x + \frac{1}{2!}x^2 + \frac{1}{3!}x^3 + \frac{1}{4!}x^4 + \cdots, \quad \text{for } x \in \mathbb{R}.$$
Replacing each occurrence of x by $-x$ gives
$$e^{-x} = 1 - x + \frac{1}{2!}x^2 - \frac{1}{3!}x^3 + \frac{1}{4!}x^4 - \cdots, \quad \text{for } x \in \mathbb{R}.$$
Therefore
$$\tfrac{1}{2}(e^x + e^{-x}) = \frac{1}{2}\left(\left(1 + x + \frac{1}{2!}x^2 + \frac{1}{3!}x^3 + \frac{1}{4!}x^4 + \cdots\right)\right.$$
$$\left.+ \left(1 - x + \frac{1}{2!}x^2 - \frac{1}{3!}x^3 + \frac{1}{4!}x^4 - \cdots\right)\right), \quad \text{for } x \in \mathbb{R};$$
that is,
$$\cosh x = 1 + \frac{1}{2!}x^2 + \frac{1}{4!}x^4 + \cdots, \quad \text{for } x \in \mathbb{R}.$$

Activity 28   *Finding the Taylor series about 0 for* $\sinh x$

Find the Taylor series about 0 for the function $f(x) = \sinh x$, and determine an interval of validity for this series.

You can see from the solutions to Example 15 and Activity 28 that the Taylor series about 0 for cosh has only even powers of x, while that for sinh has only odd powers of x. This is because cosh is an even function, while sinh is a odd function.

Notice that the Taylor series about 0 for sinh and cosh are similar to those for sin and cos, respectively. The only difference is that all the coefficients in the series for $\cosh x$ and $\sinh x$ are positive, whereas the coefficients in the series for $\cos x$ and $\sin x$ alternate in sign.

Multiplying Taylor series together

You've seen that Taylor series can be added, subtracted and multiplied by a non-zero constant. You can also multiply together two Taylor series with the same centre. The resulting Taylor series is valid for all values of x for which both original Taylor series are valid, and possibly for a larger interval of values.

The next example illustrates the multiplication of two Taylor series. It involves finding the Taylor series about 0 of the product of a polynomial and another function. Note that it's easy to write down the Taylor series about 0 of a polynomial,

$$f(x) = c_0 + c_1 x + c_2 x^2 + \cdots + c_n x^n,$$

because this is already in the form of the series in the box on page 147 (with $a = 0$, and the coefficients of all terms from x^{n+1} onwards equal to 0). It follows that the Taylor series about 0 of a polynomial is the polynomial itself! It's valid for all $x \in \mathbb{R}$.

Example 16   *Multiplying Taylor series*

Find the Taylor series about 0 for the function

$$f(x) = \frac{1 - x}{1 + x},$$

and determine an interval of validity for this series.

Solution

The Taylor series for $1 - x$ is $1 - x$, and the Taylor series for $1/(1 + x)$, found in Example 11(a), is

$$\frac{1}{1 + x} = 1 - x + x^2 - x^3 + \cdots, \quad \text{for } -1 < x < 1.$$

Therefore

$$\frac{1 - x}{1 + x} = (1 - x)(1 - x + x^2 - x^3 + \cdots)$$

$$= 1(1 - x + x^2 - x^3 + \cdots) - x(1 - x + x^2 - x^3 + \cdots)$$

$$= (1 - x + x^2 - x^3 + \cdots) - (x - x^2 + x^3 - \cdots)$$

$$= 1 - 2x + 2x^2 - 2x^3 + \cdots.$$

The Taylor series about 0 for $1 - x$ and for $1/(1 + x)$ are valid for $x \in \mathbb{R}$ and for $-1 < x < 1$, respectively. Hence the Taylor series for $(1 - x)/(1 + x)$ is valid for $-1 < x < 1$.

In the next activity you're asked to carry out two multiplications of Taylor series. In each case one of the two series is a polynomial.

Activity 29   *Multiplying Taylor series*

Find the Taylor series about 0 for each of the following functions. In each case determine an interval of validity for the series.

(a) $f(x) = x^2 \sin x$ (b) $f(x) = (1 + x) \cos x$

Earlier you saw that you can multiply a Taylor series by a non-zero constant. This is just a special case of the multiplication of two Taylor series. For example, you can obtain the Taylor series about 0 for $3e^x$ by multiplying together the Taylor series about 0 for the constant function $f(x) = 3$ and the Taylor series about 0 for e^x; the Taylor series about 0 for the function $f(x) = 3$ is simply 3, since 3 is a polynomial.

In each case where we've multiplied together two Taylor series, one of the series had only finitely many non-zero terms; that is, it was a polynomial. Multiplying together two Taylor series both of which have infinitely many non-zero terms is usually a difficult task, and you won't be asked to carry out any complete multiplications of this type in this module. However, it's fairly straightforward to multiply together the first few terms of two infinite Taylor series to find the first few terms of the product Taylor series; that is, to find a Taylor polynomial. This is illustrated in the next example.

Example 17   *Finding a Taylor polynomial by multiplication*

Find the cubic Taylor polynomial about 0 for the function $f(x) = e^x \cos x$.

Solution

💬 Multiply the series in the usual way. At each stage, include explicitly only those terms that could eventually result in final terms with power 3 or less. Ignore any terms that can lead only to final terms with power 4 or more, but use the notation '$\cdots$' to indicate that further terms exist. 💬

Using the Taylor series about 0 for e^x and for $\cos x$, we obtain

$$e^x \cos x = \left(1 + x + \frac{x^2}{2!} + \frac{x^3}{3!} + \cdots \right)\left(1 - \frac{x^2}{2!} + \cdots \right)$$

$$= 1\left(1 - \frac{x^2}{2!} + \cdots \right) + x\left(1 - \frac{x^2}{2!} + \cdots \right)$$

$$\quad + \frac{x^2}{2!}\left(1 - \frac{x^2}{2!} + \cdots \right) + \frac{x^3}{3!}\left(1 - \frac{x^2}{2!} + \cdots \right) + \cdots$$

$$= (1 - \tfrac{1}{2}x^2 + \cdots) + (x - \tfrac{1}{2}x^3 + \cdots) + (\tfrac{1}{2}x^2 - \cdots)$$

$$\quad + (\tfrac{1}{6}x^3 - \cdots) + \cdots$$

$$= 1 + x + (-\tfrac{1}{2} + \tfrac{1}{2})x^2 + (-\tfrac{1}{2} + \tfrac{1}{6})x^3 + \cdots$$

$$= 1 + x - \tfrac{1}{3}x^3 + \cdots .$$

Therefore the cubic Taylor polynomial about 0 for $f(x) = e^x \cos x$ is

$$p(x) = 1 + x - \tfrac{1}{3}x^3.$$

You can use a similar method in the next activity.

Activity 30   *Finding a Taylor polynomial by multiplication*

In Example 11(a), the binomial series was used to show that the Taylor series about 0 for $1/(1 + x)$ is

$$\frac{1}{1 + x} = 1 - x + x^2 - x^3 + \cdots, \quad \text{for } -1 < x < 1.$$

Use this Taylor series and the Taylor series for $\sin x$ to find the cubic Taylor polynomial about 0 for the function

$$f(x) = \frac{\sin x}{1 + x}.$$

4.3   Differentiating and integrating Taylor series

You've seen that the Taylor series about 0 for the function $f(x) = \sin x$ is

$$x - \frac{1}{3!} x^3 + \frac{1}{5!} x^5 - \cdots.$$

Let's consider the effect of differentiating this series term by term, in the way that we would if it had only finitely many terms and so was a polynomial. We obtain the series

$$1 - \frac{3}{3!} x^2 + \frac{5}{5!} x^4 - \cdots = 1 - \frac{1}{2!} x^2 + \frac{1}{4!} x^4 - \cdots.$$

You may recognise this series as the Taylor series about 0 for $\cos x$. So by differentiating term by term the Taylor series about 0 for $f(x) = \sin x$, we obtained the Taylor series about 0 for its derivative, $f'(x) = \cos x$.

This observation suggests that term-by-term differentiation of a Taylor series about 0 for a function f gives the Taylor series about 0 for its derivative, f'. This conjecture can be verified as follows.

Let f be a function that's differentiable infinitely many times at 0, and let $g = f'$. The Taylor series about 0 for f is

$$f(0) + f'(0)x + \frac{f''(0)}{2!} x^2 + \frac{f^{(3)}(0)}{3!} x^3 + \cdots + \frac{f^{(n)}(0)}{n!} x^n + \cdots. \qquad (9)$$

Notice here that the general term, in x^n, has been written down explicitly as part of the series.

Differentiating series (9) term by term (keeping in mind that $f(0)$, $f'(0)$, $f''(0)$, … are constants) gives the series

$$0 + f'(0) + \frac{f''(0)}{2!} 2x + \frac{f^{(3)}(0)}{3!} 3x^2 + \cdots + \frac{f^{(n)}(0)}{n!} nx^{n-1} + \cdots$$

$$= f'(0) + f''(0)x + \frac{f^{(3)}(0)}{2!} x^2 + \cdots + \frac{f^{(n)}(0)}{(n-1)!} x^{n-1} + \cdots.$$

4 Manipulating Taylor series

Since $g = f'$, we have $g(0) = f'(0)$, $g'(0) = f''(0)$, $g''(0) = f^{(3)}(0)$, and so on. Therefore we can write the series above as

$$g(0) + g'(0)x + \frac{g''(0)}{2!}\,x^2 + \cdots + \frac{g^{(n-1)}(0)}{(n-1)!}\,x^{n-1} + \cdots .$$

This is the Taylor series about 0 for $g = f'$. (The general term is expressed in terms of $n-1$ instead of n.)

Taylor series can also be integrated term by term. If the Taylor series about 0 for a function f is integrated term by term, then the result is the Taylor series about 0 of an antiderivative of f.

These properties of Taylor series are summarised in the following box. Here c_0 is written for $f(0)$, c_1 for $f'(0)$, c_2 for $f''(0)/2!$, and so on, to simplify the notation.

Differentiating and integrating Taylor series about 0

Let f be a function that is differentiable infinitely many times at 0. If the Taylor series about 0 for f is

$$c_0 + c_1 x + c_2 x^2 + c_3 x^3 + \cdots + c_n x^n + \cdots ,$$

then the Taylor series for f' is

$$c_1 + 2c_2 x + 3c_3 x^2 + 4c_4 x^3 + \cdots + n c_n x^{n-1} + \cdots ,$$

and the Taylor series for any antiderivative of f is of the form

$$c + c_0 x + \frac{c_1}{2} x^2 + \frac{c_2}{3} x^3 + \cdots + \frac{c_n}{n+1} x^{n+1} + \cdots ,$$

where c is a constant.

Any interval of validity for the Taylor series for f that is an *open* interval is also an interval of validity for the Taylor series for f' and for any antiderivative of f.

The results in the box above can be extended to Taylor series with centres other than 0, but we won't need to use such series in this module.

Example 18   *Differentiating and integrating a Taylor series*

In Example 11(a), the binomial series was used to show that

$$\frac{1}{1+x} = 1 - x + x^2 - x^3 + x^4 - \cdots, \quad \text{for } -1 < x < 1.$$

Also, by either the chain rule or the quotient rule,

$$\frac{\mathrm{d}}{\mathrm{d}x}\left(\frac{1}{1+x}\right) = -\frac{1}{(1+x)^2},$$

and by a standard integral and the rule for integrating a function of a linear expression,

$$\int \frac{1}{1+x}\,\mathrm{d}x = \ln(1+x) + c \quad (x > -1),$$

where c is a constant. Use these facts to find the Taylor series about 0 for each of the following functions. In each case state an interval of validity for the series.

(a) $f(x) = \dfrac{1}{(1+x)^2}$ (b) $f(x) = \ln(1+x)$

Solution

(a) Differentiating the series for $1/(1+x)$ gives

$$-\frac{1}{(1+x)^2} = -1 + 2x - 3x^2 + 4x^3 - \cdots, \quad \text{for } -1 < x < 1.$$

Multiplying both sides by -1 gives the required Taylor series,

$$\frac{1}{(1+x)^2} = 1 - 2x + 3x^2 - 4x^3 + \cdots, \quad \text{for } -1 < x < 1.$$

(b) Integrating the series for $1/(1+x)$ gives

$$\ln(1+x)$$
$$= c + x - \tfrac{1}{2}x^2 + \tfrac{1}{3}x^3 - \tfrac{1}{4}x^4 + \tfrac{1}{5}x^5 - \cdots, \quad \text{for } -1 < x < 1,$$

where c is a constant.

🔎 To find the value of the constant c, put $x = 0$ in the equation above and solve the resulting equation for c. 💬

Taking $x = 0$ gives $\ln 1 = c$, so $c = 0$. Therefore the required Taylor series is

$$\ln(1+x)$$
$$= x - \tfrac{1}{2}x^2 + \tfrac{1}{3}x^3 - \tfrac{1}{4}x^4 + \tfrac{1}{5}x^5 - \cdots, \quad \text{for } -1 < x < 1.$$

An alternative way to find the Taylor series in Example 18(a) is to take $\alpha = -2$ in the binomial series, as was done in Activity 17.

The result of Example 18(b) is the standard Taylor series for $\ln(1 + x)$, as you'd expect. This shows the connection between this standard series and the series for $1/(1 + x)$.

The remaining activities in this subsection require you to differentiate or integrate Taylor series.

Activity 31   *Differentiating a Taylor series*

Verify that term-by-term differentiation of the Taylor series about 0 for the function $f(x) = e^x$ leaves the series unchanged.

(This result corresponds to the fact that the derivative of e^x is e^x.)

Activity 32   *Finding the Taylor series about 0 for $\tan^{-1} x$*

In Example 13 you saw that
$$\frac{1}{1 + x^2} = 1 - x^2 + x^4 - x^6 + \cdots, \quad \text{for } -1 < x < 1.$$

In Unit 7 you saw that
$$\frac{\mathrm{d}}{\mathrm{d}x}\left(\tan^{-1} x\right) = \frac{1}{1 + x^2}.$$

Use integration to deduce the Taylor series about 0 for $\tan^{-1} x$, and state an interval of validity for this series.

Calculating π

In 1706 the mathematician John Machin used the Taylor series about 0 for $\tan^{-1}$, which you were asked to find in Activity 32, to calculate the first 100 digits of π. The series is
$$\tan^{-1} x = x - \tfrac{1}{3}x^3 + \tfrac{1}{5}x^5 - \tfrac{1}{7}x^7 + \cdots.$$

An interval of validity for this series is $-1 < x < 1$, but the series is also valid for $x = 1$. So, since $\tan^{-1} 1 = \tfrac{1}{4}\pi$, we obtain a representation for π as four times the sum of a series:
$$\pi = 4\tan^{-1} 1 = 4\left(1 - \tfrac{1}{3} + \tfrac{1}{5} - \tfrac{1}{7} + \cdots\right).$$

Unfortunately it's not practicable to use this particular series to calculate π accurately, because 1 is too far from the centre 0 of the series. However, Machin discovered the strange-looking formula
$$\pi = 16\tan^{-1}\left(\tfrac{1}{5}\right) - 4\tan^{-1}\left(\tfrac{1}{239}\right).$$

The values $\tfrac{1}{5}$ and $\tfrac{1}{239}$ are much closer to 0 than 1 is, so relatively few terms of the corresponding series need to be evaluated in order to calculate $\tan^{-1}\left(\tfrac{1}{5}\right)$ and $\tan^{-1}\left(\tfrac{1}{239}\right)$, and hence π, to 100 digits.

John Machin (1680–1751)

John Machin was at the University of Cambridge at the same time as Brook Taylor, having acted as a private tutor to Taylor beforehand. Machin was later a Fellow of the Royal Society and (for 38 years) Professor of Astronomy at Gresham College, London. He was also a member of the committee to adjudicate the claims of Newton and Leibniz to have invented the calculus.

In the final activity of this unit you're asked to use both substitution and integration to find the first few terms of the Taylor series about 0 for the inverse sine function.

Activity 33   *Finding the Taylor series about 0 for $f(x) = \sin^{-1} x$*

In Example 12, the binomial series was used to show that

$$(1+x)^{-1/2} = 1 - \tfrac{1}{2}x + \frac{1 \times 3}{2^2 \times 2!} x^2 - \frac{1 \times 3 \times 5}{2^3 \times 3!} x^3 + \cdots ;$$

that is,

$$\frac{1}{\sqrt{1+x}} = 1 - \tfrac{1}{2}x + \tfrac{3}{8}x^2 - \tfrac{5}{16}x^3 + \cdots , \quad \text{for } -1 < x < 1.$$

(a) By using substitution, find the first four terms of the Taylor series about 0 for the function $1/\sqrt{1-x^2}$. Determine an interval of validity for this series.

(b) You saw in Unit 7 that

$$\frac{\mathrm{d}}{\mathrm{d}x}\left(\sin^{-1} x\right) = \frac{1}{\sqrt{1-x^2}}.$$

By using this fact and integrating the series in part (a) term by term, find the first three non-zero terms in the Taylor series about 0 for the function $f(x) = \sin^{-1} x$, explicitly evaluating the coefficients. State an interval of validity for this series.

Learning outcomes

After studying this unit, you should be able to:

- find Taylor polynomials about particular points for particular functions

- use Taylor polynomials to find approximations for values of functions, estimating such values to a particular accuracy

- find Taylor series about particular points for particular functions

- use known Taylor series to find further Taylor series by substitution, addition, subtraction, multiplication, differentiation and integration, and deduce intervals of validity for such series from intervals of validity for the original series.

Solutions to activities

Solution to Activity 1

(a) Since $f(0) = \cos 0 = 1$, the constant Taylor polynomial about 0 for $f(x) = \cos x$ is $p(x) = 1$.

The approximation is 1 in each case; that is,
$$p(0.01) = 1 \quad \text{and} \quad p(0.1) = 1.$$
The corresponding remainders are, to five decimal places,
$$\cos(0.01) - p(0.01) = \cos(0.01) - 1 = -0.00005,$$
$$\cos(0.1) - p(0.1) = \cos(0.1) - 1 = -0.00500.$$

(b) Since $f(1) = \ln 1 = 0$, the constant Taylor polynomial about 1 for $f(x) = \ln x$ is $p(x) = 0$.

The approximation is 0 in each case; that is,
$$p(1.01) = 0 \quad \text{and} \quad p(1.1) = 0.$$
The corresponding remainders are, to five decimal places,
$$\ln(1.01) - p(1.01) = \ln(1.01) - 0 = 0.00995,$$
$$\ln(1.1) - p(1.1) = \ln(1.1) - 0 = 0.09531.$$

Solution to Activity 2

(a) We have $f(x) = \sin x$, so
$$f'(x) = \cos x.$$
Hence
$$f(0) = \sin 0 = 0 \quad \text{and} \quad f'(0) = \cos 0 = 1.$$
Thus the linear Taylor polynomial about 0 for the sine function is
$$p(x) = f(0) + f'(0)x$$
$$= 0 + x$$
$$= x.$$

(b) The linear Taylor polynomial gives the approximations
$$p(0.25) = 0.25 \quad \text{and} \quad p(0.5) = 0.5.$$
A calculator gives (to 4 d.p.)
$$\sin(0.25) = 0.2474 \quad \text{and} \quad \sin(0.5) = 0.4794.$$
Hence the two remainders are
$$\sin(0.25) - 0.25 = -0.0026,$$
$$\sin(0.5) - 0.5 = -0.0206.$$
The magnitude of the remainder is about 8 times larger at $x = 0.5$ than it is at $x = 0.25$.

Solution to Activity 3

(a) We have $f(x) = \cos x$, so
$$f'(x) = -\sin x.$$
Hence
$$f(0) = \cos 0 = 1 \quad \text{and} \quad f'(0) = -\sin 0 = 0.$$
Thus the linear Taylor polynomial about 0 for the cosine function is
$$p(x) = f(0) + f'(0)$$
$$= 1 + 0x$$
$$= 1.$$

(b) The approximation for $\cos(0.2)$ given by the linear Taylor polynomial p is $p(0.2) = 1$. To four decimal places, the remainder is
$$\cos(0.2) - 1 = -0.0199.$$

Solution to Activity 4

(a) We have $f(x) = (1 + x)^{1/2}$, so
$$f'(x) = \tfrac{1}{2}(1 + x)^{-1/2}.$$
Hence
$$f(0) = (1 + 0)^{1/2} = 1$$
and
$$f'(0) = \tfrac{1}{2}(1 + 0)^{-1/2} = \tfrac{1}{2}.$$
Thus the linear Taylor polynomial about 0 for $f(x) = (1 + x)^{1/2}$ is
$$p(x) = f(0) + f'(0)x$$
$$= 1 + \tfrac{1}{2}x, \quad \text{as required.}$$

(b) We have
$$\sqrt{1.01} = (1 + 0.01)^{1/2} = f(0.01).$$
The corresponding approximation for $\sqrt{1.01}$ is
$$p(0.01) = 1 + \tfrac{1}{2} \times 0.01 = 1.005.$$
To six decimal places, the remainder is
$$f(0.01) - p(0.01) = 1.004988 - 1.005$$
$$= -0.000012.$$

Solution to Activity 5

We have $f(x) = e^x$, so
$$f'(x) = e^x.$$
Hence
$$f(1) = e^1 = e \quad \text{and} \quad f'(1) = e^1 = e.$$

Thus the linear Taylor polynomial about 1 for $f(x) = e^x$ is
$$p(x) = f(1) + f'(1)(x - 1)$$
$$= e + e(x - 1)$$
$$= ex.$$

Solution to Activity 6

(a) We have $f(x) = \cos x$, so
$$f'(x) = -\sin x \quad \text{and} \quad f''(x) = -\cos x.$$
Hence
$$f(0) = \cos 0 = 1, \quad f'(0) = -\sin 0 = 0$$
and
$$f''(0) = -\cos 0 = -1.$$
Thus the quadratic Taylor polynomial about 0 for the cosine function is
$$p(x) = f(0) + f'(0)x + \tfrac{1}{2}f''(0)x^2$$
$$= 1 + 0x - \tfrac{1}{2}x^2$$
$$= 1 - \tfrac{1}{2}x^2.$$

(b) The corresponding approximation to $\cos(0.2)$ is
$$p(0.2) = 1 - \tfrac{1}{2}(0.2)^2 = 0.98.$$
To six decimal places, the remainder is
$$\cos(0.2) - p(0.2) = 0.980\,067 - 0.98$$
$$= 0.000\,067.$$

This remainder has much smaller magnitude than that found in Activity 3(b), so the approximation to $\cos(0.2)$ by using the quadratic Taylor polynomial $p(x) = 1 - \tfrac{1}{2}x^2$ is much better than the approximation by using the linear Taylor polynomial $p(x) = 1$.

Solution to Activity 7

We have $f(x) = \sin x$, so
$$f'(x) = \cos x \quad \text{and} \quad f''(x) = -\sin x.$$
Hence
$$f(0) = \sin 0 = 0, \quad f'(0) = \cos 0 = 1$$
and
$$f''(0) = -\sin 0 = 0.$$
Thus the quadratic Taylor polynomial about 0 for the sine function is
$$p(x) = f(0) + f'(0)x + \tfrac{1}{2}f''(0)x^2$$
$$= 0 + x + 0x^2$$
$$= x.$$

Solution to Activity 8

We have $f(x) = e^x$, so
$$f'(x) = e^x \quad \text{and} \quad f''(x) = e^x.$$
Hence
$$f(1) = e^1 = e, \quad f'(1) = e^1 = e$$
and
$$f''(1) = e^1 = e.$$
Thus the quadratic Taylor polynomial about 1 for $f(x) = e^x$ is
$$p(x) = f(1) + f'(1)(x - 1) + \tfrac{1}{2}f''(1)(x - 1)^2$$
$$= e + e(x - 1) + \tfrac{1}{2}e(x - 1)^2.$$
(By multiplying out the squared brackets and collecting like terms, this can also be written as
$$p(x) = \tfrac{1}{2}e\left(1 + x^2\right).)$$

Solution to Activity 9

(a) To find the quartic Taylor polynomial about 0 for $f(x) = \cos x$, we need to evaluate $f(0)$, $f'(0)$, $f''(0)$, $f^{(3)}(0)$ and $f^{(4)}(0)$. We have:
$$f(x) = \cos x, \qquad f(0) = 1;$$
$$f'(x) = -\sin x, \quad f'(0) = 0;$$
$$f''(x) = -\cos x, \quad f''(0) = -1;$$
$$f^{(3)}(x) = \sin x, \quad f^{(3)}(0) = 0;$$
$$f^{(4)}(x) = \cos x, \quad f^{(4)}(0) = 1.$$
Hence the quartic Taylor polynomial about 0 for the cosine function is
$$p(x) = f(0) + f'(0)x + \frac{f''(0)}{2!}x^2 + \frac{f^{(3)}(0)}{3!}x^3$$
$$+ \frac{f^{(4)}(0)}{4!}x^4$$
$$= 1 - \frac{1}{2!}x^2 + \frac{1}{4!}x^4$$
$$= 1 - \tfrac{1}{2}x^2 + \tfrac{1}{24}x^4.$$

(b) Similarly, to find the quartic Taylor polynomial about 0 for $f(x) = \sin x$, we need to evaluate $f(0)$, $f'(0)$, $f''(0)$, $f^{(3)}(0)$ and $f^{(4)}(0)$. We have:
$$f(x) = \sin x, \qquad f(0) = 0;$$
$$f'(x) = \cos x, \qquad f'(0) = 1;$$
$$f''(x) = -\sin x, \qquad f''(0) = 0;$$
$$f^{(3)}(x) = -\cos x, \quad f^{(3)}(0) = -1;$$
$$f^{(4)}(x) = \sin x, \qquad f^{(4)}(0) = 0.$$

Hence the quartic Taylor polynomial about 0 for the sine function is

$$p(x) = f(0) + f'(0)x + \frac{f''(0)}{2!}x^2 + \frac{f^{(3)}(0)}{3!}x^3$$

$$+ \frac{f^{(4)}(0)}{4!}x^4$$

$$= x - \frac{1}{3!}x^3$$

$$= x - \tfrac{1}{6}x^3.$$

(You may have noticed that the quartic Taylor polynomial about 0 for the cosine function contains terms in even powers of x only, whereas that for the sine function contains terms in odd powers of x only. This property is explained later in the subsection.)

Solution to Activity 10

(a) (i) Applying the chain rule gives

$$\frac{d}{dx}\left(\frac{1}{(1-x)^k}\right)$$

$$= \frac{d}{dx}\left((1-x)^{-k}\right)$$

$$= (-k)(1-x)^{-k-1} \times \frac{d}{dx}(1-x)$$

$$= (-k)(1-x)^{-(k+1)} \times (-1)$$

$$= k(1-x)^{-(k+1)}$$

$$= \frac{k}{(1-x)^{k+1}},$$

as required.

(ii) Applying the result from part (a)(i), with $k = 1, 2, 3$, gives

$$f(x) = \frac{1}{1-x}, \qquad f(0) = 1;$$

$$f'(x) = \frac{1}{(1-x)^2}, \qquad f'(0) = 1;$$

$$f''(x) = \frac{2}{(1-x)^3}, \qquad f''(0) = 2;$$

$$f^{(3)}(x) = \frac{3 \times 2}{(1-x)^4}$$

$$= \frac{3!}{(1-x)^4}, \quad f^{(3)}(0) = 3!.$$

(iii) Hence the cubic Taylor polynomial about 0 for f is

$$p(x) = f(0) + f'(0)x + \frac{f''(0)}{2!}x^2$$

$$+ \frac{f^{(3)}(0)}{3!}x^3$$

$$= 1 + x + \frac{2}{2!}x^2 + \frac{3!}{3!}x^3$$

$$= 1 + x + x^2 + x^3.$$

(b) (i) The 4th derivative of $f(x)$ is

$$f^{(4)}(x) = \frac{d}{dx}\left(\frac{3!}{(1-x)^4}\right)$$

$$= \frac{4 \times 3!}{(1-x)^5} = \frac{4!}{(1-x)^5},$$

the 5th derivative is

$$f^{(5)}(x) = \frac{d}{dx}\left(\frac{4!}{(1-x)^5}\right)$$

$$= \frac{5 \times 4!}{(1-x)^6} = \frac{5!}{(1-x)^6},$$

and so on. The pattern is now clear; the nth derivative will be

$$f^{(n)}(x) = \frac{n!}{(1-x)^{n+1}}.$$

(ii) By putting $x = 0$ in the formula for $f^{(n)}(x)$ above, we obtain

$$f^{(n)}(0) = \frac{n!}{(1-0)^{n+1}} = n!.$$

(iii) Hence the Taylor polynomial of degree n about 0 for f is

$$p(x) = f(0) + f'(0)x + \frac{f''(0)}{2!}x^2$$

$$+ \frac{f^{(3)}(0)}{3!}x^3 + \cdots + \frac{f^{(n)}(0)}{n!}x^n$$

$$= 1 + x + \frac{2}{2!}x^2 + \frac{3!}{3!}x^3 + \cdots + \frac{n!}{n!}x^n$$

$$= 1 + x + x^2 + x^3 + \cdots + x^n.$$

Solution to Activity 11

To find the cubic Taylor polynomial about $\pi/6$ for $f(x) = \sin x$, we evaluate $f(\pi/6)$, $f'(\pi/6)$, $f''(\pi/6)$ and $f^{(3)}(\pi/6)$, as follows:

$$f(x) = \sin x, \qquad f\left(\frac{\pi}{6}\right) = \tfrac{1}{2};$$

$$f'(x) = \cos x, \qquad f'\left(\frac{\pi}{6}\right) = \tfrac{1}{2}\sqrt{3};$$

$$f''(x) = -\sin x, \qquad f''\left(\frac{\pi}{6}\right) = -\tfrac{1}{2};$$

$$f^{(3)}(x) = -\cos x, \quad f^{(3)}\left(\frac{\pi}{6}\right) = -\tfrac{1}{2}\sqrt{3}.$$

Hence the cubic Taylor polynomial about $\pi/6$ for the sine function is

$$p(x) = f\left(\frac{\pi}{6}\right) + f'\left(\frac{\pi}{6}\right)\left(x - \frac{\pi}{6}\right)$$

$$+ \frac{f''\left(\frac{\pi}{6}\right)}{2!}\left(x - \frac{\pi}{6}\right)^2 + \frac{f^{(3)}\left(\frac{\pi}{6}\right)}{3!}\left(x - \frac{\pi}{6}\right)^3$$

$$= \frac{1}{2} + \frac{1}{2}\sqrt{3}\left(x - \frac{\pi}{6}\right) - \frac{1}{4}\left(x - \frac{\pi}{6}\right)^2$$

$$- \frac{1}{12}\sqrt{3}\left(x - \frac{\pi}{6}\right)^3.$$

Solution to Activity 13

Using the given Taylor polynomials

$$p_n(x) = 1 + x + \frac{1}{2!}x^2 + \frac{1}{3!}x^3 + \cdots + \frac{1}{n!}x^n,$$

and calculating values to six decimal places, we obtain

$$p_1(-0.05) = 1 + (-0.05) = 0.95$$

$$p_2(-0.05) = p_1(-0.05) + \tfrac{1}{2}(-0.05)^2$$
$$= 0.951\,25$$

$$p_3(-0.05) = p_2(-0.05) + \tfrac{1}{6}(-0.05)^3$$
$$= 0.951\,229 \quad \text{(to 6 d.p.)}$$

$$p_4(-0.05) = p_3(-0.05) + \tfrac{1}{24}(-0.05)^4$$
$$= 0.951\,229 \quad \text{(to 6 d.p.)}.$$

The values of $p_3(-0.05)$ and $p_4(-0.05)$ agree to six decimal places, so it is likely that

$$e^{-0.05} = 0.9512$$

to four decimal places. (This is indeed the case.)

Solution to Activity 14

Using the given Taylor polynomials, and calculating values to eight decimal places, we obtain

$$p_0(0.2) = 1$$

$$p_2(0.2) = 1 - \frac{1}{2!}(0.2)^2 = 0.98$$

$$p_4(0.2) = p_2(0.2) + \frac{1}{4!}(0.2)^4 = 0.980\,066\,67$$

$$p_6(0.2) = p_4(0.2) - \frac{1}{6!}(0.2)^6 = 0.980\,066\,58$$

$$p_8(0.2) = p_6(0.2) + \frac{1}{8!}(0.2)^8 = 0.980\,066\,58.$$

The values of $p_6(0.2)$ and $p_8(0.2)$ agree to eight decimal places, so it is likely that

$$\cos(0.2) = 0.980\,067$$

to six decimal places. (This is indeed the case.)

Solution to Activity 15

(a) From the solution to Activity 9(a), we can see that the values of $f^{(n)}(0)$ form the repeating sequence

$$1, 0, -1, 0, 1, \ldots .$$

Hence the Taylor series about 0 for $f(x) = \cos x$ is

$$1 - \frac{1}{2!}x^2 + \frac{1}{4!}x^4 - \frac{1}{6!}x^6 + \frac{1}{8!}x^8 - \cdots .$$

(b) Similarly, from the solution to Activity 9(b), we can see that the values of $f^{(n)}(0)$ form the repeating sequence

$$0, 1, 0, -1, 0, \ldots .$$

Hence the Taylor series about 0 for $f(x) = \sin x$ is

$$x - \frac{1}{3!}x^3 + \frac{1}{5!}x^5 - \frac{1}{7!}x^7 + \frac{1}{9!}x^9 - \cdots .$$

Solution to Activity 16

We proceed initially in a similar way to the solution to Activity 9(b). To find the Taylor series about 0 for $f(x) = \sin x$, we need to evaluate $f(\pi/2)$, $f'(\pi/2)$, $f''(\pi/2)$, $f^{(3)}(\pi/2)$, $\ldots$. We have:

$$f(x) = \sin x, \qquad f\left(\frac{\pi}{2}\right) = 1;$$

$$f'(x) = \cos x, \qquad f'\left(\frac{\pi}{2}\right) = 0;$$

$$f''(x) = -\sin x, \qquad f''\left(\frac{\pi}{2}\right) = -1;$$

$$f^{(3)}(x) = -\cos x, \quad f^{(3)}\left(\frac{\pi}{2}\right) = 0;$$

$$f^{(4)}(x) = \sin x, \qquad f^{(4)}\left(\frac{\pi}{2}\right) = 1.$$

The values of $f^{(n)}(\pi/2)$ form the repeating sequence

$$1, 0, -1, 0, 1, \ldots.$$

Hence, from formula (5), the Taylor series about $\pi/2$ for $f(x) = \sin x$ is

$$1 - \frac{1}{2!}\left(x - \frac{\pi}{2}\right)^2 + \frac{1}{4!}\left(x - \frac{\pi}{2}\right)^4 - \frac{1}{6!}\left(x - \frac{\pi}{2}\right)^6$$

$$+ \frac{1}{8!}\left(x - \frac{\pi}{2}\right)^8 - \cdots.$$

Solution to Activity 17

Since $1/(1+x)^2 = (1+x)^{-2}$, we take $\alpha = -2$ in the binomial series, to give

$$\frac{1}{(1+x)^2} = 1 + (-2)x + \frac{(-2)(-3)}{2!}x^2$$

$$+ \frac{(-2)(-3)(-4)}{3!}x^3 + \cdots$$

$$= 1 - 2x + 3x^2 - 4x^3 + 5x^4 - \cdots.$$

This Taylor series is valid for $-1 < x < 1$.

Solution to Activity 18

Taking $\alpha = \frac{1}{2}$ in the binomial series gives

$$(1+x)^{1/2} = 1 + \frac{1}{2}x + \frac{\frac{1}{2}(-\frac{1}{2})}{2!}x^2 + \frac{\frac{1}{2}(-\frac{1}{2})(-\frac{3}{2})}{3!}x^3$$

$$+ \frac{\frac{1}{2}(-\frac{1}{2})(-\frac{3}{2})(-\frac{5}{2})}{4!}x^4 + \cdots$$

$$= 1 + \frac{1}{2}x - \frac{1}{2^2 \times 2!}x^2 + \frac{1 \times 3}{2^3 \times 3!}x^3$$

$$- \frac{1 \times 3 \times 5}{2^4 \times 4!}x^4 + \cdots.$$

This Taylor series is valid for $-1 < x < 1$.

Solution to Activity 19

The cubic Taylor polynomial about 0 for the function $f(x) = \ln(1+x)$ is obtained from the Taylor series for $\ln(1+x)$ by deleting all the terms after $\frac{1}{3}x^3$, to give

$$p_3(x) = x - \frac{1}{2}x^2 + \frac{1}{3}x^3.$$

Solution to Activity 20

Using the series from the solution to Activity 18, we obtain, to five decimal places,

$$p_1(0.1) = 1 + \frac{1}{2}(0.1) = 1.05$$

$$p_2(0.1) = p_1(0.1) - \frac{1}{2^2 \times 2!}(0.1)^2 = 1.048\,75$$

$$p_3(0.1) = p_2(0.1) + \frac{1 \times 3}{2^3 \times 3!}(0.1)^3 = 1.048\,81$$

$$p_4(0.1) = p_3(0.1) - \frac{1 \times 3 \times 5}{2^4 \times 4!}(0.1)^4 = 1.048\,81.$$

The values of $p_3(0.1)$ and $p_4(0.1)$ agree to five decimal places, so it is likely that

$$\sqrt{1.1} = 1.049$$

to three decimal places. (This is indeed the case.)

Solution to Activity 22

(a) The Taylor series about 0 for $1/(1-x)$, from page 142, is

$$\frac{1}{1-x} = 1 + x + x^2 + x^3 + \cdots,$$

for $-1 < x < 1$. Replacing each occurrence of x by $-2x$ and using the fact that $1/(1-(-2x)) = 1/(1+2x)$ gives

$$\frac{1}{1+2x} = 1 + (-2x) + (-2x)^2 + (-2x)^3 + \cdots$$

$$= 1 - 2x + 4x^2 - 8x^3 + \cdots.$$

This is the Taylor series about 0 for $1/(1+2x)$. It is valid for $-1 < -2x < 1$; that is, for $-\frac{1}{2} < x < \frac{1}{2}$.

(This part could also be answered by taking the binomial series from page 142 for $(1+x)^\alpha$, with $\alpha = -1$, and then replacing each occurrence of x by $2x$.)

(b) The Taylor series about 0 for $\ln(1+x)$, from page 142, is

$$\ln(1+x) = x - \frac{1}{2}x^2 + \frac{1}{3}x^3 - \frac{1}{4}x^4 + \cdots,$$

for $-1 < x < 1$.

Replacing each occurrence of x by $-x$ and using the fact that $\ln(1+(-x)) = \ln(1-x)$ gives

$$\ln(1-x)$$

$$= (-x) - \frac{1}{2}(-x)^2 + \frac{1}{3}(-x)^3 - \frac{1}{4}(-x)^4 + \cdots$$

$$= -x - \frac{1}{2}x^2 - \frac{1}{3}x^3 - \frac{1}{4}x^4 - \cdots.$$

This is the Taylor series about 0 for $\ln(1-x)$. It is valid for $-1 < -x < 1$; that is, for $-1 < x < 1$.

(c) The Taylor series about 0 for $\ln(1+x)$, from page 142, is
$$\ln(1+x) = x - \tfrac{1}{2}x^2 + \tfrac{1}{3}x^3 - \tfrac{1}{4}x^4 + \cdots,$$
for $-1 < x < 1$. Replacing each occurrence of x by $3x$ gives
$$\ln(1+3x)$$
$$= (3x) - \tfrac{1}{2}(3x)^2 + \tfrac{1}{3}(3x)^3 - \tfrac{1}{4}(3x)^4 + \cdots$$
$$= 3x - \frac{3^2}{2}x^2 + \frac{3^3}{3}x^3 - \frac{3^4}{4}x^4 + \cdots.$$
This is the Taylor series about 0 for $\ln(1+3x)$. It is valid for $-1 < 3x < 1$; that is, for $-\tfrac{1}{3} < x < \tfrac{1}{3}$.

(d) The Taylor series about 0 for e^x, from page 142, is
$$e^x = 1 + x + \frac{1}{2!}x^2 + \frac{1}{3!}x^3 + \cdots, \quad \text{for } x \in \mathbb{R}.$$
Replacing each occurrence of x by x^3 gives the Taylor series about 0 for e^{x^3}:
$$e^{x^3} = 1 + (x^3) + \frac{1}{2!}(x^3)^2 + \frac{1}{3!}(x^3)^3 + \cdots$$
$$= 1 + x^3 + \frac{1}{2!}x^6 + \frac{1}{3!}x^9 + \cdots, \quad \text{for } x \in \mathbb{R}.$$

Solution to Activity 23

The Taylor series about 0 for $1/(1+x)$ is given as
$$\frac{1}{1+x} = 1 - x + x^2 - x^3 + \cdots,$$
for $-1 < x < 1$. Replacing each occurrence of x by $x - 1$ in this equation, we obtain
$$\frac{1}{1+(x-1)}$$
$$= 1 - (x-1) + (x-1)^2 - (x-1)^3 + \cdots.$$
But $1/(1+(x-1)) = 1/x$. Therefore the Taylor series about 1 for $1/x$ is
$$\frac{1}{x} = 1 - (x-1) + (x-1)^2 - (x-1)^3 + \cdots.$$
This Taylor series is valid for $-1 < x - 1 < 1$; that is, for $0 < x < 2$.

Solution to Activity 24

In each part, we use the Taylor series about 0 for $1/(1+x)$, from page 142, which is
$$\frac{1}{1+x} = 1 - x + x^2 - x^3 + \cdots,$$
for $-1 < x < 1$.

(a) Replacing each occurrence of x by $\tfrac{2}{3}x$ in this equation, we obtain
$$\frac{1}{1+\tfrac{2}{3}x} = 1 - \left(\tfrac{2}{3}x\right) + \left(\tfrac{2}{3}x\right)^2 - \left(\tfrac{2}{3}x\right)^3 + \cdots$$
$$= 1 - \tfrac{2}{3}x + \tfrac{4}{9}x^2 - \tfrac{8}{27}x^3 + \cdots.$$
It follows that the Taylor series about 0 for $g(x) = 3/(3+2x) = 1/\left(1+\tfrac{2}{3}x\right)$ is
$$\frac{3}{3+2x} = 1 - \tfrac{2}{3}x + \tfrac{4}{9}x^2 - \tfrac{8}{27}x^3 + \cdots.$$
This Taylor series is valid for $-1 < \tfrac{2}{3}x < 1$; that is, for $-\tfrac{3}{2} < x < \tfrac{3}{2}$.

(b) Replacing each occurrence of x by $2(x+1)$ in the series for $1/(1+x)$, we obtain
$$\frac{1}{1+2(x+1)}$$
$$= 1 - (2(x+1)) + (2(x+1))^2 - (2(x+1))^3 + \cdots$$
$$= 1 - 2(x+1) + 4(x+1)^2 - 8(x+1)^3 + \cdots.$$
It follows that the Taylor series about -1 for $1/(3+2x) = 1/(1+2(x+1))$ is
$$\frac{1}{3+2x} = 1 - 2(x+1) + 4(x+1)^2$$
$$- 8(x+1)^3 + \cdots.$$
This Taylor series is valid for $-1 < 2(x+1) < 1$; that is, for $-\tfrac{1}{2} < x+1 < \tfrac{1}{2}$ or equivalently $-\tfrac{3}{2} < x < -\tfrac{1}{2}$.

Solution to Activity 25

Using the given Taylor series about 0 for $\ln(1+x)$ and $\ln(1-x)$, we obtain
$$\ln(1+x) - \ln(1-x)$$
$$= \left(x - \tfrac{1}{2}x^2 + \tfrac{1}{3}x^3 - \tfrac{1}{4}x^4 + \tfrac{1}{5}x^5 - \cdots\right)$$
$$- \left(-x - \tfrac{1}{2}x^2 - \tfrac{1}{3}x^3 - \tfrac{1}{4}x^4 - \tfrac{1}{5}x^5 - \cdots\right)$$
$$= 2x + \tfrac{2}{3}x^3 + \tfrac{2}{5}x^5 + \cdots;$$
that is,
$$\ln\left(\frac{1+x}{1-x}\right) = 2x + \tfrac{2}{3}x^3 + \tfrac{2}{5}x^5 + \cdots.$$
The Taylor series for $\ln(1+x)$ and $\ln(1-x)$ are each valid for $-1 < x < 1$, so the Taylor series derived here is also valid for $-1 < x < 1$.

Solution to Activity 26

If $t = 1.5$, then the corresponding value of x is
$$x = \frac{1.5 - 1}{1.5 + 1} = \frac{0.5}{2.5} = \frac{1}{5} = 0.2.$$

Using the series given, we obtain, to six decimal places,
$$p_1(0.2) = 2 \times 0.2 = 0.4$$
$$p_3(0.2) = p_1(0.2) + \tfrac{2}{3}(0.2)^3 = 0.405\,333$$
$$p_5(0.2) = p_3(0.2) + \tfrac{2}{5}(0.2)^5 = 0.405\,461$$
$$p_7(0.2) = p_5(0.2) + \tfrac{2}{7}(0.2)^7 = 0.405\,465$$
$$p_9(0.2) = p_7(0.2) + \tfrac{2}{9}(0.2)^9 = 0.405\,465.$$

The values of $p_7(0.2)$ and $p_9(0.2)$ agree to six decimal places, so it is likely that
$$\ln(1.5) = \ln\left(\frac{1 + 0.2}{1 - 0.2}\right) = 0.4055$$

to four decimal places. (This is indeed the case.)

Solution to Activity 27

The given Taylor series is
$$\frac{1}{(1+x)^2} = 1 - 2x + 3x^2 - 4x^3 + \cdots,$$

for $-1 < x < 1$.

Using this series and replacing each occurrence of x by $\tfrac{1}{3}x$ gives
$$\frac{1}{(3+x)^2} = \frac{1}{3^2} \times \frac{1}{(1 + \tfrac{1}{3}x)^2}$$
$$= \frac{1}{3^2}\left(1 - 2\left(\tfrac{1}{3}x\right) + 3\left(\tfrac{1}{3}x\right)^2 - 4\left(\tfrac{1}{3}x\right)^3 + \cdots\right)$$
$$= \frac{1}{3^2}\left(1 - \frac{2}{3}x + \frac{3}{3^2}x^2 - \frac{4}{3^3}x^3 + \cdots\right)$$
$$= \frac{1}{3^2} - \frac{2}{3^3}x + \frac{3}{3^4}x^2 - \frac{4}{3^5}x^3 + \cdots.$$

This Taylor series is valid for $-1 < \tfrac{1}{3}x < 1$; that is, for $-3 < x < 3$.

Solution to Activity 28

We use the formula
$$\sinh x = \tfrac{1}{2}(e^x - e^{-x}).$$

The Taylor series about 0 for e^x is
$$e^x = 1 + x + \frac{x^2}{2!} + \frac{x^3}{3!} + \frac{x^4}{4!} + \cdots, \quad \text{for } x \in \mathbb{R}.$$

On replacing each occurrence of x by $-x$, we obtain
$$e^{-x} = 1 - x + \frac{x^2}{2!} - \frac{x^3}{3!} + \frac{x^4}{4!} - \cdots, \quad \text{for } x \in \mathbb{R}.$$

Therefore
$$\tfrac{1}{2}(e^x - e^{-x}) = \frac{1}{2}\left(\left(1 + x + \frac{x^2}{2!} + \frac{x^3}{3!} + \frac{x^4}{4!} + \cdots\right)\right.$$
$$\left. - \left(1 - x + \frac{x^2}{2!} - \frac{x^3}{3!} + \frac{x^4}{4!} - \cdots\right)\right)$$
$$= x + \frac{1}{3!}x^3 + \frac{1}{5!}x^5 + \cdots,$$

for $x \in \mathbb{R}$; that is,
$$\sinh x = x + \frac{1}{3!}x^3 + \frac{1}{5!}x^5 + \cdots, \quad \text{for } x \in \mathbb{R}.$$

Solution to Activity 29

(a) Using the Taylor series about 0 for $\sin x$, from page 142, we obtain
$$x^2 \sin x = x^2\left(x - \frac{1}{3!}x^3 + \frac{1}{5!}x^5 - \cdots\right)$$
$$= x^3 - \frac{1}{3!}x^5 + \frac{1}{5!}x^7 - \cdots, \quad \text{for } x \in \mathbb{R}.$$

(b) Using the Taylor series about 0 for $\cos x$, from page 142, we obtain
$$(1 + x)\cos x = (1 + x)\left(1 - \frac{1}{2!}x^2 + \frac{1}{4!}x^4 - \cdots\right)$$
$$= 1\left(1 - \frac{1}{2!}x^2 + \frac{1}{4!}x^4 - \cdots\right)$$
$$+ x\left(1 - \frac{1}{2!}x^2 + \frac{1}{4!}x^4 - \cdots\right)$$
$$= \left(1 - \frac{1}{2!}x^2 + \frac{1}{4!}x^4 - \cdots\right)$$
$$+ \left(x - \frac{1}{2!}x^3 + \frac{1}{4!}x^5 - \cdots\right)$$
$$= 1 + x - \frac{1}{2!}x^2 - \frac{1}{2!}x^3 + \frac{1}{4!}x^4 + \frac{1}{4!}x^5 - \cdots,$$

for $x \in \mathbb{R}$.

Solution to Activity 30

Using the Taylor series about 0 for $1/(1 + x)$ and $\sin x$, and ignoring all terms that lead to 4th or higher powers of x, we obtain
$$\frac{\sin x}{1 + x} = (1 - x + x^2 - \cdots)\left(x - \frac{1}{3!}x^3 + \cdots\right)$$
$$= \left(x - \frac{1}{3!}x^3 + \cdots\right) - x(x - \cdots) + x^2(x - \cdots) - \cdots$$
$$= (x - \tfrac{1}{6}x^3 + \cdots) - (x^2 - \cdots) + (x^3 - \cdots) - \cdots$$
$$= x - x^2 + \tfrac{5}{6}x^3 - \cdots.$$

Hence the cubic Taylor polynomial about 0 for $f(x) = (\sin x)/(1+x)$ is
$$p(x) = x - x^2 + \tfrac{5}{6}x^3.$$

Solution to Activity 31

The Taylor series about 0 for e^x is
$$1 + x + \frac{1}{2!}x^2 + \frac{1}{3!}x^3 + \frac{1}{4!}x^4 + \cdots .$$
Differentiating this series gives
$$0 + 1 + \frac{2}{2!}x + \frac{3}{3!}x^2 + \frac{4}{4!}x^3 + \cdots$$
$$= 1 + x + \frac{1}{2!}x^2 + \frac{1}{3!}x^3 + \cdots ,$$
which is the same series, as required.

Solution to Activity 32

We have
$$\frac{1}{1+x^2} = 1 - x^2 + x^4 - x^6 + \cdots ,$$
for $-1 < x < 1$. Integrating both sides of this equation gives
$$\int \frac{1}{1+x^2}\,dx = \int (1 - x^2 + x^4 - x^6 + \cdots)\,dx;$$
that is,
$$\tan^{-1} x = c + x - \tfrac{1}{3}x^3 + \tfrac{1}{5}x^5 - \tfrac{1}{7}x^7 + \cdots ,$$
for $-1 < x < 1$, where c is a constant. Taking $x = 0$ gives $\tan^{-1} 0 = c$, so $c = 0$. Therefore
$$\tan^{-1} x = x - \tfrac{1}{3}x^3 + \tfrac{1}{5}x^5 - \tfrac{1}{7}x^7 + \cdots ,$$
for $-1 < x < 1$.

Solution to Activity 33

(a) The given series is
$$\frac{1}{\sqrt{1+x}} = 1 - \tfrac{1}{2}x + \tfrac{3}{8}x^2 - \tfrac{5}{16}x^3 + \cdots ,$$
for $-1 < x < 1$. Replacing each occurrence of x by $-x^2$ gives
$$\frac{1}{\sqrt{1-x^2}} = 1 - \tfrac{1}{2}(-x^2) + \tfrac{3}{8}(-x^2)^2 - \tfrac{5}{16}(-x^2)^3 + \cdots$$
$$= 1 + \tfrac{1}{2}x^2 + \tfrac{3}{8}x^4 + \tfrac{5}{16}x^6 + \cdots .$$
This Taylor series is valid for $-1 < -x^2 < 1$. The left-hand inequality here is $-1 < -x^2$, which is equivalent to $1 > x^2$; that is, $-1 < x < 1$. The right-hand inequality is $-x^2 < 1$, which is equivalent to $x^2 > -1$ and therefore does not place any restriction on x, since the square of any real number is non-negative. Thus this Taylor series is valid for $-1 < x < 1$.

(b) Integrating both sides of the equation above gives
$$\int \frac{1}{\sqrt{1-x^2}}\,dx = \int (1 + \tfrac{1}{2}x^2 + \tfrac{3}{8}x^4 + \cdots)\,dx;$$
that is,
$$\sin^{-1} x = c + x + \tfrac{1}{6}x^3 + \tfrac{3}{40}x^5 + \cdots ,$$
for $-1 < x < 1$, where c is a constant. Putting $x = 0$ gives $\sin^{-1} 0 = c$, so $c = 0$. Therefore
$$\sin^{-1} x = x + \tfrac{1}{6}x^3 + \tfrac{3}{40}x^5 + \cdots ,$$
for $-1 < x < 1$.

Acknowledgements

Grateful acknowledgement is made to the following sources:

Page 145: Mark Hobbs, for the idea for the cartoon

Every effort has been made to contact copyright holders. If any have been inadvertently overlooked the publishers will be pleased to make the necessary arrangements at the first opportunity.

Complex numbers

Introduction

As you know, every positive real number has two square roots, one positive and one negative. For example, the positive real number 9 has square roots 3 and -3. Another way to express this fact is to say that the equation

$$x^2 = 9$$

has solutions 3 and -3. Suppose now that you want to find a square root of a *negative* number, such as -1. That is, you want to solve the equation

$$x^2 = -1.$$

You may believe that this equation has no solutions; after all, the square of any real number is positive or zero. In this unit you'll learn about a system of numbers, known as the *complex numbers*, in which -1 and all other negative numbers have square roots.

The complex numbers are created by first introducing a new number, written as i, with the property that $i^2 = -1$ (so i is a square root of -1). It may seem like cheating to simply define i in this way, but you'll see that the resulting new system of numbers is incredibly powerful and useful. The other complex numbers are created by multiplying i by any real number, and then adding any real number. For example, the following are complex numbers:

$$3 + 4i, \quad -\sqrt{2} + 99i \quad \text{and} \quad 0.7 - \pi i.$$

Each real number can also be considered to be a complex number (3 is $3 + 0i$, for example). The number i is a solution of the equation $x^2 = -1$, and there's a second solution of this equation, namely $-i$.

The first publication to include a reference to complex numbers was the book *Ars Magna* (1545) by Gerolamo Cardano (1501–1576). The possibility of using complex numbers first emerged when Italian mathematicians were developing methods for solving cubic equations, such as $x^3 + x^2 + 6x + 3 = 0$. Both Scipione del Ferro (1465–1526) and Niccolò Fontana Tartaglia (1499/1500–1557) independently discovered how to solve any cubic equation, using methods that sometimes involve complex numbers. Tartaglia revealed his method in secret to Cardano, who later published it in his *Ars Magna*. This angered Tartaglia, who insulted Cardano for revealing the method. Cardano, in his defence, claimed to have also seen del Ferro's method, which was unpublished, and so he no longer felt obliged to keep the method of solving cubic equations secret.

Niccolò Fontana Tartaglia

At first, complex numbers may seem abstract, because they don't obviously represent physical quantities in the way that real numbers do. However, they're of fundamental importance in mathematics – as you'll begin to see in this unit – and they're an essential tool in many scientific disciplines, such as electromagnetism, fluid dynamics and quantum mechanics.

Figure 1   A transistor

Quantum mechanics, for instance, is about the motion of very small objects, such as atoms. The foundational equations of the subject involve complex numbers.

Discoveries in quantum mechanics led to the development of the modern transistor, midway through the last century. Transistors (one is shown in Figure 1) are devices used to control current in circuits, and are an essential part of electronic systems, such as those found in cars, computers and portable media players.

It's instructive to think of complex numbers geometrically, using the *complex plane*, which is a plane such as that shown in Figure 2. Each complex number is represented by a point on the plane. For instance, the complex number $2 + 3i$ is represented by the point with coordinates $(2, 3)$. You'll learn more about the complex plane in Section 2.

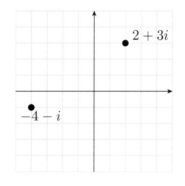

Figure 2   The complex plane

In higher-level modules involving complex numbers you can find out how some simple formulas involving complex numbers give rise to *fractals* in the complex plane, which are intricate shapes with repetitive structures, such as that shown in Figure 3.

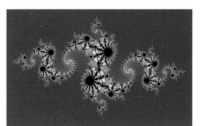

Figure 3   A fractal in the complex plane

Not only do complex numbers have fascinating geometric properties that give rise to beautiful fractals, but the system of complex numbers also has some useful algebraic properties that the system of real numbers lacks. For instance, you saw in Unit 2 that, if you're working only with the real numbers, then some quadratic equations have no solutions. An example is the equation $x^2 - 4x + 5 = 0$: if you write this equation as $(x - 2)^2 + 1 = 0$, then you can see that for every real number x the left-hand side is greater than or equal to 1, and hence the equation has no solutions that are real numbers. You'll see in Section 3 that if you're allowed to use complex numbers, then every quadratic equation has at least one solution. In fact, you'll meet an even stronger result: if you're allowed to use complex numbers, then every *polynomial equation* has at least one solution. A polynomial equation is an equation of the form 'polynomial expression = 0' (where the polynomial expression has degree at least 1), such as

$$5x^6 + 8 = 0 \quad \text{or} \quad x^7 - 13x^5 + \tfrac{5}{3}x^2 - 2 = 0.$$

In Section 4 you'll be shown *Euler's formula*,

$$e^{i\theta} = \cos\theta + i\sin\theta.$$

This is a hugely important equation that relates the exponential function to the trigonometric functions. Euler's formula allows you to write complex numbers in a helpful manner, called *exponential form*, which is widely used in mathematics, engineering and other scientific subjects.

Some of the blue boxes in this unit give you a taste of some of the ways in which complex numbers are used in higher-level mathematics. Remember that these boxes are only for your interest; you won't be assessed on their contents.

1   Arithmetic with complex numbers

In this section you'll learn the details of what complex numbers are, and how you can add, subtract, multiply and divide them. You'll also learn about another arithmetic operation, called *complex conjugation*, which is particular to the complex numbers.

1.1   What are complex numbers?

To define the complex numbers we start by considering the equation

$$x^2 = -1.$$

This equation has no solutions that are real numbers, because the square of any real number is non-negative. To overcome this problem, we introduce a new number, which we call i, and declare that i is a solution of the equation.

> The number i is defined to have the property $i^2 = -1$.

So i is a square root of -1. You learned in Section 4 of Unit 1 that the symbol $\sqrt{}$ is used to denote the non-negative square root of a non-negative real number. In other texts you may see i written as $\sqrt{-1}$, even though neither -1 nor i is a non-negative real number. This notation isn't used in this module, as it can be misleading. To see why, remember the rule $\sqrt{a}\sqrt{b} = \sqrt{ab}$, also from Unit 1, which is true when a and b are non-negative real numbers. If you try to apply this rule with $a = b = -1$, then you obtain the incorrect statement

$$\sqrt{-1}\sqrt{-1} = \sqrt{(-1)\times(-1)} = \sqrt{1} = 1.$$

This statement is wrong because $\sqrt{-1}\sqrt{-1}$ should equal -1, not 1.

To avoid this kind of pitfall, it's best not to use the notation $\sqrt{-1}$, except in certain particular circumstances, such as those described in Subsection 3.1, where you'll meet expressions involving $\pm\sqrt{}$.

Let's now look at how the complex numbers are obtained by combining this new number i with the real numbers. For instance, you can multiply i by a real number such as 5 to give another number, $5i$. You can then add $5i$ to a real number such as 3 to give another number, $3 + 5i$. The complex numbers are all the numbers that you can obtain in this way.

Complex numbers

A **complex number** is a number of the form $a + bi$, where a and b are real numbers.

The set of all complex numbers is denoted by $\mathbb{C}$.

For example, $-7 + 3i$ and $\frac{3}{5} + 19i$ are complex numbers. Using the usual conventions of algebra, we can write some complex numbers in a form simpler than $a + bi$. For example, we write

$$
\begin{array}{lcl}
45 + (-11)i & \text{as} & 45 - 11i \\
3 + 1i & \text{as} & 3 + i \\
6 + 0i & \text{as} & 6 \\
0 + (-1)i & \text{as} & -i \\
0 + 0i & \text{as} & 0.
\end{array}
$$

Note that since i is a square root of -1, the number $-i$ is also a square root of -1, as you'd expect. You'll see this confirmed later.

In the rest of this section, you'll meet some of the basic properties of complex numbers, and practise manipulating them. To start with, here are two important definitions.

> **Real and imaginary parts**
>
> For any complex number $z = a + bi$, the real number a is called the **real part** of z and the real number b is called the **imaginary part** of z. We write
>
> $$\mathrm{Re}(z) = a \quad \text{and} \quad \mathrm{Im}(z) = b.$$

For example,

$$\mathrm{Re}(-7 + 3i) = -7 \quad \text{and} \quad \mathrm{Im}(-7 + 3i) = 3.$$

Also,

$$\mathrm{Re}(5i) = 0 \quad \text{and} \quad \mathrm{Im}(5i) = 5.$$

Notice that it is b, and not bi, that is the imaginary part of $a + bi$. For example, the imaginary part of $-7 + 3i$ is 3, not $3i$.

If the real part of a complex number is 0, then the complex number is sometimes called an **imaginary number** or a **purely imaginary number**. For instance, the complex numbers $5i$ and $-i$ are imaginary numbers.

If the imaginary part of a complex number is 0, then that complex number is in fact a real number. For instance, the complex number 5 (which you could write as $5 + 0i$) is also a real number. In the same way, *every* real number is a complex number. This implies that the set of real numbers is a subset of the set of complex numbers; that is, $\mathbb{R} \subseteq \mathbb{C}$.

> **Activity 1**   *Identifying real and imaginary parts*
>
> Write down the real and imaginary part of each of the following complex numbers.
>
> (a) $2 + 9i$ (b) 4 (c) $-7i$ (d) 0 (e) i (f) $1 - i$

You can also write complex numbers in the form $a + ib$, which is equivalent to $a + bi$, and both forms are used. Your choice may depend on the nature of the real number b. For instance, you may prefer to write $1 + i\sqrt{2}$ rather than $1 + \sqrt{2}i$, to avoid possible confusion with $1 + \sqrt{2i}$.

Over the centuries, mathematicians have struggled with definitions of numbers. Few people have trouble understanding the natural numbers $1, 2, 3, \ldots$, but the concept of zero was more troublesome. One of the first people to bring the idea to Europe was Fibonacci (Leonardo of Pisa) in his *Liber Abaci* (1202), the text that spread the Hindu–Arabic numeral system through Europe. Even so, the symbol 0 was not widely used in Europe until the seventeenth century, and in 1759 the English mathematician Francis Maseres wrote of the negative numbers that they

> darken the very whole doctrines of the equations and make dark of the things which are in their nature excessively obvious and simple.

Likewise, many mathematicians at first doubted the validity of complex numbers, which Cardano had described in *Ars Magna* as 'some recondite third kind of thing'. In fact, the renowned French philosopher and mathematician René Descartes (1596–1650) coined the term *imaginary numbers* for real number multiples of i because he considered them to be illusory.

Today we're aware of the many uses of different types of numbers, and the foundations of mathematics are well established, so there's no longer any doubt about the validity of zero, negative numbers or complex numbers.

Francis Maseres (1731–1824)

1.2 Adding and subtracting complex numbers

You can add or subtract complex numbers by adding or subtracting their real and imaginary parts separately. For example,

$$(5 + 6i) + (3 + 2i) = \underbrace{(5 + 3)}_{\substack{\text{add real} \\ \text{parts}}} + \underbrace{(6 + 2)}_{\substack{\text{add imaginary} \\ \text{parts}}} i = 8 + 8i,$$

and

$$(5 + 6i) - (3 + 2i) = \underbrace{(5 - 3)}_{\substack{\text{subtract} \\ \text{real parts}}} + \underbrace{(6 - 2)}_{\substack{\text{subtract} \\ \text{imaginary parts}}} i = 2 + 4i.$$

In essence, to add or subtract complex numbers you treat i as a variable and add or subtract in the normal way.

Example 1 *Adding and subtracting complex numbers*

Let $z = 7 + 19i$ and $w = 13 - 10i$. Work out $z + w$ and $z - w$.

Solution

$$(7 + 19i) + (13 - 10i) = (7 + 13) + (19 + (-10))i = 20 + 9i$$
$$(7 + 19i) - (13 - 10i) = (7 - 13) + (19 - (-10))i = -6 + 29i$$

Activity 2 *Adding and subtracting complex numbers*

Work out $z + w$ and $z - w$ for each case below.

(a) $z = 2 + 5i, \quad w = -7 + 13i$ \qquad (b) $z = -4i, \quad w = -9i$

(c) $z = 3 - 7i, \quad w = 3 - 7i$ \qquad (d) $z = 3 + 7i, \quad w = 3 - 7i$

(e) $z = \frac{1}{6} - \frac{1}{3}i, \quad w = -\frac{1}{3} + \frac{1}{6}i$ \qquad (f) $z = 1.2, \quad w = 3.4i$

Many familiar rules for adding and subtracting real numbers also apply to complex numbers. For instance, the order in which you add two complex numbers z and w doesn't matter:

$$z + w = w + z.$$

Also, any three complex numbers u, v and w satisfy

$$(u + v) + w = u + (v + w).$$

You've met similar rules before, when you learned about addition of vectors, in Unit 5, and addition of matrices, in Unit 9. Recall that an operation (in this case, addition of complex numbers) that obeys the first rule is said to be *commutative*, and an operation that obeys the second rule is said to be *associative*. Together the two rules tell you that you can add several complex numbers in any order that you choose.

The number 0 has the same role in the arithmetic of complex numbers as it does in the arithmetic of real numbers, in that adding 0 to any number leaves that number unchanged.

You should approach the next activity using the usual rules of algebra, remembering to treat i like a variable.

Activity 3 *Adding and subtracting several complex numbers*

Let $u = 4 + 6i$, $v = -3 + 5i$ and $w = 2 - i$. Work out the following.

(a) $u + v + w$ \qquad (b) $w + v + u$ \qquad (c) $u - (v + w)$ \qquad (d) $u - (v - w)$

1.3 Multiplying complex numbers

You can multiply two complex numbers using the usual rules of algebra and the fact that $i^2 = -1$, as shown in the next example.

Example 2 *Multiplying complex numbers*

Find the product of $3 + 2i$ and $5 + i$.

Solution

🗨 Multiply out the brackets. 🗨

$$(3 + 2i)(5 + i) = 15 + 3i + 10i + 2i^2$$
$$= 15 + 13i + 2i^2$$

🗨 Simplify using $i^2 = -1$. 🗨

$$= 15 + 13i + 2(-1)$$
$$= 15 + 13i - 2$$
$$= 13 + 13i$$

As usual, you can also write products using the $\times$ symbol. For instance, the product $(3 + 2i)(5 + i)$ can also be written as

$$(3 + 2i) \times (5 + i).$$

Activity 4 *Multiplying complex numbers*

Find the following products of complex numbers.

(a) $(1 + 3i)(2 + 4i)$ (b) $(-2 + 3i)(4 - 7i)$ (c) $3i(4 - 5i)$

(d) $7(-2 + 5i)$ (e) $(2 - 3i)(2 + 3i)$ (f) $\left(\frac{1}{2} + i\right)\left(1 + \frac{1}{2}i\right)$

Multiplication of complex numbers, like addition of complex numbers, is both *commutative* and *associative*. This means that, for any complex numbers z and w,

$$z \times w = w \times z,$$

and, for any complex numbers u, v and w,

$$u \times (v \times w) = (u \times v) \times w.$$

Multiplication of complex numbers is also *distributive* over addition of complex numbers; that is, for any complex numbers u, v and w,

$$u \times (v + w) = u \times v + u \times w.$$

When you add and multiply real numbers, you probably apply the commutative, associative and distributive laws without thinking about them. You should be comfortable doing the same for complex numbers.

The numbers 0 and 1 play the same roles in the multiplication of complex numbers as they do in the multiplication of real numbers. That is, multiplying a number by 0 gives the answer 0, and multiplying a number by 1 leaves that number unchanged.

Activity 5 *Adding and multiplying several complex numbers*

Let $u = 1 + 2i$, $v = 4 - 3i$ and $w = -i$. Work out the following.

(a) $u(v + w)$ (b) $uv + uw$ (c) uvw

When multiplying a complex number z by itself, you should write z^2, rather than zz or $z \times z$, just as for real numbers. Other positive integer powers of a complex number z, such as z^3 or z^{100}, are defined in the usual way. When z is not zero, the zeroth power z^0 of z is defined to be 1, just as for real numbers. You'll learn about negative integer powers later on.

The index laws from Section 4 of Unit 1 continue to hold when the base numbers are complex numbers and the powers are positive integers. For example, one of these laws for complex numbers states that, if z and w are complex numbers and n is a positive integer, then

$$(zw)^n = z^n w^n.$$

In fact, once you learn about negative powers you'll see that these laws hold when the powers are any integers (not necessarily positive integers).

Activity 6 *Working out powers of i*

Work out i^0, i^1, i^2, i^3, i^4, i^5 and i^6. Predict the pattern that would emerge if you continued to work out higher powers of i.

As you learn more about complex numbers, you'll come to see that the system of complex numbers has richer properties than the system of real numbers. One example of this is in taking square roots of numbers.

You know that each positive real number has two square roots. For example, the number 3 has the two square roots $\pm\sqrt{3}$. If you're working with the complex numbers, then it's also true that each *negative* real number has two square roots. For example, the number -3 has the two square roots $\pm i\sqrt{3}$, because

$$\left(i\sqrt{3}\right)^2 = i^2\left(\sqrt{3}\right)^2 = (-1)\times 3 = -3$$

and

$$\left(-i\sqrt{3}\right)^2 = \left(i\times\left(-\sqrt{3}\right)\right)^2 = i^2\left(-\sqrt{3}\right)^2 = (-1)\times 3 = -3.$$

As you'll see later, these are the only two square roots of -3. In general, we have the following useful fact.

Square roots of a negative real number

If d is a positive real number, then the square roots of $-d$ are $\pm i\sqrt{d}$.

For example, the square roots of -4 are $\pm i\sqrt{4}$, that is, $\pm 2i$.

Activity 7   *Checking the square roots of a negative number*

Show that $3i$ and $-3i$ are both square roots of -9.

Gauss in his prime

Gaussian integers

As you know, an integer p greater than 1 whose only integer factors are ± 1 and $\pm p$ is called a *prime number*, or just a *prime*. The first few primes are

2, 3, 5, 7, 11, ...

Notice that even though 2 is a prime,

$$(1+i)(1-i) = 1 - i + i - i^2 = 2.$$

This shows that $1+i$ and $1-i$ are both factors of 2, so if we allow not only integer factors but also factors that are complex numbers whose real and imaginary parts are integers, then 2 is no longer a prime! A complex number $a + bi$ for which a and b are integers is known as a *Gaussian integer*, after the German mathematician Carl Friedrich Gauss (1777–1855), who first developed them.

Just as any ordinary integer x can be factorised in two 'trivial' ways as $x = 1 \times x$ and $x = (-1) \times (-x)$, so any Gaussian integer z can be factorised in four trivial ways as

$$z = 1 \times z = (-1) \times (-z) = i \times (-iz) = (-i) \times (iz).$$

If these are the only ways in which a Gaussian integer z can be factorised as a product of two Gaussian integers, then z is called a *Gaussian prime*. You've seen that 2 is not a Gaussian prime, and neither is 5, because

$$(2+i)(2-i) = 5.$$

However, it can be shown that 3 is a Gaussian prime, as is $1+i$, and in fact there are infinitely many Gaussian primes.

You can learn about the Gaussian integers in more advanced modules on number theory.

1.4 Complex conjugation

Before you find out how to divide complex numbers, it's useful for you to learn about another operation that you can perform on complex numbers, called *complex conjugation*.

Complex conjugation

The **complex conjugate** of $a + bi$ is $a - bi$.

The complex conjugate of z is denoted by $\overline{z}$.

The operation of transforming z to $\overline{z}$ is called **complex conjugation**.

For example,

$$\text{if } z = -3 + 2i \quad \text{then} \quad \overline{z} = -3 - 2i, \quad \text{and}$$
$$\text{if } z = 5 - 3i \quad \text{then} \quad \overline{z} = 5 + 3i.$$

Activity 8 *Finding complex conjugates*

Find the complex conjugate of each of the following complex numbers.

(a) $4 + 2i$ (b) $-3 - 8i$ (c) $9i$ (d) 5

Notice that if z is a real number, then $\overline{z} = z$. So complex conjugation has no effect on real numbers.

In the next activity you're asked to show that to undo complex conjugation, you just apply complex conjugation again.

Activity 9 *Applying complex conjugation twice*

Let $z = a + bi$ and $w = \overline{z}$. Show that $\overline{w} = z$.

There are some more properties of complex conjugation in the box below. The last property involves division of complex numbers, which you'll meet shortly.

These properties, and all the other complex number properties stated in this unit, hold for all complex numbers for which the expressions in them are defined. For example, the fourth property below holds for all complex numbers z and w with $w \neq 0$.

Some properties of complex conjugation

$$\overline{z + w} = \overline{z} + \overline{w}$$
$$\overline{z - w} = \overline{z} - \overline{w}$$
$$\overline{zw} = \overline{z}\,\overline{w}$$
$$\overline{z/w} = \overline{z}/\overline{w}$$

You can prove these properties by writing $z = a + bi$ and $w = c + di$. This gives

$$\overline{z + w} = \overline{(a + bi) + (c + di)}$$
$$= \overline{(a + c) + (b + d)i}$$
$$= (a + c) - (b + d)i$$
$$= (a - bi) + (c - di)$$
$$= \overline{z} + \overline{w}.$$

In the same way you can show that $\overline{z - w} = \overline{z} - \overline{w}$.

To prove the third property, let's work out the sides of the equation separately. We have

$$\overline{z}\,\overline{w} = (a - bi)(c - di)$$
$$= ac - adi - bci + bdi^2$$
$$= (ac - bd) - (ad + bc)i.$$

Also,

$$zw = (a + bi)(c + di)$$
$$= ac + adi + bci + bdi^2$$
$$= (ac - bd) + (ad + bc)i,$$

which gives

$$\overline{zw} = (ac - bd) - (ad + bc)i.$$

So both $\overline{z}\,\overline{w}$ and $\overline{zw}$ are equal to $(ac - bd) - (ad + bc)i$, which implies that $\overline{zw} = \overline{z}\,\overline{w}$.

The fourth property will be proved in the next subsection, once you've seen how to divide complex numbers.

In the next activity you're asked to prove two further properties of complex conjugation.

Activity 10   *Proving two identities involving complex numbers*

By writing $z = a + bi$, prove the following identities.

(a) $z + \overline{z} = 2\operatorname{Re}(z)$ (b) $z - \overline{z} = 2i\operatorname{Im}(z)$

Here's the property of complex conjugation that's useful when you want to divide complex numbers: whenever you multiply a complex number by its complex conjugate, you obtain a real number. To see why this is, recall the formula for the difference of two squares from Unit 1:

$$(A + B)(A - B) = A^2 - B^2.$$

Given any complex number $z = a + bi$, we can apply the difference of two squares formula with $A = a$ and $B = bi$ to give

$$\underbrace{(a + bi)}_{z}\underbrace{(a - bi)}_{\overline{z}} = a^2 - (bi)^2 = a^2 - b^2 i^2 = a^2 + b^2.$$

So we have the useful fact below.

> For any complex number $z = a + bi$,
> $$z\overline{z} = a^2 + b^2.$$

For example,

$$(1 + 2i)(1 - 2i) = 1^2 + 2^2 = 1 + 4 = 5.$$

Activity 11   *Multiplying complex numbers by their complex conjugates*

Multiply the following complex numbers by their complex conjugates.

(a) $2 + 3i$ (b) $-1 - 2i$ (c) $5i$ (d) -2

1.5   Dividing complex numbers

In this subsection you'll learn how to divide complex numbers, making use of the complex conjugation operation that you met in the previous subsection.

Suppose, for example, that you want to divide $5 + 3i$ by $1 + 2i$. You can write the result as

$$\frac{5 + 3i}{1 + 2i}.$$

To see that this really is a complex number, you can simplify it by multiplying the top and bottom of the fraction by the complex conjugate of the denominator. For our fraction, the denominator is $1 + 2i$, so its complex conjugate is $1 - 2i$. Multiplying the top and bottom of the fraction by $1 - 2i$ gives

$$\frac{5+3i}{1+2i} = \frac{(5+3i)(1-2i)}{(1+2i)(1-2i)} = \frac{5-10i+3i-6i^2}{1^2+2^2} = \frac{11-7i}{5}.$$

You can write this number as

$$\tfrac{1}{5}(11-7i) \quad \text{or} \quad \tfrac{11}{5} - \tfrac{7}{5}i.$$

The second alternative has the form $a + bi$, which shows that it is indeed a complex number. However, it's fine to leave the answer in any of the final three forms above.

Simplifying fractions in this way may remind you of simplifying fractions involving surds, such as

$$\frac{1+5\sqrt{3}}{\sqrt{2}+\sqrt{3}},$$

which you met in Section 4 of Unit 1. To do this, you used a conjugate of an expression involving surds, which performs a similar role to the complex conjugate.

Example 3   *Dividing complex numbers*

Write the fraction $\dfrac{1+3i}{5-i}$ as a single complex number.

Solution

Multiply the top and bottom of the fraction by the complex conjugate of the denominator, which is $5 + i$, and simplify the resulting expression.

$$\frac{1+3i}{5-i} = \frac{(1+3i)(5+i)}{(5-i)(5+i)}$$

$$= \frac{5+i+15i+3i^2}{5^2+(-1)^2}$$

$$= \frac{2+16i}{26}$$

$$= \frac{1+8i}{13}$$

You can check that the answer that you obtain from a division of complex numbers is correct by using multiplication. In the example that you've just seen, for instance, you find that

$$\tfrac{1}{13}(1+8i) \times (5-i) = \tfrac{1}{13}(5+39i-8i^2) = \tfrac{1}{13}(13+39i) = 1+3i,$$

as expected.

Activity 12 *Dividing complex numbers*

Write each of the following fractions as a single complex number.

(a) $\dfrac{1}{-2+3i}$ (b) $\dfrac{2i}{1+i}$ (c) $\dfrac{11-8i}{2i}$ (d) $\dfrac{1}{i}$ (e) $\dfrac{1}{-i}$

(f) $\dfrac{4+7i}{-1+2i}$ (g) $\dfrac{8+3i}{1+3i}$ (h) $\dfrac{-2+5i}{-4-i}$

It isn't possible to divide a complex number by 0, just as it isn't possible to divide a real number by 0.

As for real numbers, if z is a non-zero complex number, then the number $1/z$ is called the **reciprocal** of z. Also, as for real numbers,

$$\frac{1}{z} \text{ is denoted by } z^{-1}, \quad \frac{1}{z^2} \text{ is denoted by } z^{-2}, \quad \frac{1}{z^3} \text{ is denoted by } z^{-3},$$

and so on.

As mentioned earlier, the index laws from Unit 1 hold when the base numbers are complex numbers and the powers are any integers, positive, negative or zero. For example, the following index laws hold for all complex numbers z and w and all integers m and n:

$$z^m z^n = z^{m+n}, \quad \frac{z^m}{z^n} = z^{m-n} \quad \text{and} \quad (zw)^n = z^n w^n.$$

When you're using complex numbers as base numbers, you should be careful to apply index laws only in cases in which the indices (such as m and n above) are integers. This is because the definitions of expressions such as $z^{1/2}$, where z is a complex number, are beyond the scope of this module. As you'll see in Section 3, all complex numbers other than 0 have two square roots, so an expression such as $z^{1/2}$ is potentially ambiguous since it could refer to either of the square roots.

Finally, as promised, here's the proof of the fourth property of complex conjugates stated in the box on page 186. The property is

$$\overline{z/w} = \overline{z}/\overline{w}.$$

If $w \neq 0$, then

$$(z/w) \times w = z, \quad \text{so} \quad \overline{(z/w) \times w} = \overline{z}.$$

Hence, by the third property in the box on page 186,

$$\overline{z/w} \times \overline{w} = \overline{z}.$$

Dividing both sides by $\overline{w}$ gives the property stated above.

2 Geometry with complex numbers

In this section you'll learn how complex numbers can be represented by points in a plane, called the *complex plane*, which gives a rich geometric way of interpreting the arithmetic operations described in the previous section. You'll see that you can add and subtract complex numbers represented by points in the complex plane in a similar way to how you add and subtract vectors.

2.1 The complex plane

You saw in Unit 1 that the real numbers can be represented as points on a line, called the **real line** or the **number line**, as shown in Figure 4.

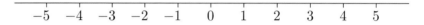

Figure 4   Part of the real line

Since a complex number is made up of two real numbers, its real part and its imaginary part, it can be represented by a point in a plane.

> ### The complex plane
>
> The **complex plane** is a plane in which the complex number $a + bi$ is represented by the point (a, b).
>
> The horizontal axis is called the **real axis** and the vertical axis is called the **imaginary axis**.

For example, the complex number $3 + 4i$ is represented in the complex plane by the point $(3, 4)$. This complex number is shown, with others, in Figure 5. Notice that the origin represents the complex number 0.

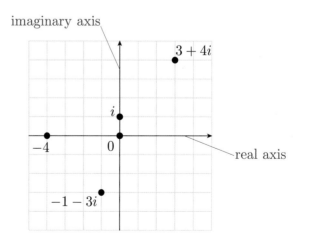

Figure 5   Complex numbers in the complex plane

The grid in Figure 5 is a **unit grid**, which means that adjacent horizontal lines in the grid are separated by one unit, and adjacent vertical lines are also separated by one unit. All the grids that you'll see in this unit are unit grids.

Note that for simplicity we usually don't distinguish between complex numbers and the points that represent them in the complex plane. For example, we say that the complex number i lies on the imaginary axis, rather than that the point representing the complex number i lies on the imaginary axis.

Activity 13   *Marking complex numbers in the complex plane*

Mark the following complex numbers on a diagram of the complex plane:

$$2 - 4i, \qquad -3 + 2i, \qquad 3, \qquad -i \qquad \text{and} \qquad 4i.$$

The complex plane is also known as the **Argand diagram**, after a French mathematician with the surname Argand, who in 1806 wrote an essay on representing complex numbers geometrically in a plane.

Recent research has shown that reliable biographical information about Argand is extremely limited; not even his first name is known! There is no evidence that he was a certain Swiss-born man called Jean-Robert Argand, as was previously believed. Information in one of Argand's publications suggests that he was a scientifically oriented technician, based in the Parisian clock-making industry.

The idea of introducing a complex plane had been proposed before, by the English mathematician John Wallis (1616–1703), and separately by the Norwegian–Danish mathematician Caspar Wessel (1745–1818), but these earlier proposals failed to gain popular acceptance.

Let's consider what happens in the complex plane when you add two complex numbers. By the usual rule for adding complex numbers,

$$(a + bi) + (c + di) = (a + c) + (b + d)i.$$

So if you add the complex numbers represented by the points (a, b) and (c, d), then you get the complex number represented by the point $(a + c, b + d)$. That is, you just add the coordinates separately, in the same way that you add the components separately when you add vectors.

Because of this, you can add two complex numbers in the complex plane by drawing (or imagining) a parallelogram, as illustrated in Figure 6. This is the **parallelogram law** for the addition of complex numbers, which is similar to the parallelogram law for vector addition.

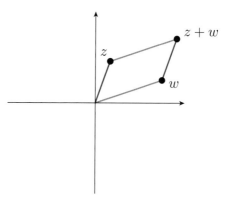

Figure 6   The parallelogram law for the addition of complex numbers

Next let's consider what happens in the complex plane when you multiply a complex number by a real number. We have

$$m(a + bi) = ma + mbi.$$

So if you multiply the complex number represented by the point (a, b) by the real number m, then you get the complex number represented by the point (ma, mb). That is, you just multiply the coordinates separately by the real number, in the same way that you multiply the components separately when you multiply a vector by a scalar.

The effect of this is that when you multiply a complex number z by a real number m, the resulting complex number mz remains on the line that passes through the origin and z, but is $|m|$ times as far from the origin as z is. If m is positive, then mz lies on the same side of the origin as z, and if m is negative, then mz lies on the opposite side of the origin from z. These effects are illustrated in Figure 7. They're similar to the effects of multiplying a vector by a scalar.

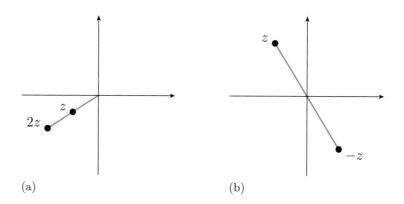

Figure 7   (a) Multiplication by 2 (b) Multiplication by -1

Complex conjugation also has a simple geometric interpretation in the complex plane: the number $\bar{z} = a - bi$ is the image of $z = a + bi$ under reflection in the real axis, as shown in Figure 8.

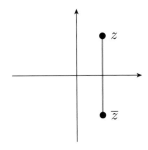

Figure 8   Complex conjugation in the complex plane

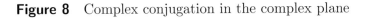

Activity 14   *Adding complex numbers, multiplying complex numbers by real numbers, and complex conjugation in the complex plane*

On a copy (or several copies) of the diagram below, mark the complex numbers in parts (a)–(f). Do this by thinking geometrically, in the ways described above, rather than by first writing z and w in the form $a + bi$ and using the algebraic methods from Section 1.

(a) $z + w$ (b) $2z$ (c) $\bar{z}$ (d) $z + \bar{z}$ (e) $-w$ (f) $z - w$

(Remember that $z - w = z + (-w)$.)

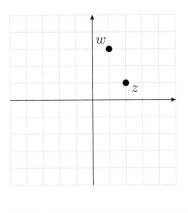

You can check your answers to Activity 14 by writing z and w in the form $a + bi$ and using the methods from Section 1. You can see from the diagram that $z = 2 + i$ and $w = 1 + 3i$. Therefore, for example,

$$z + w = (2 + i) + (1 + 3i) = (2 + 1) + (1 + 3)i = 3 + 4i.$$

If you plot this answer $3 + 4i$ in the complex plane, as shown in Figure 9, then you obtain the same point that you found in Activity 14(a) by using the parallelogram law.

193

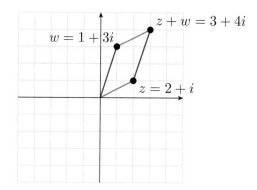

Figure 9   Adding $2 + i$ and $1 + 3i$ in the complex plane

2.2 Modulus of a complex number

You saw in Section 2 of Unit 2 that the *modulus* of a real number x, which is denoted by $|x|$ and is also called the *magnitude* or *absolute value* of x, is the distance of x from zero. For example, $|3| = 3$ and $|-3| = 3$. Essentially, the modulus of a real number x is the 'size' of x.

In the same way, the **modulus** (or **absolute value**) of a complex number z, which is denoted by $|z|$, is its distance from the origin, and is a measure of its size. (We don't use the word 'magnitude' for complex numbers.) Pythagoras' theorem gives the formula below for the modulus of a complex number, which is illustrated in Figure 10.

> **Modulus of a complex number**
>
> Let $z = a + bi$. The **modulus** $|z|$ of z is its distance from the origin, given by
> $$|z| = \sqrt{a^2 + b^2}.$$
> The plural of 'modulus' is *moduli*.

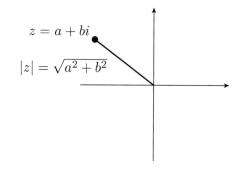

Figure 10   The distance between the origin and $z = a + bi$ is $|z| = \sqrt{a^2 + b^2}$.

Let's calculate the moduli of some particular complex numbers. For example,

$$|3 - 4i| = \sqrt{3^2 + (-4)^2} = \sqrt{9 + 16} = \sqrt{25} = 5$$

and

$$|-7| = \sqrt{(-7)^2} = \sqrt{49} = 7.$$

As illustrated by the second example, if z is a real number, then $|z|$ is just the usual modulus of this real number.

Activity 15 *Finding the moduli of complex numbers*

Find the moduli of the following complex numbers.

(a) $3 + 4i$ (b) $-4 + 3i$ (c) 0 (d) -31 (e) $17i$

(f) $7 - i\sqrt{15}$ (g) $1 + i$ (h) $19 + 19i$ (i) $-i$ (j) $-\frac{1}{2} + \frac{\sqrt{3}}{2}i$

In Subsection 1.4 you saw that, for any complex number $z = a + bi$,

$$z\overline{z} = a^2 + b^2.$$

The expression $a^2 + b^2$ is equal to $|z|^2$, so we have the useful identity

$$z\overline{z} = |z|^2.$$

We can obtain another useful identity by replacing z by zw in the identity $|z|^2 = z\overline{z}$, to give

$$|zw|^2 = zw\overline{zw}.$$

You learned earlier that $\overline{zw} = \overline{z}\,\overline{w}$, so

$$|zw|^2 = zw\overline{zw} = zw\overline{z}\,\overline{w} = z\overline{z}w\overline{w} = |z|^2|w|^2.$$

Hence $|zw|^2 = |z|^2|w|^2$, and taking square roots gives the useful identity

$$|zw| = |z||w|.$$

From this identity you can deduce a third useful identity, as follows. If $w \neq 0$, then

$$|z| = \left|\frac{z}{w} \times w\right| = \left|\frac{z}{w}\right||w|, \quad \text{so} \quad \left|\frac{z}{w}\right| = \frac{|z|}{|w|}.$$

Properties of modulus

$$z\overline{z} = |z|^2$$

$$|zw| = |z||w|$$

$$\left|\frac{z}{w}\right| = \frac{|z|}{|w|}$$

Activity 16   *Proving identities involving modulus*

By writing $z = a + bi$, show that $|-z| = |z|$ and $|\bar{z}| = |z|$.

If you divide both sides of the identity $z\bar{z} = |z|^2$ by $\bar{z}$, then you obtain

$$z = \frac{|z|^2}{\bar{z}}.$$

Taking the reciprocal of both sides of this equation gives you a neat formula for finding $1/z$, as follows.

$$\frac{1}{z} = \frac{\bar{z}}{|z|^2}$$

For example, the reciprocal of $1 + 3i$ is

$$\frac{1}{1 + 3i} = \frac{\overline{1 + 3i}}{|1 + 3i|^2} = \frac{1 - 3i}{1^2 + 3^2} = \frac{1 - 3i}{10}.$$

Activity 17   *Working out the reciprocals of complex numbers*

Find the reciprocals of the following complex numbers.

(a) $2 + i$ (b) $-1 - 3i$ (c) $2i$

2.3 Argument of a complex number

You can completely specify a particular complex number by stating its modulus, that is, its distance from the origin in the complex plane, together with the direction in which it lies from the origin. This direction is usually specified by stating a particular angle associated with the complex number, which we call an *argument* of the complex number. You'll learn about the arguments of a complex number in this subsection. Together, the modulus and an argument of a complex number can be used to express the complex number in a helpful form, called *polar form*, which you'll meet in the next subsection.

Arguments of a complex number

An **argument** of a non-zero complex number z is an angle in radians measured anticlockwise from the positive real axis to the line between the origin and z.

The number 0 doesn't have an argument.

For example, one argument of the complex number $-4 + 4i$ is $3\pi/4$, as shown in Figure 11(a). You can see that this angle is $3\pi/4$ because it's three-quarters of a half-turn, and a half-turn is π radians. Other arguments of the same complex number are $-5\pi/4$ and $11\pi/4$, as shown in Figures 11(b) and (c). The angle $-5\pi/4$ is negative because it's measured clockwise, rather than anticlockwise.

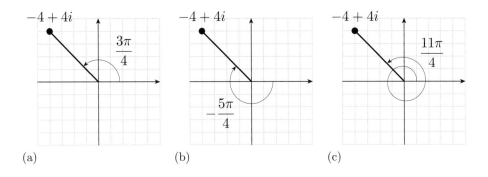

(a)   (b)   (c)

Figure 11   Three different arguments of $-4 + 4i$

You've encountered this sort of situation before, in which the same direction is specified by different angles. For example, it occurred when you worked with the directions of vectors in Section 6 of Unit 5. The angles $-5\pi/4$ and $11\pi/4$ each have the same rotational effect as $3\pi/4$, because they each differ from $3\pi/4$ by an integer multiple of 2π:

$$-\frac{5\pi}{4} = \frac{3\pi}{4} - 2\pi \quad \text{and} \quad \frac{11\pi}{4} = \frac{3\pi}{4} + 2\pi.$$

In fact, you can see that each non-zero complex number has infinitely many arguments, because you can add any integer multiple of 2π to an argument to obtain another argument. Exactly one of these arguments lies in the interval $(-\pi, \pi]$, and it's often the simplest one to use.

> **Principal argument of a complex number**
>
> The **principal argument** of a non-zero complex number z is the argument of z that lies in the interval $(-\pi, \pi]$. This angle is denoted by $\mathrm{Arg}(z)$.

For example, the principal argument of $z = -4 + 4i$ is $3\pi/4$. That is,

$$\mathrm{Arg}(-4 + 4i) = \frac{3\pi}{4}.$$

In some other texts, the principal argument is called the **principal value of the argument**, and sometimes the interval $[0, 2\pi)$ is used rather than $(-\pi, \pi]$.

Let's now consider how to find the principal argument of a complex number. If the complex number lies on one of the axes, then you can find the principal argument just from a sketch, as the next example demonstrates.

Example 4   *Finding the principal argument of a complex number that lies on one of the axes*

Find the principal argument of the complex number $3i$.

Solution

🔍 Sketch $3i$ in the complex plane. 💬

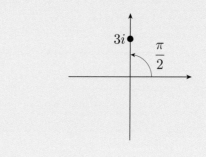

From the diagram, $\mathrm{Arg}(3i) = \pi/2$.

Activity 18   *Finding the principal argument of a complex number that lies on one of the axes*

Find the principal argument of each of the following complex numbers.

(a) $\frac{7}{2}i$ (b) $-4i$ (c) -3 (d) 2

The method for finding the principal argument of a complex number that doesn't lie on one of the axes is similar to the method for finding the direction of a two-dimensional vector from its components, which you met in Unit 5. It involves finding values of inverse tangent, so you may find it helpful to refer to Table 1, which contains the tangents of special angles that you met in Unit 4.

Table 1   Tangents of special angles

θ in radians	$\tan\theta$
$\dfrac{\pi}{6}$	$\dfrac{1}{\sqrt{3}}$
$\dfrac{\pi}{4}$	1
$\dfrac{\pi}{3}$	$\sqrt{3}$

Example 5 *Finding the principal argument of a complex number that doesn't lie on one of the axes*

Find the principal argument of the complex number $-1 + i\sqrt{3}$.

Solution

🔍 Sketch $-1 + i\sqrt{3}$ in the complex plane. The important thing is to get it in the correct quadrant. Label the principal argument θ, and label by ϕ the acute angle between the real axis and the line from the origin to z. 💭

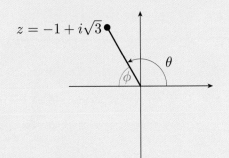

🔍 Draw a line from z to the real axis that is perpendicular to the real axis to form a right-angled triangle. Mark the lengths of the horizontal and vertical sides of the triangle. 💭

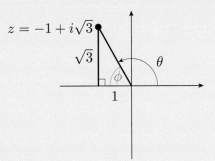

🔍 Use the triangle to work out the acute angle ϕ, and hence work out the principal argument θ. 💭

From the diagram,

$$\tan\phi = \frac{\sqrt{3}}{1} = \sqrt{3}.$$

Therefore $\phi = \pi/3$. So the principal argument is

$$\theta = \pi - \phi = \pi - \frac{\pi}{3} = \frac{2\pi}{3}.$$

Activity 19 *Finding the principal arguments of complex numbers that don't lie on one of the axes*

Find the principal argument of each of the following complex numbers.

(a) $1 + i$ (b) $1 - i\sqrt{3}$ (c) $-\sqrt{3} - i$ (d) $2\sqrt{3} - 2i$

Possible origin of the term 'argument'

2.4 Polar form

All the complex numbers that you've met so far have been written in the form $a + bi$, for real numbers a and b. This form is known as the **Cartesian form** of a complex number. In this subsection you'll learn about an alternative way to write complex numbers, using the modulus and argument, known as *polar form*. In fact, the idea is not entirely new to you, as you met a similar procedure in Unit 5 when you saw how to find the components of a vector from its magnitude and direction.

To find the polar form of a non-zero complex number z, we begin with the Cartesian form $z = a + bi$, and express a and b in terms of the modulus and one of the arguments of z. Let's write r for the modulus $|z|$, and θ for one of the arguments, as shown in Figure 12. In this case θ happens to be the principal argument of z, but the discussion that follows is valid no matter what the choice of argument.

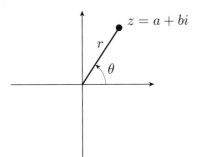

Figure 12   A complex number $z = a + bi$ with modulus r and argument θ

To see how to write a and b in terms of r and θ, first consider the complex number w that has the same argument as z, namely θ, but whose modulus is 1, as shown in Figure 13(a). This complex number w lies on the unit circle, and hence it follows from what you saw in Unit 4, Subsection 2.2, that its coordinates are $(\cos\theta, \sin\theta)$. This is true whatever the size of the argument θ.

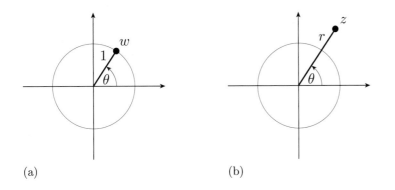

(a)   (b)

Figure 13   The complex numbers (a) w, with modulus 1 and argument θ (b) z, with modulus r and argument θ

In other words,

$$w = \cos\theta + i\sin\theta.$$

Since $z = rw$, as illustrated in Figure 13(b), it follows that

$$z = r(\cos\theta + i\sin\theta).$$

This is the *polar form* of z, in which z is written in terms of its modulus and one of its arguments.

> **Polar form of a complex number**
>
> A non-zero complex number z is in **polar form** if it is expressed as
>
> $$z = r(\cos\theta + i\sin\theta).$$
>
> Here r is the modulus of z, and θ is an argument of z.

For example, the complex number z with modulus 2 and argument $3\pi/4$, which is shown in Figure 14, can be written in polar form as

$$z = 2\left(\cos\left(\frac{3\pi}{4}\right) + i\sin\left(\frac{3\pi}{4}\right)\right).$$

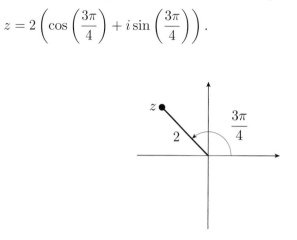

Figure 14   The complex number z with modulus 2 and argument $3\pi/4$

As you saw in the previous subsection, any angle that differs from $3\pi/4$ by an integer multiple of 2π is also an argument of the complex number z in Figure 14. For instance, $-5\pi/4$ and $11\pi/4$ are also arguments of z, so you can alternatively write z in polar form as

$$z = 2\left(\cos\left(-\frac{5\pi}{4}\right) + i\sin\left(-\frac{5\pi}{4}\right)\right)$$

or

$$z = 2\left(\cos\left(\frac{11\pi}{4}\right) + i\sin\left(\frac{11\pi}{4}\right)\right).$$

However, unless there's a good reason not to do so, you should use the principal argument when writing a complex number in polar form, which in this case is our original argument $3\pi/4$.

The number 0 doesn't have an argument, so it doesn't have a polar form either. If you want to write the number zero, then you should just use the symbol 0, whether you're working with Cartesian or polar forms.

Let's now consider how to convert between the Cartesian and polar forms of a complex number. To convert a complex number from polar form to Cartesian form you need to work out values of sine and cosine. You can use your calculator to do this, but you'll develop a better understanding of the procedure if instead you use techniques from Unit 4 for working out sines and cosines of simple fractions of π, and refer to Table 2, which contains the sines and cosines of special angles from Section 1 of Unit 4.

Table 2   Sines and cosines of special angles

θ in radians	$\sin\theta$	$\cos\theta$
0	0	1
$\dfrac{\pi}{6}$	$\dfrac{1}{2}$	$\dfrac{\sqrt{3}}{2}$
$\dfrac{\pi}{4}$	$\dfrac{1}{\sqrt{2}}$	$\dfrac{1}{\sqrt{2}}$
$\dfrac{\pi}{3}$	$\dfrac{\sqrt{3}}{2}$	$\dfrac{1}{2}$
$\dfrac{\pi}{2}$	1	0

Example 6   *Converting from polar form to Cartesian form*

Write the complex number

$$2\left(\cos\left(\frac{3\pi}{4}\right)+i\sin\left(\frac{3\pi}{4}\right)\right)$$

in Cartesian form.

Solution

🔍 Evaluate the cosine and sine, then expand the brackets. 💬

$$2\left(\cos\left(\frac{3\pi}{4}\right)+i\sin\left(\frac{3\pi}{4}\right)\right)=2\left(-\frac{1}{\sqrt{2}}+i\frac{1}{\sqrt{2}}\right)=-\sqrt{2}+i\sqrt{2}$$

Activity 20   *Converting from polar form to Cartesian form*

Write the following complex numbers in Cartesian form.

(a) $3(\cos 0+i\sin 0)$ (b) $7\left(\cos\left(\frac{\pi}{2}\right)+i\sin\left(\frac{\pi}{2}\right)\right)$

(c) $6(\cos\pi+i\sin\pi)$ (d) $\cos\left(-\frac{\pi}{2}\right)+i\sin\left(-\frac{\pi}{2}\right)$

(e) $5(\cos(-\pi)+i\sin(-\pi))$ (f) $4\left(\cos\left(\frac{\pi}{3}\right)+i\sin\left(\frac{\pi}{3}\right)\right)$

(g) $2\left(\cos\left(-\frac{\pi}{4}\right)+i\sin\left(-\frac{\pi}{4}\right)\right)$ (h) $\sqrt{3}\left(\cos\left(\frac{5\pi}{6}\right)+i\sin\left(\frac{5\pi}{6}\right)\right)$

To convert a complex number from Cartesian form to polar form, you need to calculate its modulus and principal argument.

Example 7   *Converting from Cartesian form to polar form*

Write the complex number $-2 - 2\sqrt{3}\,i$ in polar form.

Solution

🔍 First find the modulus. 💬

The modulus is
$$r = \sqrt{(-2)^2 + \left(-2\sqrt{3}\right)^2} = \sqrt{4 + 12} = \sqrt{16} = 4.$$

🔍 To find the principal argument, sketch $z = -2 - 2\sqrt{3}\,i$ in the complex plane. The important thing is to get it in the correct quadrant. Label the principal argument θ, and label by ϕ the acute angle between the real axis and the line from the origin to z. 💬

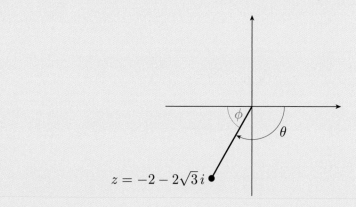

🔍 Draw a line from z to the real axis that is perpendicular to the real axis, to form a right-angled triangle. Mark the lengths of the horizontal and vertical sides of the triangle. 💬

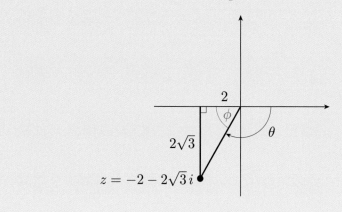

> ❧ Use the triangle to work out the acute angle ϕ, and hence work out the principal argument θ. ❧
>
> From the diagram,
>
> $$\tan \phi = \frac{2\sqrt{3}}{2} = \sqrt{3}.$$
>
> Therefore $\phi = \pi/3$. So
>
> $$\theta = -(\pi - \phi) = -\left(\pi - \frac{\pi}{3}\right) = -\frac{2\pi}{3}.$$
>
> ❧ Write z in polar form. ❧
>
> Hence
>
> $$z = 4\left(\cos\left(-\frac{2\pi}{3}\right) + i\sin\left(-\frac{2\pi}{3}\right)\right).$$

When you convert a complex number from Cartesian form to polar form, you can readily check your answer by converting back. For example, for the complex number in Example 7,

$$z = 4\left(\cos\left(-\frac{2\pi}{3}\right) + i\sin\left(-\frac{2\pi}{3}\right)\right) = 4\left(-\frac{1}{2} - i\frac{\sqrt{3}}{2}\right) = -2 - 2\sqrt{3}\,i.$$

You can use your solutions to Activities 18 and 19 to help you with the next activity.

Activity 21 *Converting from Cartesian form to polar form*

Write the following complex numbers in polar form.

(a) $\frac{7}{2}i$ (b) $-4i$ (c) -3 (d) 2 (e) $1 + i$ (f) $1 - i\sqrt{3}$

(g) $-\sqrt{3} - i$ (h) $2\sqrt{3} - 2i$

2.5 Multiplication and division in polar form

The Cartesian form of a complex number is convenient for adding and subtracting complex numbers, because to add or subtract complex numbers you just add or subtract their real and imaginary parts separately. In this subsection you'll see that polar form is more suited for multiplication and division.

Consider two complex numbers in polar form, $z = r(\cos\theta + i\sin\theta)$ and $w = s(\cos\phi + i\sin\phi)$. Then

$$
\begin{aligned}
zw &= r(\cos\theta + i\sin\theta) \times s(\cos\phi + i\sin\phi) \\
&= rs(\cos\theta\cos\phi + i\cos\theta\sin\phi + i\sin\theta\cos\phi + i^2\sin\theta\sin\phi) \\
&= rs\big((\cos\theta\cos\phi - \sin\theta\sin\phi) + i(\cos\theta\sin\phi + \sin\theta\cos\phi)\big).
\end{aligned}
$$

Recall the angle sum identities for sine and cosine, from Section 4 of Unit 4:
$$\sin(\theta + \phi) = \sin\theta\cos\phi + \cos\theta\sin\phi$$
$$\cos(\theta + \phi) = \cos\theta\cos\phi - \sin\theta\sin\phi.$$

Using these identities we obtain
$$zw = rs(\cos(\theta + \phi) + i\sin(\theta + \phi)).$$

This shows that to multiply two complex numbers in polar form, you *multiply their moduli* and *add their arguments*.

> **Product of complex numbers in polar form**
>
> Let $z = r(\cos\theta + i\sin\theta)$ and $w = s(\cos\phi + i\sin\phi)$. Then
> $$zw = rs\big(\cos(\theta + \phi) + i\sin(\theta + \phi)\big).$$

Example 8   *Finding the product of complex numbers in polar form*

Let
$$z = 10\left(\cos\left(\frac{3\pi}{5}\right) + i\sin\left(\frac{3\pi}{5}\right)\right)$$
and
$$w = 5\left(\cos\left(\frac{4\pi}{5}\right) + i\sin\left(\frac{4\pi}{5}\right)\right).$$

Find zw in polar form.

Solution

Multiply the moduli and add the arguments.
$$zw = 50\left(\cos\left(\frac{3\pi}{5} + \frac{4\pi}{5}\right) + i\sin\left(\frac{3\pi}{5} + \frac{4\pi}{5}\right)\right)$$
$$= 50\left(\cos\left(\frac{7\pi}{5}\right) + i\sin\left(\frac{7\pi}{5}\right)\right)$$

The argument $7\pi/5$ doesn't lie in the interval $(-\pi, \pi]$, so it isn't the principal argument of zw. To find the principal argument, subtract an integer multiple of 2π from $7\pi/5$ to obtain an angle that lies in the interval $(-\pi, \pi]$.

Since
$$\frac{7\pi}{5} - 2\pi = \frac{7\pi}{5} - \frac{10\pi}{5} = -\frac{3\pi}{5},$$
it follows that
$$zw = 50\left(\cos\left(-\frac{3\pi}{5}\right) + i\sin\left(-\frac{3\pi}{5}\right)\right).$$

In the next activity, remember to use the *principal* argument in the polar form in your answers.

Activity 22 *Finding the product of complex numbers in polar form*

Find zw in polar form in each of the following cases.

(a) $z = 12\left(\cos\left(\frac{\pi}{5}\right) + i\sin\left(\frac{\pi}{5}\right)\right),\quad w = 4\left(\cos\left(\frac{\pi}{10}\right) + i\sin\left(\frac{\pi}{10}\right)\right)$

(b) $z = 8\left(\cos\left(\frac{7\pi}{8}\right) + i\sin\left(\frac{7\pi}{8}\right)\right),\quad w = 5\left(\cos\left(\frac{3\pi}{4}\right) + i\sin\left(\frac{3\pi}{4}\right)\right)$

(c) $z = \cos\left(\frac{8\pi}{9}\right) + i\sin\left(\frac{8\pi}{9}\right),\quad w = \cos\left(\frac{8\pi}{9}\right) + i\sin\left(\frac{8\pi}{9}\right)$

You've seen that to find the product of two complex numbers in polar form you multiply their moduli and add their arguments. You do the same to find the product of three or more complex numbers in polar form. For example, the product of

$$u = 3\left(\cos\left(\frac{4\pi}{5}\right) + i\sin\left(\frac{4\pi}{5}\right)\right),$$

$$v = 2\left(\cos\left(-\frac{2\pi}{5}\right) + i\sin\left(-\frac{2\pi}{5}\right)\right) \text{ and}$$

$$w = 7\left(\cos\left(\frac{\pi}{5}\right) + i\sin\left(\frac{\pi}{5}\right)\right)$$

is

$$uvw = (3 \times 2 \times 7)\left(\cos\left(\frac{4\pi}{5} - \frac{2\pi}{5} + \frac{\pi}{5}\right) + i\sin\left(\frac{4\pi}{5} - \frac{2\pi}{5} + \frac{\pi}{5}\right)\right)$$

$$= 42\left(\cos\left(\frac{3\pi}{5}\right) + i\sin\left(\frac{3\pi}{5}\right)\right).$$

Activity 23 *Finding the product of several complex numbers in polar form*

Find the product of the following three complex numbers in polar form:

$$u = 4\left(\cos\left(\frac{3\pi}{7}\right) + i\sin\left(\frac{3\pi}{7}\right)\right)$$

$$v = \cos\left(\frac{\pi}{7}\right) + i\sin\left(\frac{\pi}{7}\right)$$

$$w = 2\left(\cos\left(\frac{5\pi}{7}\right) + i\sin\left(\frac{5\pi}{7}\right)\right).$$

Let's now look at how to divide two complex numbers in polar form. As before, let $z = r(\cos\theta + i\sin\theta)$ and $w = s(\cos\phi + i\sin\phi)$. At the end of Subsection 2.2, you saw a formula for the reciprocal of a non-zero complex number, which gives

$$\frac{1}{w} = \frac{\overline{w}}{|w|^2}.$$

Remember that $|w| = s$. Multiplying both sides of the equation above by z gives

$$\begin{aligned}
\frac{z}{w} &= \frac{z\overline{w}}{|w|^2} \\
&= \frac{r(\cos\theta + i\sin\theta) \times s(\cos\phi - i\sin\phi)}{s^2} \\
&= \frac{r}{s}\left(\cos\theta\cos\phi - i\cos\theta\sin\phi + i\sin\theta\cos\phi - i^2\sin\theta\sin\phi\right) \\
&= \frac{r}{s}\left((\cos\theta\cos\phi + \sin\theta\sin\phi) + i(\sin\theta\cos\phi - \cos\theta\sin\phi)\right).
\end{aligned}$$

Recall the angle difference identities for sine and cosine, from Section 4 of Unit 4:

$$\sin(\theta - \phi) = \sin\theta\cos\phi - \cos\theta\sin\phi$$
$$\cos(\theta - \phi) = \cos\theta\cos\phi + \sin\theta\sin\phi.$$

Using these identities we obtain

$$\frac{z}{w} = \frac{r}{s}(\cos(\theta - \phi) + i\sin(\theta - \phi)).$$

This shows that to divide two complex numbers in polar form, you *divide their moduli* and *subtract their arguments*.

Quotient of complex numbers in polar form

Let $z = r(\cos\theta + i\sin\theta)$ and $w = s(\cos\phi + i\sin\phi)$. Then

$$\frac{z}{w} = \frac{r}{s}(\cos(\theta - \phi) + i\sin(\theta - \phi)).$$

Example 9   *Finding the quotient of complex numbers in polar form*

Let

$$z = 10\left(\cos\left(\frac{\pi}{5}\right) + i\sin\left(\frac{\pi}{5}\right)\right)$$

and

$$w = 5\left(\cos\left(\frac{7\pi}{5}\right) + i\sin\left(\frac{7\pi}{5}\right)\right).$$

Find z/w in polar form.

Solution

🗨 Divide the moduli and subtract the arguments. 🗨

$$\frac{z}{w} = 2\left(\cos\left(\frac{\pi}{5} - \frac{7\pi}{5}\right) + i\sin\left(\frac{\pi}{5} - \frac{7\pi}{5}\right)\right)$$

$$= 2\left(\cos\left(-\frac{6\pi}{5}\right) + i\sin\left(-\frac{6\pi}{5}\right)\right).$$

🗨 The argument $-6\pi/5$ doesn't lie in the interval $(-\pi, \pi]$, so it isn't the principal argument of z/w. To find the principal argument, add an integer multiple of 2π to $-6\pi/5$ to obtain an angle that lies in the interval $(-\pi, \pi]$. 🗨

Since

$$-\frac{6\pi}{5} + 2\pi = -\frac{6\pi}{5} + \frac{10\pi}{5} = \frac{4\pi}{5},$$

it follows that

$$\frac{z}{w} = 2\left(\cos\left(\frac{4\pi}{5}\right) + i\sin\left(\frac{4\pi}{5}\right)\right).$$

Activity 24   *Finding the quotient of complex numbers in polar form*

Find z/w in polar form in each of the following cases.

(a) $z = 12\left(\cos\left(\frac{\pi}{5}\right) + i\sin\left(\frac{\pi}{5}\right)\right)$, $w = 4\left(\cos\left(\frac{\pi}{10}\right) + i\sin\left(\frac{\pi}{10}\right)\right)$

(b) $z = 8\left(\cos\left(\frac{3\pi}{8}\right) + i\sin\left(\frac{3\pi}{8}\right)\right)$, $w = 4\left(\cos\left(\frac{5\pi}{8}\right) + i\sin\left(\frac{5\pi}{8}\right)\right)$

(c) $z = \cos\left(\frac{8\pi}{9}\right) + i\sin\left(\frac{8\pi}{9}\right)$, $w = \cos\left(\frac{8\pi}{9}\right) + i\sin\left(\frac{8\pi}{9}\right)$

Using the polar form of complex numbers you can now visualise in the complex plane how to multiply one complex number by another, as the following example demonstrates.

Example 10   *Visualising multiplication by $2i$ geometrically*

Describe the geometric effect of multiplying a complex number by $2i$.

Solution

🗨 Start by finding the polar form of $2i$. 🗨

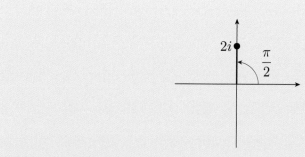

From the diagram,

$$2i = 2\left(\cos\left(\frac{\pi}{2}\right) + i\sin\left(\frac{\pi}{2}\right)\right).$$

🔍 Consider a general complex number z in polar form, to be multiplied by $2i$. 💭

Now let $z = r(\cos\theta + i\sin\theta)$.

🔍 Find the polar form of $z \times 2i$. 💭

Then

$$z \times 2i = r(\cos\theta + i\sin\theta) \times 2\left(\cos\left(\frac{\pi}{2}\right) + i\sin\left(\frac{\pi}{2}\right)\right)$$
$$= 2r\left(\cos\left(\theta + \frac{\pi}{2}\right) + i\sin\left(\theta + \frac{\pi}{2}\right)\right).$$

🔍 If you find it helpful, sketch z and $z \times 2i$ in the complex plane to help you understand how $z \times 2i$ is obtained from z geometrically. 💭

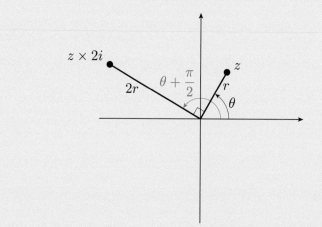

Therefore, multiplying z by $2i$ corresponds to an anticlockwise rotation of z through a quarter turn ($\pi/2$ radians) and a scaling of z by the factor 2.

Activity 25 *Multiplying a complex number by $-i$*

Describe the geometric effect of multiplying a complex number by $-i$.

2.6 De Moivre's formula

You've seen how to multiply two or more complex numbers in polar form, so it's now possible to consider powers of complex numbers in polar form. There's a helpful formula for working out powers, known as *de Moivre's formula*, named after the French mathematician Abraham de Moivre. ('De Moivre' is pronounced as 'de mwa-vr', where the 'e' is spoken like the 'u' in 'number'.) To obtain this formula, we apply the formulas for products and quotients of complex numbers found in the previous subsection, as follows.

You saw that to find the product of two or more complex numbers in polar form, you multiply their moduli (to give the modulus of the product) and add their arguments (to give an argument of the product). Applying this procedure to n copies of the complex number $z = r(\cos\theta + i\sin\theta)$ gives

$$z^n = \underbrace{r \times r \times \cdots \times r}_{\text{multiply moduli}} \big(\cos(\underbrace{\theta + \theta + \cdots + \theta}_{\text{add arguments}}) + i\sin(\underbrace{\theta + \theta + \cdots + \theta}_{\text{add arguments}})\big).$$

That is,

$$z^n = r^n(\cos n\theta + i\sin n\theta).$$

This is de Moivre's formula, for positive integers. In fact the formula is valid for *all* integers n, as stated below.

> **De Moivre's formula**
>
> Let $z = r(\cos\theta + i\sin\theta)$. Then, for any integer n,
>
> $$z^n = r^n(\cos n\theta + i\sin n\theta).$$

So far you've only seen why de Moivre's formula is true for positive integers. When $n = 0$ it's certainly true, because then both sides of the formula are equal to 1. To see why the formula is true for negative integers, begin with any positive integer n, and write the numbers 1 and z^n in polar form:

$$1 = \cos 0 + i\sin 0 \quad \text{and} \quad z^n = r^n(\cos n\theta + i\sin n\theta).$$

Now apply the formula for quotients of complex numbers in polar form to the complex numbers 1 and z^n. Dividing the moduli and subtracting the arguments gives

$$\frac{1}{z^n} = \frac{1}{r^n}(\cos(0 - n\theta) + i\sin(0 - n\theta)) = r^{-n}(\cos(-n\theta) + i\sin(-n\theta)).$$

Since z^{-n} is the same as $1/z^n$, we obtain

$$z^{-n} = r^{-n}(\cos(-n\theta) + i\sin(-n\theta)).$$

Because $-n$ can represent any negative integer, this confirms that de Moivre's formula is also true for negative integers.

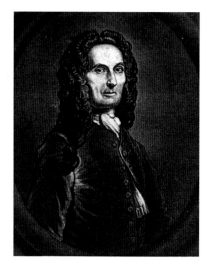

Abraham de Moivre
(1667–1754)

Arguably Abraham de Moivre's greatest contributions to mathematics were in the theory of probability. In 1733, in a paper published in Latin, he was the first person to discuss the normal distribution, an important mathematical tool for modelling probabilities. In 1738 he included an English translation of the paper in the second edition of his book *The Doctrine of Chances: A method of calculating the probabilities of events in play*. It is said that de Moivre correctly predicted the day of his own death after observing that he was sleeping 15 minutes longer each night. Assuming that this would continue, he predicted that he would die on the day that he slept for 24 hours, and did indeed die on that day, 27 November 1754.

De Moivre's formula allows you to find powers of complex numbers in polar form quickly. To find powers of complex numbers in Cartesian form, you can convert to polar form, find the power, then convert back to Cartesian form, as the following example demonstrates.

Example 11 *Working out powers of complex numbers*

Find $\left(-\sqrt{3}+i\right)^5$ in Cartesian form.

Solution

🔍 Write $-\sqrt{3}+i$ in polar form. To do this, first find the modulus. 💬

The modulus of $-\sqrt{3}+i$ is

$$r = \sqrt{\left(-\sqrt{3}\right)^2 + 1^2} = \sqrt{3+1} = \sqrt{4} = 2.$$

🔍 Then find the principal argument, by first sketching $-\sqrt{3}+i$ in the complex plane. 💬

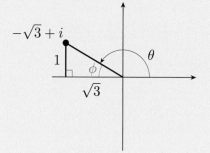

From the diagram,

$$\tan\phi = \frac{1}{\sqrt{3}}.$$

Therefore $\phi = \pi/6$. So

$$\theta = \pi - \frac{\pi}{6} = \frac{5\pi}{6}.$$

Hence

$$-\sqrt{3} + i = 2\left(\cos\left(\frac{5\pi}{6}\right) + i\sin\left(\frac{5\pi}{6}\right) \right).$$

🔍 Apply de Moivre's formula. 💬

Therefore

$$\left(-\sqrt{3} + i\right)^5 = 2^5 \left(\cos\left(5 \times \frac{5\pi}{6}\right) + i\sin\left(5 \times \frac{5\pi}{6}\right) \right)$$

$$= 32\left(\cos\left(\frac{25\pi}{6}\right) + i\sin\left(\frac{25\pi}{6}\right) \right).$$

🔍 Convert to Cartesian form. To help do this by hand, first rewrite the polar form using the principal argument. 💬

Since

$$\frac{25\pi}{6} = 4\pi + \frac{\pi}{6},$$

we obtain

$$\left(-\sqrt{3} + i\right)^5 = 32\left(\cos\left(\frac{\pi}{6}\right) + i\sin\left(\frac{\pi}{6}\right) \right)$$

$$= 32\left(\frac{\sqrt{3}}{2} + \frac{i}{2} \right)$$

$$= 16\sqrt{3} + 16i.$$

Activity 26   *Working out powers of complex numbers*

Work out the Cartesian forms of the following complex numbers.

(a) $(1+i)^3$ (b) $\left(2^{1/3}\left(\cos\left(\frac{\pi}{9}\right) + i\sin\left(\frac{\pi}{9}\right) \right) \right)^{12}$ (c) $\left(-1 + i\sqrt{3}\right)^7$

(d) $\left(\sqrt{3} + i\right)^{-6}$ (e) $(2 + 2i)^{-5}$

In the final activity of this section you can learn how to work with complex numbers on the computer.

Activity 27   *Manipulating complex numbers with the CAS*

Work through Subsection 13.1 of the *Computer algebra guide*.

3 Polynomial equations

A **polynomial equation** is an equation of the form
'polynomial expression $= 0$', where the polynomial expression has degree
at least 1. For example,

$$5x^6 + 8 = 0 \quad \text{and} \quad x^7 - 13x^5 + \tfrac{5}{3}x^2 - 2 = 0$$

are polynomial equations, and every linear or quadratic equation is a
polynomial equation.

At the start of this unit you were told the remarkable fact that by
introducing a solution i of the quadratic equation

$$x^2 + 1 = 0$$

to form the complex numbers, you make it possible to find at least one
solution of *any* quadratic equation. In this subsection, you'll learn how to
find all the solutions of any quadratic equation, including any solutions
that are not real numbers. You'll also learn about *the fundamental theorem
of algebra*, which shows that in fact every *polynomial* equation has at least
one solution in the set of complex numbers.

3.1 Quadratic equations

As you know, a *quadratic equation* is an equation of the
form $az^2 + bz + c = 0$, where $a \neq 0$. For example,

$$2z^2 - 5z - 1 = 0 \quad \text{and} \quad z^2 - 6z + 25 = 0$$

are quadratic equations. We use the variable z here (rather than the more
familiar x, say) because we want to work with complex numbers, and it's
traditional to use the letter z for a variable that represents a complex
number. For the moment, let's restrict our attention to quadratic
equations in which the coefficients a, b and c are real numbers, and leave
the possibility that a, b and c might be complex numbers that aren't
necessarily real to the end of this subsection.

You saw in Section 4 of Unit 2 that the number of **real solutions**
(solutions that are real numbers) of the quadratic equation
$az^2 + bz + c = 0$ depends on the value of the *discriminant* $b^2 - 4ac$. The
equation has

- two real solutions if $b^2 - 4ac > 0$
- one real solution if $b^2 - 4ac = 0$
- no real solutions if $b^2 - 4ac < 0$.

For example, the quadratic equation $2z^2 - 5z - 1 = 0$ has discriminant

$$(-5)^2 - 4 \times 2 \times (-1) = 25 + 8 = 33,$$

so it has two real solutions. In contrast, the quadratic
equation $z^2 - 6z + 25 = 0$ has discriminant

$$(-6)^2 - 4 \times 1 \times 25 = 36 - 100 = -64,$$

so it has no real solutions.

Although some quadratic equations have no real solutions, every quadratic equation has either one or two solutions that are complex numbers, which we call **complex solutions**. Complex solutions can be real numbers (because a real number is a special type of complex number), but they can also be complex numbers that are not real, like $1 + i$ or $-7i$.

One way to find the complex solutions of a quadratic equation is to use the method of completing the square, in much the same way as in Unit 2. The only difference is that now you have to allow square roots of negative numbers.

Example 12   *Solving a quadratic equation that has no real solutions by completing the square*

Solve the quadratic equation $z^2 - 6z + 25 = 0$ by completing the square.

Solution

Completing the square gives

$$(z - 3)^2 + 16 = 0;$$

that is,

$$(z - 3)^2 = -16.$$

🗨 Take the square root of both sides. Remember from Subsection 1.3 that if d is a positive real number, then the square roots of $-d$ are $\pm i\sqrt{d}$. 💬

Therefore

$$z - 3 = \pm i\sqrt{16};$$

that is,

$$z - 3 = \pm 4i,$$

so

$$z = 3 \pm 4i.$$

Remember that you can check the solutions of a quadratic equation by substituting them back into the equation. For the quadratic equation in Example 12, we have

$$(3 + 4i)^2 - 6(3 + 4i) + 25 = (3 + 4i)(3 + 4i) - 6(3 + 4i) + 25$$
$$= 9 + 12i + 12i + 16i^2 - 18 - 24i + 25$$
$$= (9 - 16 - 18 + 25) + i(12 + 12 - 24)$$
$$= 0.$$

You can check the other solution, $3 - 4i$, in the same way.

Activity 28   *Solving quadratic equations that have no real solutions by completing the square*

Solve the following quadratic equations by completing the square.

(a) $z^2 - 2z + 2 = 0$ (b) $z^2 + 4z + 13 = 0$ (c) $z^2 + 25 = 0$

Another way to find the complex solutions of a quadratic equation is to use the usual quadratic formula.

The quadratic formula

The solutions of the quadratic equation $az^2 + bz + c = 0$, where a, b and c are real numbers, are given by

$$z = \frac{-b \pm \sqrt{b^2 - 4ac}}{2a}.$$

As you saw earlier, the quadratic formula gives two real solutions of the quadratic equation if $b^2 - 4ac > 0$ and one real solution if $b^2 - 4ac = 0$.

When $b^2 - 4ac < 0$, there's a problem with the quadratic formula, because the square root sign $\sqrt{}$ cannot be used with a negative number inside it. For convenience, we make an exception here, and when d is a positive real number we allow the notation $\pm\sqrt{-d}$ to mean the two square roots of the negative number $-d$, which you learned in Subsection 1.3 are $\pm i\sqrt{d}$. This practice doesn't cause errors, because the $\pm$ symbol means that you'll always consider both square roots of a negative number at once.

For example, if $b^2 - 4ac = -16$ then the quadratic formula involves the term

$$\pm\sqrt{-16},$$

which means the two square roots of -16, namely $\pm 4i$.

Example 13   *Solving a quadratic equation that has no real solutions using the quadratic formula*

Solve the quadratic equation $z^2 + 10z + 34 = 0$ using the quadratic formula.

Solution

🔍 Use the quadratic formula. 💭

$$z = \frac{-10 \pm \sqrt{10^2 - 4 \times 1 \times 34}}{2 \times 1}$$

$$= \frac{-10 \pm \sqrt{100 - 136}}{2}$$

$$= \frac{-10 \pm \sqrt{-36}}{2}$$

🔍 The term $\pm\sqrt{-36}$ means the two square roots of -36, namely $\pm 6i$. 💭

$$= \frac{-10 \pm 6i}{2}$$

$$= -5 \pm 3i$$

Activity 29   *Solving quadratic equations using the quadratic formula*

Solve the following quadratic equations by using the quadratic formula, or a simpler method if possible.

(a) $z^2 + 2z + 2 = 0$ (b) $z^2 + 6z + 9 = 0$ (c) $3z^2 + 5 = 0$

(d) $z^2 - 4z + 8 = 0$ (e) $z^2 + 3z = 0$ (f) $2z^2 - 3z + 5 = 0$

You can see from the quadratic formula that when a, b and c are real numbers such that $b^2 - 4ac < 0$, the two complex solutions of the quadratic equation $az^2 + bz + c = 0$ are complex conjugates of each other. For example, the two solutions $-5 + 3i$ and $-5 - 3i$ of the quadratic equation $z^2 + 10z + 34 = 0$ in Example 13 are complex conjugates of each other. Two complex numbers that are complex conjugates of each other are together called a **complex conjugate pair**.

The next example shows how you can choose any complex conjugate pair and then find a quadratic equation whose solutions are that complex conjugate pair.

Example 14   *Finding a quadratic equation with a given pair of solutions*

Find, in its simplest form, a quadratic equation that has solutions $2 \pm i$.

Solution

🔍 For any numbers u and v, a quadratic equation with solutions u and v is $(z - u)(z - v) = 0$. 💬

A quadratic equation with solutions $2 \pm i$ is

$$(z - (2 + i))(z - (2 - i)) = 0.$$

🔍 To simplify this equation, expand the brackets. Do this directly, or, to do it slightly more efficiently, first write the expression $(z - (2 + i))(z - (2 - i))$ as a difference of two squares, by rewriting $z - (2 + i)$ as $(z - 2) - i$ and $z - (2 - i)$ as $(z - 2) + i$. 💬

Simplifying gives

$$((z - 2) - i)((z - 2) + i) = 0$$

🔍 Apply the difference of two squares formula $(A - B)(A + B) = A^2 - B^2$ with $A = z - 2$ and $B = i$. 💬

$$(z - 2)^2 - i^2 = 0$$
$$z^2 - 4z + 4 + 1 = 0$$
$$z^2 - 4z + 5 = 0.$$

So a quadratic equation with solutions $2 \pm i$ is $z^2 - 4z + 5 = 0$.

The procedure in Example 14 always gives a quadratic equation in which the coefficient of z^2 is 1. However, you can multiply the equation through by any non-zero number to give a quadratic equation that has the same solutions but in which the coefficient of z^2 is not 1.

Activity 30 *Finding quadratic equations with given pairs of solutions*

Find, in their simplest forms, quadratic equations with the following pairs of solutions.

(a) $1 \pm 2i$ (b) $-3 \pm 4i$ (c) $\pm 7i$ (d) $1 \pm \frac{1}{2}i$

So far all the quadratic equations $az^2 + bz + c = 0$ that you've met have had real coefficients a, b and c, and this is the only type of quadratic equation that you'll solve in this module. However, the quadratic formula also gives the solutions of quadratic equations in which a, b and c are complex numbers that aren't necessarily real. For such an equation, the expression $\pm\sqrt{b^2 - 4ac}$ represents the two square roots of a complex number. You'll learn how to find square roots, and other roots, of complex numbers in the next subsection.

3.2 Roots of complex numbers

As you know, if a is any number, then any solution x of the equation

$$x^2 = a$$

is called a *square root* of a. For example, the equation

$$x^2 = 4$$

has two solutions; in other words, the number 4 has two square roots, namely 2 and -2. Similarly, you've seen that the equation

$$x^2 = -9$$

has two solutions; in other words, the number -9 has two square roots, namely $3i$ and $-3i$.

Notice that in both the cases $a = 4$ and $a = -9$ the pairs of square roots lie symmetrically on opposite sides of the origin, as shown in Figure 15.

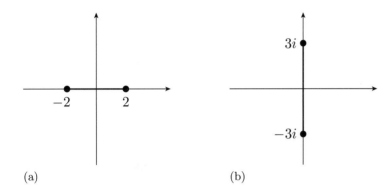

(a)   (b)

Figure 15   The square roots of (a) 4 (b) -9

You can investigate this symmetry property of square roots further in the next activity.

Activity 31   *Investigating the symmetry of square roots*

Use the *Square roots of real numbers* applet to investigate the solutions of the equation $x^2 - a = 0$, that is, the square roots of a, as a varies.

In general, any solution z of the equation

$$z^n = a,$$

where a is a complex number and n is a positive integer, is called an **nth root** of a. (We say 'square root' rather than '2nd root', and 'cube root' rather than '3rd root', as we do for real numbers.) In this subsection you'll learn how to find all the solutions of equations of this form. You'll see that, if a is non-zero, then there are exactly n solutions, positioned symmetrically around the origin. If a is 0, then there's only one solution, namely 0.

Let's start by looking at equations of the form $z^n = 1$, such as $z^3 = 1$ and $z^4 = 1$. Solutions of equations of this form are called **roots of unity**; the word 'unity' refers to the number 1. More specifically,

- the solutions of the equation $z^2 = 1$ are the **square roots of unity**,
- the solutions of the equation $z^3 = 1$ are the **cube roots of unity**,
- the solutions of the equation $z^4 = 1$ are the **fourth roots of unity**,

and so on.

Let's consider the cube roots of unity. You know that 1 is a cube root of unity, because $1^3 = 1$. There are two other cube roots though, namely

$$\tfrac{1}{2}\left(-1 + i\sqrt{3}\right) \quad \text{and} \quad \tfrac{1}{2}\left(-1 - i\sqrt{3}\right).$$

You'll see how to find such roots shortly, but for now let's check that these numbers really are cube roots of unity. To check the first one, let's first find the square and then the cube of the expression inside the brackets:

$$\left(-1 + i\sqrt{3}\right)^2 = 1 - 2i\sqrt{3} + i^2\left(\sqrt{3}\right)^2$$
$$= 1 - 2i\sqrt{3} - 3$$
$$= -2 - 2i\sqrt{3},$$

so

$$\left(-1 + i\sqrt{3}\right)^3 = \left(-1 + i\sqrt{3}\right)^2\left(-1 + i\sqrt{3}\right)$$
$$= \left(-2 - 2i\sqrt{3}\right)\left(-1 + i\sqrt{3}\right)$$
$$= 2 - 2i\sqrt{3} + 2i\sqrt{3} - 2i^2\left(\sqrt{3}\right)^2$$
$$= 2 + 6$$
$$= 8.$$

Therefore

$$\left(\frac{-1 + i\sqrt{3}}{2}\right)^3 = \frac{\left(-1 + i\sqrt{3}\right)^3}{2^3} = \frac{8}{8} = 1.$$

So $\tfrac{1}{2}\left(-1 + i\sqrt{3}\right)$ is indeed a cube root of unity.

Activity 32   *Checking a cube root of unity*

Check that $\tfrac{1}{2}\left(-1 - i\sqrt{3}\right)$ is a cube root of unity.

The three cube roots of unity all have modulus 1, as you can check directly if you wish. To see why, suppose that z is a cube root of unity, so $z^3 = 1$.

Taking the modulus of both sides of this equation gives

$$|z^3| = 1.$$

Now

$$|z^3| = |z \times z \times z| = |z| \times |z| \times |z| = |z|^3,$$

so it follows that

$$|z|^3 = 1.$$

Therefore $|z| = 1$; that is, z has modulus 1.

You can see that a similar argument will hold for any nth root of unity, for any positive integer n. So, for any positive integer n, the nth roots of unity all have modulus 1.

The three cube roots of unity are shown in the complex plane in Figure 16. Because they all have modulus 1, they all lie on the **unit circle**, which is the circle of radius 1 that is centred on the origin.

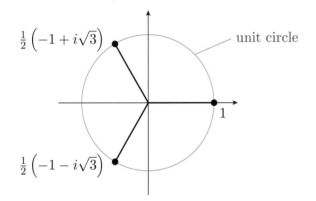

Figure 16   The cube roots of unity

It appears from Figure 16 that the cube roots of unity are equally spaced around the unit circle, and you'll see shortly that this is indeed so. More generally, you'll see that for any positive integer n, there are n solutions of the equation $z^n = 1$ and they're equally spaced around the unit circle. One of these solutions is the number 1, of course, which lies on the positive part of the real axis.

The next example illustrates a method for finding the nth roots of unity, for any positive integer n, using the case $n = 5$ as an example. You'll see later in the subsection that you can use essentially the same method to find the nth roots of any complex number.

You might find it particularly helpful to watch the tutorial clip for the following example.

Example 15   *Finding the fifth roots of unity*

Solve the equation $z^5 = 1$. Sketch the solutions in the complex plane.

Solution

🔍 Write the unknown z in polar form, in terms of an unknown modulus r and an unknown argument θ. Also write the number on the right-hand side of the equation in polar form. 💭

Let $z = r(\cos\theta + i\sin\theta)$. Also, $1 = \cos 0 + i\sin 0$. So the equation is

$$(r(\cos\theta + i\sin\theta))^5 = \cos 0 + i\sin 0.$$

🔍 Use de Moivre's formula to find the polar form of the left-hand side. 💭

De Moivre's formula gives

$$r^5(\cos 5\theta + i\sin 5\theta) = \cos 0 + i\sin 0.$$

🔍 Find r by comparing the moduli of the two sides of this equation. The left-hand side has modulus r^5, and the right-hand side has modulus 1. 💭

Comparing moduli gives

$$r^5 = 1, \quad \text{so} \quad r = 1.$$

🔍 Now find θ by comparing the arguments of the two sides of the equation. The left-hand side has argument 5θ, and the right-hand side has argument 0. However, it *doesn't* follow that $5\theta = 0$. Instead it follows that $5\theta = 0 + 2m\pi$, for some integer m. So there are infinitely many possible values of 5θ, and hence infinitely many possible values of θ. 💭

Comparing arguments gives

$$5\theta = 0 + 2m\pi = 2m\pi, \quad \text{where } m \text{ is an integer.}$$

Hence

$$\theta = \frac{2m\pi}{5}, \quad \text{where } m \text{ is an integer.}$$

🔍 Find the five values of θ given by $m = 0, 1, 2, 3, 4$. (You'll see after the example that other integers m don't give further solutions. In general, if the exponent in the original equation is n, then you should find the values of θ given by n consecutive integer values of m, starting with $m = 0$.) 💭

Taking $m = 0, 1, 2, 3, 4$ gives the following values of θ:

$$\theta = 0, \frac{2\pi}{5}, \frac{4\pi}{5}, \frac{6\pi}{5}, \frac{8\pi}{5}.$$

Write out the solutions. It's convenient to label them as z_0, z_1, z_2, z_3, z_4.

The solutions are

$$z_0 = \cos 0 + i \sin 0 = 1$$

$$z_1 = \cos\left(\frac{2\pi}{5}\right) + i \sin\left(\frac{2\pi}{5}\right)$$

$$z_2 = \cos\left(\frac{4\pi}{5}\right) + i \sin\left(\frac{4\pi}{5}\right)$$

$$z_3 = \cos\left(\frac{6\pi}{5}\right) + i \sin\left(\frac{6\pi}{5}\right)$$

$$z_4 = \cos\left(\frac{8\pi}{5}\right) + i \sin\left(\frac{8\pi}{5}\right).$$

Sketch the solutions in the complex plane. Each solution has modulus 1, so they all lie on the unit circle. Plot the solution $z_0 = 1$, and then sketch z_1, z_2, z_3 and z_4, in that order, by marking regularly spaced points separated by the angle $2\pi/5$ anticlockwise around the unit circle. Just estimate each angle $2\pi/5$; there's no need for a precise drawing.

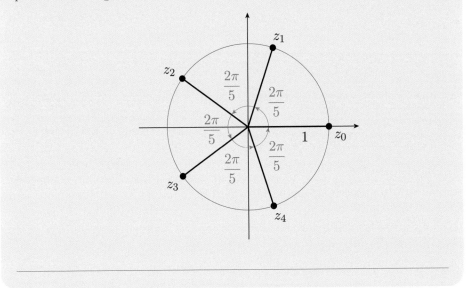

In the solution to Example 15 the fifth roots of unity were given in polar form, with arguments in the interval $[0, 2\pi)$ rather than principal arguments (remember that principal arguments lie in the interval $(-\pi, \pi]$). In general when you're finding roots of complex numbers, it's usually more convenient to use arguments in the interval $[0, 2\pi)$ rather than principal arguments.

To help you see why values of m other than 0, 1, 2, 3 and 4 don't give further solutions of the equation $z^5 = 1$ in Example 15, let's try some of these other values of m, to see what happens.

For example, if you take $m = 5$, then you obtain the solution

$$z = \cos\left(\frac{10\pi}{5}\right) + i\sin\left(\frac{10\pi}{5}\right).$$

Since $10\pi/5 = 2\pi = 2\pi + 0$, this solution is the same as the solution z_0 found in the example. Similarly, if you take $m = 6$, then you obtain the solution

$$z = \cos\left(\frac{12\pi}{5}\right) + i\sin\left(\frac{12\pi}{5}\right).$$

Since $12\pi/5 = 2\pi + 2\pi/5$, this solution is the same as the solution z_1 found in the example. Once you've taken m to be 0, 1, 2, 3 and 4, the solutions that you obtain just start to repeat. The same thing happens if you take negative values of m.

Here's an algebraic explanation of this repeating behaviour. When you use the method in Example 15 to find the nth roots of unity for some value of n, each possible value of θ is of the form

$$\theta = \frac{2m\pi}{n}, \quad \text{where } m \text{ is an integer.}$$

Consider any integer m. It can be written in the form

$$m = qn + r,$$

where q is an integer and r is the remainder after m is divided by n. (For example, if $n = 5$, then the integer $m = 14$, for instance, can be written as $14 = 2 \times 5 + 4$.) So the value of θ corresponding to m can be written as

$$\theta = \frac{2(qn + r)\pi}{n} = q \times 2\pi + \frac{2r\pi}{n},$$

where q is an integer, and r is one of the integers $0, 1, \ldots, n - 1$. That is, the value of θ corresponding to m differs from the value of θ corresponding to one of the integers $0, 1, \ldots, n - 1$ by an integer multiple of 2π. Hence the solution z arising from the integer m is the same as the solution arising from one of the integers $0, 1, \ldots, n - 1$.

The following box summarises the main steps of the method used in Example 15. The method is stated for a general equation $z^n = a$, where a is any non-zero complex number, rather than just for equations of the form $z^n = 1$, because it applies in this more general situation, as you'll see later in this subsection.

Strategy:
To find the complex solutions of the equation $z^n = a$, where $a \neq 0$

1. Write the unknown z in polar form, in terms of an unknown modulus r and an unknown argument θ, and write the number a in polar form.

2. Substitute the polar forms of z and a into the equation, and apply de Moivre's formula to find the polar form of the left-hand side.

3. Compare moduli to find the value of r.

4. Compare arguments to find n successive possible values of θ.

5. Hence write down the n possible values of z.

It is usually convenient to use arguments in the interval $[0, 2\pi)$.

The solutions found in Example 15 were left in polar form because in that form they're exact, and it's difficult to find the exact Cartesian form of all of them. Also, the polar form helps you to see that the solutions give five equally spaced points around the unit circle. The solution z_0 was given in both polar form and Cartesian form. This is because its Cartesian form is so simple ($z_0 = 1$) that it would be strange not to mention this.

In the next activity you're asked to find roots of unity in both polar form *and* Cartesian form, because it's fairly straightforward to give exact solutions in both forms. You saw the solutions of the equation in part (a) of this activity earlier in the subsection, but you should obtain them again, using the strategy.

Activity 33 *Finding roots of unity*

Solve the following equations. Give your answers in both polar form and Cartesian form. Sketch the solutions in the complex plane.

(a) $z^3 = 1$ (b) $z^4 = 1$ (c) $z^6 = 1$

Now let's look at equations of the form

$$z^n = a,$$

where a is any non-zero complex number. Before we use the strategy above to solve an equation like this, let's look at a particular example of such an equation.

Consider the equation

$$z^3 = -8.$$

It has one real solution, namely -2, because $(-2)^3 = -8$. It also has two other complex solutions, namely $1 + i\sqrt{3}$ and $1 - i\sqrt{3}$, which you can check yourself. All three solutions are shown in the complex plane in Figure 17.

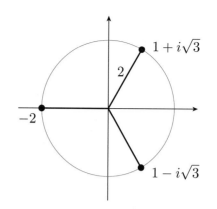

Figure 17   The cube roots of -8

The three solutions don't lie on the unit circle; instead they lie on the circle of radius 2 centred at the origin. To see why, suppose that z is any solution of the equation, so $z^3 = -8$. Taking the modulus of both sides of this equation gives

$$|z^3| = 8, \quad \text{so} \quad |z|^3 = 8.$$

Therefore

$$|z| = 8^{1/3} = 2.$$

That is, z has modulus 2, and therefore lies on the circle of radius 2 centred on the origin.

It appears from Figure 17 that the three solutions are equally spaced around this circle, and indeed they are. In general, the following fact holds.

> For each non-zero number a, the equation $z^n = a$ has n complex solutions, and these are equally spaced around a circle centred on the origin.

The next example illustrates how to apply the strategy that you've seen in this subsection to find all the complex solutions of an equation of the form $z^n = a$, where a is non-zero. Again, you might find it helpful to watch the tutorial clip.

Example 16   *Finding the roots of a complex number*

Solve the equation $z^4 = 4i$. Sketch the solutions in the complex plane.

Solution

💬 Write the unknown z in polar form, in terms of an unknown modulus r and an unknown argument θ. Also write the number on the right-hand side of the equation in polar form. 💬

Let $z = r(\cos\theta + i\sin\theta)$. The complex number $4i$ has modulus 4 and principal argument $\pi/2$, so its polar form is

$$4i = 4\left(\cos\frac{\pi}{2} + i\sin\frac{\pi}{2}\right).$$

So the equation is

$$(r(\cos\theta + i\sin\theta))^4 = 4\left(\cos\frac{\pi}{2} + i\sin\frac{\pi}{2}\right).$$

🔍 Use de Moivre's formula to find the polar form of the left-hand side. 💬

De Moivre's formula gives

$$r^4(\cos 4\theta + i\sin 4\theta) = 4\left(\cos\frac{\pi}{2} + i\sin\frac{\pi}{2}\right).$$

🔍 Find r by comparing the moduli of each side of the equation. 💬

Comparing moduli gives

$$r^4 = 4, \quad \text{so} \quad r = 4^{1/4} = \sqrt{2}.$$

🔍 Find θ by comparing the arguments of the two sides of the equation. 💬

Comparing arguments gives

$$4\theta = \frac{\pi}{2} + 2m\pi, \quad \text{where } m \text{ is an integer.}$$

Therefore

$$\theta = \frac{\pi}{8} + \frac{m\pi}{2}, \quad \text{where } m \text{ is an integer.}$$

🔍 Find the values of θ given by $m = 0, 1, 2, 3$. 💬

The values of θ for $m = 0, 1, 2, 3$ are

$$\frac{\pi}{8}, \quad \frac{5\pi}{8}, \quad \frac{9\pi}{8}, \quad \frac{13\pi}{8}.$$

🔍 Write out the solutions. It's convenient to label them as z_0, z_1, z_2 and z_3. 💬

The solutions are

$$z_0 = \sqrt{2}\left(\cos\left(\frac{\pi}{8}\right) + i\sin\left(\frac{\pi}{8}\right)\right)$$

$$z_1 = \sqrt{2}\left(\cos\left(\frac{5\pi}{8}\right) + i\sin\left(\frac{5\pi}{8}\right)\right)$$

$$z_2 = \sqrt{2}\left(\cos\left(\frac{9\pi}{8}\right) + i\sin\left(\frac{9\pi}{8}\right)\right)$$

$$z_3 = \sqrt{2}\left(\cos\left(\frac{13\pi}{8}\right) + i\sin\left(\frac{13\pi}{8}\right)\right).$$

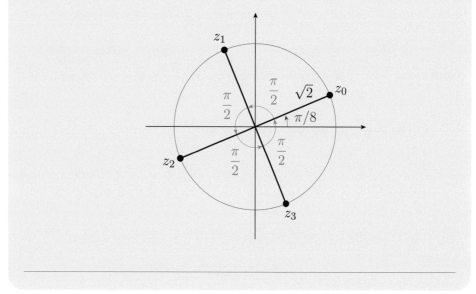

Sketch the solutions in the complex plane. Each solution has modulus $\sqrt{2}$, so they all lie on the circle of radius $\sqrt{2}$ centred at the origin. Sketch the solution z_0, and then sketch z_1, z_2 and z_3, in that order, by marking regularly spaced points separated by angles $\pi/2$ anticlockwise around the circle.

As expected, the solutions of the equation $z^4 = 4i$ in Example 16 are equally spaced round a circle centred on the origin. Note that the infinitely many possible values of the argument, $\theta = \pi/8 + m\pi/2$, where m is an integer, give repeating solutions of the equation $z^4 = 4i$ in a similar way to the solutions of $z^n = 1$ described earlier.

Activity 34   *Finding roots of complex numbers*

Solve the following equations. Give the solutions to parts (a) and (b) in both polar form and Cartesian form, and give the solutions to part (c) in polar form only. Sketch the solutions in the complex plane.

(a) $z^6 = 64$ (b) $z^3 = -8$ (c) $z^5 = -1 - i$

3.3 The fundamental theorem of algebra

As you learned earlier, a *polynomial equation* is an equation of the form 'polynomial expression $= 0$', where the polynomial expression has degree at least 1. The coefficients in the polynomial expression can be complex numbers. For example, the following equations are all polynomial equations:

$$z^5 + 1 + i = 0, \quad 3z^2 + \tfrac{11}{4}z - 18 = 0 \quad \text{and} \quad z^3 - (17 + 3i)z + 2 = 0.$$

The first of these equations can be rearranged as $z^5 = -1 - i$, which is an equation of the type that you learned how to solve in the previous subsection. The second equation is a quadratic equation. **Cubic equations** (such as the third equation above) and **quartic equations** are polynomial equations in which the polynomial expressions have degrees 3 and 4, respectively. This subsection is about *the fundamental theorem of algebra*, which shows that every polynomial equation has at least one solution.

Before you meet the fundamental theorem of algebra, let's first consider an example that will help you to understand it. In Example 12 on page 215 you saw that the solutions of the quadratic equation $z^2 - 6z + 25 = 0$ are $3 + 4i$ and $3 - 4i$. It follows that you can factorise the quadratic $z^2 - 6z + 25$ as

$$z^2 - 6z + 25 = \left(z - (3 + 4i)\right)\left(z - (3 - 4i)\right).$$

More generally, if z_1 and z_2 are the solutions of the quadratic equation $az^2 + bz + c = 0$ (there may be only one solution, in which case $z_1 = z_2$), then you can factorise the quadratic $az^2 + bz + c$ as

$$az^2 + bz + c = a(z - z_1)(z - z_2).$$

The fundamental theorem of algebra says that it's not only quadratics that can be factorised like this, but in fact any polynomial expression can be factorised in a similar way.

The fundamental theorem of algebra

Every polynomial

$$a_n z^n + a_{n-1} z^{n-1} + \cdots + a_1 z + a_0$$

of degree $n \geq 1$ has a factorisation

$$a_n(z - z_1)(z - z_2) \cdots (z - z_n),$$

where $z_1, z_2, \ldots, z_n$ are complex numbers, some of which may be equal to others.

The fundamental theorem of algebra was first proved by Carl Friedrich Gauss, and a proof was also given by Argand, who was mentioned in Subsection 2.1. The proof requires techniques more advanced than those in this module and is given in higher-level modules.

The fundamental theorem of algebra tells you that any polynomial equation, say

$$a_n z^n + a_{n-1} z^{n-1} + \cdots + a_1 z + a_0 = 0,$$

can be written in the form

$$a_n(z - z_1)(z - z_2) \cdots (z - z_n) = 0.$$

It follows that the polynomial equation has solutions $z_1, z_2, \ldots, z_n$, some of which may be equal to others. In particular, *every polynomial equation has at least one complex solution.*

Although the fundamental theorem of algebra tells you that every polynomial equation has at least one complex solution, it doesn't tell you how to *find* any solutions. Often finding solutions is difficult, and you have to use a computer. You can learn how to do that in the next activity.

Activity 35 *Solving polynomial equations with the CAS*

Work through Subsection 13.2 of the *Computer algebra guide.*

Insolvability of the quintic

Not only is there a formula for the solutions of a quadratic equation in terms of its coefficients, but there are also formulas for the solutions of cubic equations and quartic equations in terms of their coefficients. These formulas are long, and difficult to evaluate without a computer. For polynomial equations of higher degree, however, it's impossible to find formulas involving the usual arithmetic operations that give all the solutions of all the equations. For example, the quintic equation

$$z^5 + 3z + 6 = 0$$

is said to be *insolvable* because, although it has five solutions, it's impossible to obtain these solutions from the coefficients 1, 3 and 6 by using only the operations $+$, $-$, $\times$, $\div$ and $\sqrt[n]{}$.

One of the first mathematicians to develop the theory of insolvable polynomial equations was the French Republican Évariste Galois ('Galois' is pronounced 'Gal-wah'). Galois' discoveries led to the development of the subject now known as *Galois theory*, in which the solutions of polynomial equations are studied systematically. Sadly, Galois didn't receive full recognition for his work in his lifetime, because he died aged only twenty, as a result of a duel.

Évariste Galois (1811–1832)

4 Exponential form

In this section you'll learn about a more concise version of polar form, called *exponential form*. You'll see that when you write complex numbers in exponential form, some of their properties, such as the formula for multiplication and de Moivre's formula, become more intuitive.

4.1 Euler's formula

To find the exponential form of a complex number from its polar form, you use a formula called *Euler's formula*. This formula gives a meaning for the expression $e^{i\theta}$, where θ is a real number. So far you've learned what the expression e^x means only when x is a real number, but you can get some idea of what the natural meaning of $e^{i\theta}$ might be by considering Taylor series. Recall from Unit 11 that the Taylor series about 0 for e^x is

$$e^x = 1 + x + \frac{x^2}{2!} + \frac{x^3}{3!} + \frac{x^4}{4!} + \frac{x^5}{5!} + \frac{x^6}{6!} + \frac{x^7}{7!} + \cdots.$$

Let's try substituting $i\theta$ for x in this series. Since you've learned about Taylor series only for *real* numbers, you haven't been shown that you're allowed to do this (in fact you are: it's justified in more advanced modules). Nonetheless, you'll see that the substitution can help you understand why Euler's formula makes sense. We obtain

$$e^{i\theta} = 1 + i\theta + \frac{(i\theta)^2}{2!} + \frac{(i\theta)^3}{3!} + \frac{(i\theta)^4}{4!} + \frac{(i\theta)^5}{5!} + \frac{(i\theta)^6}{6!} + \frac{(i\theta)^7}{7!} + \cdots$$

$$= 1 + i\theta + \frac{i^2\theta^2}{2!} + \frac{i^3\theta^3}{3!} + \frac{i^4\theta^4}{4!} + \frac{i^5\theta^5}{5!} + \frac{i^6\theta^6}{6!} + \frac{i^7\theta^7}{7!} + \cdots.$$

To simplify this expression, notice the following pattern:

$$\underbrace{i^0 = 1, \quad i^1 = i, \quad i^2 = -1, \quad i^3 = -i,}_{\text{This pattern } 1,i,-1,-i \text{ repeats.}} \quad i^4 = 1, \quad i^5 = i, \ldots$$

(You may remember this pattern from Activity 6.) It follows that

$$e^{i\theta} = 1 + i\theta - \frac{\theta^2}{2!} - i\frac{\theta^3}{3!} + \frac{\theta^4}{4!} + i\frac{\theta^5}{5!} - \frac{\theta^6}{6!} - i\frac{\theta^7}{7!} + \cdots$$

$$= \left(1 - \frac{\theta^2}{2!} + \frac{\theta^4}{4!} - \frac{\theta^6}{6!} + \cdots\right) + i\left(\theta - \frac{\theta^3}{3!} + \frac{\theta^5}{5!} - \frac{\theta^7}{7!} + \cdots\right).$$

You also saw in Unit 11 that the Taylor series about 0 for $\cos\theta$ and $\sin\theta$ are

$$\cos\theta = 1 - \frac{\theta^2}{2!} + \frac{\theta^4}{4!} - \frac{\theta^6}{6!} + \cdots \quad \text{and} \quad \sin\theta = \theta - \frac{\theta^3}{3!} + \frac{\theta^5}{5!} - \frac{\theta^7}{7!} + \cdots.$$

Therefore

$$e^{i\theta} = \cos\theta + i\sin\theta.$$

This equation is **Euler's formula**. It's named after its discoverer, the Swiss mathematician Leonard Euler (1707–1783), who was mentioned in Unit 3. Euler obtained the formula in much the way that we have.

The manipulation above shows that if the Taylor series about 0 for e^x is valid with $i\theta$ instead of x, then Euler's formula must hold. So Euler's formula seems to be the natural definition of $e^{i\theta}$, and hence we use it to define $e^{i\theta}$.

Euler's formula

Let θ be a real number. Then $e^{i\theta}$ is defined by **Euler's formula**

$$e^{i\theta} = \cos\theta + i\sin\theta.$$

When $\theta = \pi$, Euler's formula says that $e^{i\pi} = \cos\pi + i\sin\pi$; that is, $e^{i\pi} = -1$. This equation can be rearranged to give the equation below, which is known as **Euler's equation**.

Euler's equation

$$e^{i\pi} + 1 = 0$$

This equation, which is also sometimes called *Euler's identity*, is one of the most famous equations in mathematics, because it relates the five fundamental numbers 0, 1, i, e and π.

Euler's formula $e^{i\theta} = \cos\theta + i\sin\theta$ tells us that a complex number z in polar form

$$z = r(\cos\theta + i\sin\theta)$$

can be written in a more concise way as

$$z = re^{i\theta}.$$

This is the *exponential form* of a complex number, promised at the start of this subsection.

Exponential form of a complex number

A non-zero complex number z is in **exponential form** if it is expressed as

$$z = re^{i\theta},$$

where r is the modulus of z and θ is an argument of z.

For example, because the complex number $3i$ has modulus 3 and principal argument $\pi/2$, it has exponential form $3e^{i\pi/2}$. It also has other exponential forms, corresponding to different choices of argument of $3i$, such as $3e^{5\pi i/2}$ and $3e^{-3\pi i/2}$. However, you should use the principal argument when writing a complex number in exponential form, unless there's a good reason not to do so.

The number 0 doesn't have a polar form, as you've seen, and it doesn't have an exponential form either. When working with complex numbers in exponential form, you should write the number zero using the usual symbol 0.

Because the exponential form of a complex number is just a concise way to write its polar form, the process of converting between the Cartesian and exponential forms of a complex number is much the same as the process of converting between its Cartesian and polar forms, which you learned in Section 2.

Example 17 *Converting from exponential form to Cartesian form*

Write the complex number $4e^{-5\pi i/6}$ in Cartesian form.

Solution

🔍 Write the number in polar form, evaluate the cosine and sine, and multiply out the brackets. 💬

$$4e^{-5\pi i/6} = 4\left(\cos\left(-\frac{5\pi}{6}\right) + i\sin\left(-\frac{5\pi}{6}\right)\right)$$

$$= 4\left(-\frac{\sqrt{3}}{2} - \frac{i}{2}\right)$$

$$= -2\sqrt{3} - 2i$$

You can use your solutions to Activity 20 on page 203 to help you with the next activity.

Activity 36 *Converting from exponential form to Cartesian form*

Write the following complex numbers in Cartesian form.

(a) $3e^{i0}$ (b) $7e^{i\pi/2}$ (c) $6e^{i\pi}$ (d) $e^{-i\pi/2}$ (e) $5e^{-i\pi}$

(f) $4e^{i\pi/3}$ (g) $2e^{-i\pi/4}$ (h) $\sqrt{3}e^{5\pi i/6}$

Example 18 *Converting from Cartesian form to exponential form*

Write the complex number $1 - i$ in exponential form.

Solution

🔍 First find the modulus. 💬

The modulus is

$$r = \sqrt{1^2 + (-1)^2} = \sqrt{1 + 1} = \sqrt{2}.$$

To find the principal argument, sketch $1 - i$ in the complex plane.

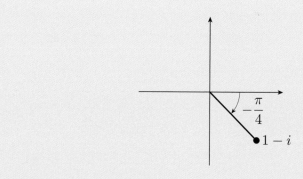

From the diagram, the principal argument is $-\pi/4$. Therefore
$$1 - i = \sqrt{2}e^{-i\pi/4}.$$

You can use your solutions to Activity 21 on page 205 to help you with the next activity.

Activity 37   *Converting from Cartesian form to exponential form*

Write the following complex numbers in exponential form.

(a) $7i/2$ (b) $-4i$ (c) -3 (d) 2 (e) $1 + i$ (f) $1 - i\sqrt{3}$

(g) $-\sqrt{3} - i$ (h) $2\sqrt{3} - 2i$

It's often better to use the exponential form $re^{i\theta}$ of a complex number, rather than its polar form $r(\cos\theta + i\sin\theta)$, because it's shorter. Another reason for preferring the exponential form is that some of the formulas involving polar form that you met earlier become more intuitive when complex numbers are expressed in exponential form.

Consider, for example, the formula for the product of two complex numbers in polar form:

$$\underbrace{r(\cos\theta + i\sin\theta)}_{re^{i\theta}} \times \underbrace{s(\cos\phi + i\sin\phi)}_{se^{i\phi}} = \underbrace{rs(\cos(\theta + \phi) + i\sin(\theta + \phi))}_{rse^{i(\theta+\phi)}}.$$

If you write the complex numbers in exponential form, then this formula becomes

$$re^{i\theta} \times se^{i\phi} = rse^{i(\theta+\phi)}.$$

This version of the formula is more intuitive, and hence easier to remember and use, because it agrees with the usual index laws for multiplying powers of a real number.

In particular, when $r = s = 1$ you obtain the following equation, which looks like it follows from a familiar index law, but involves complex numbers.

$$e^{i\theta}e^{i\phi} = e^{i(\theta + \phi)}$$

Similarly, de Moivre's formula,

$$\underbrace{\left(r(\cos\theta + i\sin\theta)\right)^n}_{\left(re^{i\theta}\right)^n} = \underbrace{r^n(\cos n\theta + i\sin n\theta)}_{r^n e^{in\theta}},$$

is simpler and more intuitive when written using exponential form:

$$\left(re^{i\theta}\right)^n = r^n e^{in\theta}.$$

Choosing $r = 1$ gives the rule below, which again looks like it follows from a familiar index law, but involves complex numbers.

$$\left(e^{i\theta}\right)^n = e^{in\theta}$$

Activity 38   Writing a formula for the quotient of two complex numbers in exponential form

The formula for the quotient of two complex numbers in polar form is

$$\frac{r(\cos\theta + i\sin\theta)}{s(\cos\phi + i\sin\phi)} = \frac{r}{s}(\cos(\theta - \phi) + i\sin(\theta - \phi)).$$

Write this formula using exponential form.

Activity 39   Working with complex numbers in exponential form

Express each of the following products, quotients and powers of complex numbers as a single complex number in exponential form.

(a) $e^{i\pi/8} \times e^{3\pi i/8}$ (b) $\left(e^{i\pi/8}\right)^4$ (c) $\dfrac{e^{3\pi i/8}}{e^{i\pi/8}}$ (d) $\dfrac{e^{i\pi/8}}{e^{3\pi i/8}}$

You can use Euler's formula to obtain further useful formulas, by combining it with properties of sine and cosine. For example, if you replace θ by $-\theta$ in Euler's formula then you obtain

$$e^{-i\theta} = \cos(-\theta) + i\sin(-\theta).$$

You saw in Unit 4 that
$$\cos(-\theta) = \cos\theta \quad \text{and} \quad \sin(-\theta) = -\sin\theta,$$
which give the following formula for $e^{-i\theta}$.

$$e^{-i\theta} = \cos\theta - i\sin\theta$$

Since $\cos\theta - i\sin\theta$ is the complex conjugate of $\cos\theta + i\sin\theta$, we can make the following useful observation.

The complex conjugate of $e^{i\theta}$ is $e^{-i\theta}$.

The equation $e^{-i\theta} = \cos\theta - i\sin\theta$ is used in the next subsection to obtain formulas for $\sin\theta$ and $\cos\theta$ in terms of $e^{i\theta}$ and $e^{-i\theta}$.

Activity 40   *Proving an identity by using Euler's formula and properties of sine and cosine*

Using Euler's formula, prove the identity
$$e^{i(\theta + 2\pi)} = e^{i\theta}.$$

Most large wind turbines generate an alternating current

Complex impedance

In an electrical circuit powered by a direct current (from a battery, for example), the current J, measured in amperes, and the voltage V, measured in volts, are related by *Ohm's law*, which says that

$$V = JR,$$

where R is the resistance of the circuit, measured in ohms.

The electric power in our homes is not supplied by a direct current. Instead it's supplied by an alternating current, generated by an alternating voltage. The intensities of the alternating current J and voltage V oscillate with time, and are typically given by equations such as

$$J = J_0 \sin\omega t \quad \text{and} \quad V = V_0 \sin(\omega t + \phi),$$

where J_0 and V_0 are the maximum values of the current and voltage, respectively, ω determines the rate of oscillation of both the current and the voltage, and ϕ measures how far the current and voltage are from being synchronised.

The graphs of these equations are illustrated in Figure 18.

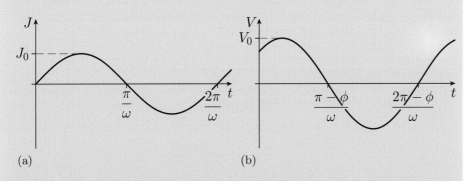

(a)   (b)

Figure 18   The graphs of (a) $J = J_0 \sin \omega t$ (b) $V = V_0 \sin(\omega t + \phi)$

Electrical engineers use complex numbers in exponential form to manipulate equations arising from alternating currents. They define the *complex current* $\mathbf{J}$ to equal $J_0 e^{i\omega t}$ and the *complex voltage* $\mathbf{V}$ to equal $V_0 e^{i(\omega t + \phi)}$. It follows that

$$\mathrm{Im}(\mathbf{J}) = \mathrm{Im}(J_0 e^{i\omega t}) = J_0 \sin \omega t$$

and

$$\mathrm{Im}(\mathbf{V}) = \mathrm{Im}(V_0 e^{i(\omega t + \phi)}) = V_0 \sin(\omega t + \phi).$$

So the current J is the imaginary part of the complex current $\mathbf{J}$ and the voltage V is the imaginary part of the complex voltage $\mathbf{V}$. The *complex impedance* $\mathbf{Z}$ is defined to be the ratio $\mathbf{V}/\mathbf{J}$. It can be shown that $\mathbf{Z}$ measures the various ways in which an electrical circuit resists the flow of an alternating current. By rearranging the equation $\mathbf{Z} = \mathbf{V}/\mathbf{J}$ you obtain a version of Ohm's law for alternating currents:

$$\mathbf{V} = \mathbf{Z}\mathbf{J}.$$

The actual alternating voltage can be found by comparing the imaginary parts of each side of this equation.

4.2 Trigonometric identities from de Moivre's formula and Euler's formula

In Unit 4 you saw some trigonometric identities, such as

$$\sin 2\theta = 2 \sin \theta \cos \theta \quad \text{and} \quad \cos 2\theta = 2 \cos^2 \theta - 1.$$

In this final subsection you'll learn how you can use de Moivre's formula and Euler's formula, together with the binomial theorem from Unit 10, to obtain new trigonometric identities. This illustrates the fact that techniques involving complex numbers can often be used to deduce results about real functions.

One way to find new trigonometric identities is to use the special case of de Moivre's formula given in the box below. It's obtained by taking the modulus r to be 1 in the general formula on page 211 and swapping the sides.

> **Special case of de Moivre's formula**
>
> $$\cos n\theta + i \sin n\theta = (\cos \theta + i \sin \theta)^n$$

Example 19   *Using de Moivre's formula to find trigonometric identities*

Use de Moivre's formula to obtain the following trigonometric identities:

$$\cos 3\theta = 4\cos^3 \theta - 3\cos \theta$$
$$\sin 3\theta = 3\sin \theta - 4\sin^3 \theta.$$

Solution

💬 Use the special case of de Moivre's formula. Because the required identities involve 3θ, take $n = 3$. 💬

By de Moivre's formula,

$$\cos 3\theta + i \sin 3\theta = (\cos \theta + i \sin \theta)^3$$

💬 Apply the binomial theorem. 💬

$$\begin{aligned}
&= (\cos \theta)^3 + 3(\cos \theta)^2 (i \sin \theta) + 3(\cos \theta)(i \sin \theta)^2 \\
&\quad + (i \sin \theta)^3 \\
&= \cos^3 \theta + 3i \cos^2 \theta \sin \theta - 3\cos \theta \sin^2 \theta - i \sin^3 \theta \\
&= (\cos^3 \theta - 3\cos \theta \sin^2 \theta) + i(3\cos^2 \theta \sin \theta - \sin^3 \theta).
\end{aligned}$$

💬 To obtain the first identity, use the fact that the real part of the left-hand side is equal to the real part of the right-hand side. To express $\sin^2 \theta$ in terms of $\cos \theta$, use the identity $\sin^2 \theta + \cos^2 \theta = 1$. 💬

Therefore

$$\begin{aligned}
\cos 3\theta &= \cos^3 \theta - 3\cos \theta \sin^2 \theta \\
&= \cos^3 \theta - 3\cos \theta (1 - \cos^2 \theta) \\
&= 4\cos^3 \theta - 3\cos \theta
\end{aligned}$$

💬 To obtain the second identity, use the fact that the imaginary part of the left-hand side is equal to the imaginary part of the right-hand side. 💬

and

$$\begin{aligned}
\sin 3\theta &= 3\cos^2\theta\sin\theta - \sin^3\theta \\
&= 3(1 - \sin^2\theta)\sin\theta - \sin^3\theta \\
&= 3\sin\theta - 4\sin^3\theta.
\end{aligned}$$

When you've obtained a new trigonometric identity, it's worth trying it out with some specific values of the variable θ, to check that you haven't made an error. Consider, for example, the identity obtained in Example 19:

$$\cos 3\theta = 4\cos^3\theta - 3\cos\theta.$$

When $\theta = 0$,

$$\text{LHS} = 1 \quad \text{and} \quad \text{RHS} = 4 - 3 = 1.$$

When $\theta = \pi/3$,

$$\text{LHS} = -1 \quad \text{and} \quad \text{RHS} = 4 \times \left(\tfrac{1}{2}\right)^3 - 3 \times \tfrac{1}{2} = -1.$$

When $\theta = \pi/2$, both LHS and RHS are 0.

So the identity certainly holds for these particular values of θ, as expected.

Activity 41   *Using de Moivre's formula to find trigonometric identities*

Use de Moivre's formula to obtain the trigonometric identities

$$\cos 4\theta = 8\cos^4\theta - 8\cos^2\theta + 1$$
$$\sin 4\theta = 4\sin\theta\cos\theta(\cos^2\theta - \sin^2\theta).$$

To keep your working short, you may find it helpful to write $c = \cos\theta$ and $s = \sin\theta$.

Another way to obtain new trigonometric identities is to start by finding formulas for $\sin\theta$ and $\cos\theta$ in terms of $e^{i\theta}$ and $e^{-i\theta}$, where θ is a real number. To do this, recall Euler's formula and the complex conjugate form of Euler's formula, obtained in the previous subsection:

$$\begin{aligned}
e^{i\theta} &= \cos\theta + i\sin\theta \\
e^{-i\theta} &= \cos\theta - i\sin\theta.
\end{aligned}$$

Adding the two equations gives

$$e^{i\theta} + e^{-i\theta} = 2\cos\theta, \quad \text{so} \quad \frac{e^{i\theta} + e^{-i\theta}}{2} = \cos\theta.$$

Subtracting the bottom equation from the top equation gives

$$e^{i\theta} - e^{-i\theta} = 2i\sin\theta, \quad \text{so} \quad \frac{e^{i\theta} - e^{-i\theta}}{2i} = \sin\theta.$$

These are the formulas that we need.

$$\cos\theta = \frac{e^{i\theta} + e^{-i\theta}}{2}$$

$$\sin\theta = \frac{e^{i\theta} - e^{-i\theta}}{2i}$$

The next example shows you how you can use the first of these formulas to obtain a trigonometric identity. (In fact this trigonometric identity is one of the identities from Example 19, in a rearranged form.) You also have to use the rules below, which you met in the previous subsection.

$$e^{i\theta}e^{i\phi} = e^{i(\theta+\phi)}$$

$$\left(e^{i\theta}\right)^n = e^{in\theta}$$

Example 20   *Using the formula* $\cos\theta = \frac{1}{2}\left(e^{i\theta} + e^{-i\theta}\right)$ *to obtain a trigonometric identity*

Use the formula $\cos\theta = \frac{1}{2}\left(e^{i\theta} + e^{-i\theta}\right)$ to obtain the identity

$$\cos^3\theta = \tfrac{1}{4}\left(\cos 3\theta + 3\cos\theta\right).$$

Solution

We have $\cos\theta = \frac{1}{2}\left(e^{i\theta} + e^{-i\theta}\right)$. Therefore

$$\cos^3\theta = \frac{1}{2^3}\left(e^{i\theta} + e^{-i\theta}\right)^3$$

Use the binomial theorem.

$$= \frac{1}{8}\left((e^{i\theta})^3 + 3(e^{i\theta})^2e^{-i\theta} + 3e^{i\theta}(e^{-i\theta})^2 + (e^{-i\theta})^3\right)$$

Simplify by using the rule $(e^{i\theta})^n = e^{in\theta}$.

$$= \frac{1}{8}\left(e^{3i\theta} + 3e^{2i\theta}e^{-i\theta} + 3e^{i\theta}e^{-2i\theta} + e^{-3i\theta}\right)$$

Simplify by using the rule $e^{i\theta}e^{i\phi} = e^{i(\theta+\phi)}$.

$$= \frac{1}{8}\left(e^{3i\theta} + 3e^{i\theta} + 3e^{-i\theta} + e^{-3i\theta}\right)$$

Rearrange to obtain expressions of the form $\frac{1}{2}(e^{i\alpha} + e^{-i\alpha})$, and then use the formula given in the question again.

$$= \frac{1}{4}\left(\left(\frac{e^{3i\theta}+e^{-3i\theta}}{2}\right)+3\left(\frac{e^{i\theta}+e^{-i\theta}}{2}\right)\right)$$

$$= \frac{1}{4}\left(\cos 3\theta + 3\cos\theta\right).$$

Activity 42   *Using the formulas* $\cos\theta = \frac{1}{2}\left(e^{i\theta}+e^{-i\theta}\right)$ *and* $\sin\theta = \frac{1}{2i}\left(e^{i\theta}-e^{-i\theta}\right)$ *to obtain trigonometric identities*

Use the formulas
$$\cos\theta = \frac{1}{2}\left(e^{i\theta}+e^{-i\theta}\right) \quad \text{and} \quad \sin\theta = \frac{1}{2i}\left(e^{i\theta}-e^{-i\theta}\right)$$
to obtain the following identities.

(a) $\sin^3\theta = \frac{1}{4}\left(3\sin\theta - \sin 3\theta\right)$ (b) $\cos^4\theta = \frac{1}{8}\left(\cos 4\theta + 4\cos 2\theta + 3\right)$

The examples and activities in this section have shown you how to use complex numbers to deduce new trigonometric identities that express $\sin n\theta$ and $\cos n\theta$ in terms of powers of $\sin\theta$ and $\cos\theta$, and vice versa. This should have given you some idea of the power of complex numbers, and an appreciation of the fact that their uses are far from 'imaginary'.

Quaternions

You've seen that when you work with complex numbers, you're performing arithmetic with pairs of real numbers. The Irish mathematician William Rowan Hamilton was the first to realise how to perform arithmetic with *quadruples* of real numbers. He did this, in a flash of inspiration, while walking beside the Royal Irish Canal near Dublin on 16 October 1843. His idea was to use numbers of the form $a + bi + cj + dk$, where a, b, c and d are real numbers, and
$$i^2 = j^2 = k^2 = ijk = -1.$$
Hamilton scratched this foundational equation on to Broom Bridge as he passed by. His scratches are no longer visible and instead a plaque records the event. Hamilton called his new system of numbers the **quaternions**. You can perform all the usual arithmetic operations with quaternions, with one crucial difference: multiplication is not commutative. For example, you can show that
$$ij = k, \quad \text{whereas} \quad ji = -k.$$
Soon after the discovery of the quaternions, a system of arithmetic with *octuples* of real numbers was developed, called the **octonions** (or **Cayley numbers**). Multiplication of octonions is neither commutative nor associative. This makes them tricky to manipulate!

The plaque on Broom Bridge, Dublin, that marks Hamilton's discovery

I'm sorry, the number you have dialled is imaginary. Please rotate your phone through 90 degrees and redial.

Learning outcomes

After studying this unit, you should be able to:

- understand what complex numbers are, and carry out arithmetical operations on them
- work with the complex plane
- understand modulus and argument
- understand the polar form of a complex number, and convert between Cartesian form and polar form
- multiply and divide complex numbers in polar form
- understand and use de Moivre's formula
- find all solutions of quadratic equations, including complex solutions
- find roots of complex numbers
- understand the fundamental theorem of algebra
- state Euler's formula
- understand the exponential form of a complex number, and convert between this form and other forms
- use de Moivre's formula and Euler's formula to obtain trigonometric identities.

Closing remarks

Well done for completing MST124 (or skipping to the last page)! You've covered a broad range of topics, which will provide you with the essential mathematical skills that you need to develop as an engineer, scientist, economist or mathematician.

Let's review some of the key topics that you met, and see how they fit together. You learned a good deal about functions, which are among the most fundamental objects in mathematics. The exponential function is of particular significance, not least because of its use in exponential models of real-life situations. The trigonometric functions are also of great importance, and their many practical applications include measuring distances and modelling waves. In this final unit you met Euler's remarkable formula $e^{i\theta} = \cos\theta + i\sin\theta$, which brings together the exponential and trigonometric functions by using complex numbers.

With compound interest, savings increase exponentially

Another class of functions that you studied are the polynomial functions. You saw that you can approximate functions by Taylor polynomials, which is often extremely useful for understanding properties of functions and performing calculations with them.

You saw that functions and sequences can be represented geometrically by their graphs. Graphs help to quickly communicate the key properties of functions and sequences, and they also provide a simple way to represent physical quantities such as velocity and acceleration.

Through studying gradients of graphs you came to learn about differentiation, and then about integration, which is the reverse of differentiation. The theory surrounding these two concepts, which is known as calculus, is an essential part of almost every discipline that involves mathematics, from finance to medicine. You'll make good use of calculus in higher-level modules involving mathematics.

The acceleration of a diving peregrine falcon can be represented by a graph and analysed using calculus

In Unit 5 you learned about another way of modelling real-life phenomena, namely by using vectors. Trigonometry is crucial when you're working with vectors, because you can use it to calculate the directions of vectors. You also learned some geometry in Unit 5, and then, in this final unit, you saw how by using the complex plane you can associate the rich structure of the complex numbers with two-dimensional geometry.

Yet another central topic that you encountered is matrices, which have a huge range of applications, in modelling networks, solving linear equations, higher-dimensional calculus, and many other topics.

The MST124 authors hope that you feel inspired to continue to study mathematics, whether it's through engineering, science, statistics or any other subject with a mathematical component.

Solutions to activities

Solution to Activity 1

(a) $\operatorname{Re}(2 + 9i) = 2, \quad \operatorname{Im}(2 + 9i) = 9$

(b) $\operatorname{Re}(4) = 4, \quad \operatorname{Im}(4) = 0$

(c) $\operatorname{Re}(-7i) = 0, \quad \operatorname{Im}(-7i) = -7$

(d) $\operatorname{Re}(0) = 0, \quad \operatorname{Im}(0) = 0$

(e) $\operatorname{Re}(i) = 0, \quad \operatorname{Im}(i) = 1$

(f) $\operatorname{Re}(1 - i) = 1, \quad \operatorname{Im}(1 - i) = -1$

Solution to Activity 2

(a) $(2 + 5i) + (-7 + 13i) = (2 + (-7)) + (5 + 13)i$
$$= -5 + 18i$$

$(2 + 5i) - (-7 + 13i) = (2 - (-7)) + (5 - 13)i$
$$= 9 - 8i$$

(b) $(-4i) + (-9i) = ((-4) + (-9))i$
$$= -13i$$

$(-4i) - (-9i) = ((-4) - (-9))i$
$$= 5i$$

(c) $(3 - 7i) + (3 - 7i) = (3 + 3) + ((-7) + (-7))i$
$$= 6 - 14i$$

$(3 - 7i) - (3 - 7i) = (3 - 3) + ((-7) - (-7))i$
$$= 0$$

(d) $(3 + 7i) + (3 - 7i) = (3 + 3) + (7 + (-7))i$
$$= 6$$

$(3 + 7i) - (3 - 7i) = (3 - 3) + (7 - (-7))i$
$$= 14i$$

(e) $\left(\frac{1}{6} - \frac{1}{3}i\right) + \left(-\frac{1}{3} + \frac{1}{6}i\right)$
$$= \left(\frac{1}{6} + \left(-\frac{1}{3}\right)\right) + \left(\left(-\frac{1}{3}\right) + \frac{1}{6}\right)i$$
$$= -\frac{1}{6} - \frac{1}{6}i$$

$\left(\frac{1}{6} - \frac{1}{3}i\right) - \left(-\frac{1}{3} + \frac{1}{6}i\right)$
$$= \left(\frac{1}{6} - \left(-\frac{1}{3}\right)\right) + \left(\left(-\frac{1}{3}\right) - \frac{1}{6}\right)i$$
$$= \frac{1}{2} - \frac{1}{2}i$$

(f) $z + w = 1.2 + 3.4i$
$z - w = 1.2 - 3.4i$

Solution to Activity 3

(a) $u + v + w = (4 + 6i) + (-3 + 5i) + (2 - i)$
$$= (4 + (-3) + 2) + (6 + 5 + (-1))i$$
$$= 3 + 10i$$

(b) By part (a),
$$w + v + u = u + v + w = 3 + 10i.$$

(c) $u - (v + w) = u - v - w$
$$= (4 + 6i) - (-3 + 5i) - (2 - i)$$
$$= (4 - (-3) - 2) + (6 - 5 - (-1))i$$
$$= 5 + 2i$$

(d) $u - (v - w) = u - v + w$
$$= (4 + 6i) - (-3 + 5i) + (2 - i)$$
$$= (4 - (-3) + 2) + (6 - 5 + (-1))i$$
$$= 9$$

Solution to Activity 4

(a) $(1 + 3i)(2 + 4i) = 2 + 4i + 6i + 12i^2$
$$= 2 + 4i + 6i - 12$$
$$= -10 + 10i$$

(b) $(-2 + 3i)(4 - 7i) = -8 + 14i + 12i - 21i^2$
$$= -8 + 14i + 12i + 21$$
$$= 13 + 26i$$

(c) $3i(4 - 5i) = 12i - 15i^2$
$$= 12i + 15$$
$$= 15 + 12i$$

(d) $7(-2 + 5i) = -14 + 35i$

(e) $(2 - 3i)(2 + 3i) = 4 + 6i - 6i - 9i^2$
$$= 4 + 6i - 6i + 9$$
$$= 13$$

(f) $\left(\frac{1}{2} + i\right)\left(1 + \frac{1}{2}i\right) = \frac{1}{2} + \frac{1}{4}i + i + \frac{1}{2}i^2$
$$= \frac{1}{2} + \frac{1}{4}i + i - \frac{1}{2}$$
$$= \frac{5}{4}i$$

Solution to Activity 5

(a) $u(v + w) = (1 + 2i)((4 - 3i) + (-i))$

$\qquad = (1 + 2i)(4 - 4i)$

$\qquad = 4 - 4i + 8i - 8i^2$

$\qquad = 4 - 4i + 8i + 8$

$\qquad = 12 + 4i$

(b) By part (a),

$\qquad uv + uw = u(v + w) = 12 + 4i.$

(c) $uvw = (1 + 2i)((4 - 3i)(-i))$

$\qquad = (1 + 2i)(-4i + 3i^2)$

$\qquad = (1 + 2i)(-3 - 4i)$

$\qquad = -3 - 4i - 6i - 8i^2$

$\qquad = -3 - 4i - 6i + 8$

$\qquad = 5 - 10i$

Solution to Activity 6

$i^0 = 1$

$i^1 = i$

$i^2 = -1$

$i^3 = (i^2)i = (-1)i = -i$

$i^4 = (i^3)i = (-i)i = -i^2 = 1$

$i^5 = (i^4)i = (1)i = i$

$i^6 = (i^5)i = (i)i = -1$

The powers of i are, in order,

$$\underbrace{1,\ i,\ -1,\ -i,}\ \underbrace{1,\ i,\ -1,\ -i,}\ \underbrace{1,\ i,\ -1,\ -i,} \ldots .$$

This pattern repeats

Solution to Activity 7

Since

$$(3i)^2 = 3^2 i^2 = 9 \times (-1) = -9,$$

it follows that $3i$ is a square root of -9. Since

$$(-3i)^2 = (-3)^2 i^2 = 9 \times (-1) = -9,$$

it follows that $-3i$ is also a square root of -9.

Solution to Activity 8

(a) $4 - 2i$

(b) $-3 + 8i$

(c) $-9i$

(d) 5

Solution to Activity 9

As $z = a + bi$, it follows that $w = \bar{z} = a - bi$.
Therefore

$$\overline{w} = \overline{a - bi} = a + bi = z.$$

Solution to Activity 10

Let $z = a + bi$.

(a) $z + \bar{z} = (a + bi) + (a - bi) = 2a = 2\operatorname{Re}(z)$

(b) $z - \bar{z} = (a + bi) - (a - bi) = 2bi = 2i\operatorname{Im}(z)$

Solution to Activity 11

(a) $(2 + 3i)(2 - 3i) = 2^2 + 3^2 = 4 + 9 = 13$

(b) $(-1 - 2i)(-1 + 2i) = (-1)^2 + (-2)^2 = 1 + 4 = 5$

(c) $(5i) \times (-5i) = 5^2 = 25$

(d) $(-2) \times (-2) = 4$

Solution to Activity 12

(a) $\dfrac{1}{-2 + 3i} = \dfrac{-2 - 3i}{(-2 + 3i)(-2 - 3i)}$

$\qquad = \dfrac{-2 - 3i}{(-2)^2 + 3^2}$

$\qquad = \dfrac{-2 - 3i}{13}$

(b) $\dfrac{2i}{1 + i} = \dfrac{2i(1 - i)}{(1 + i)(1 - i)}$

$\qquad = \dfrac{2i - 2i^2}{1^2 + 1^2}$

$\qquad = \dfrac{2 + 2i}{2}$

$\qquad = 1 + i$

(c) To simplify this fraction, you could multiply the top and bottom of the fraction by the complex conjugate of the denominator, namely $-2i$. However, it's simpler to multiply the top and bottom of the fraction by $-i$, as follows.

$\dfrac{11 - 8i}{2i} = \dfrac{(11 - 8i)(-i)}{2i(-i)}$

$\qquad = \dfrac{-11i + 8i^2}{-2i^2}$

$\qquad = \dfrac{-11i - 8}{2}$

$\qquad = \dfrac{-8 - 11i}{2}$

(d) $\dfrac{1}{i} = \dfrac{-i}{i \times (-i)} = \dfrac{-i}{1} = -i$

(e) $\dfrac{1}{-i} = \dfrac{i}{-i \times i} = \dfrac{i}{1} = i$

(f) $\begin{aligned}\dfrac{4+7i}{-1+2i} &= \dfrac{(4+7i)(-1-2i)}{(-1+2i)(-1-2i)} \\ &= \dfrac{-4-8i-7i-14i^2}{(-1)^2+2^2} \\ &= \dfrac{10-15i}{5} \\ &= 2-3i\end{aligned}$

(g) $\begin{aligned}\dfrac{8+3i}{1+3i} &= \dfrac{(8+3i)(1-3i)}{(1+3i)(1-3i)} \\ &= \dfrac{8-24i+3i-9i^2}{1^2+3^2} \\ &= \dfrac{17-21i}{10}\end{aligned}$

(h) $\begin{aligned}\dfrac{-2+5i}{-4-i} &= \dfrac{(-2+5i)(-4+i)}{(-4-i)(-4+i)} \\ &= \dfrac{8-2i-20i+5i^2}{(-4)^2+(-1)^2} \\ &= \dfrac{3-22i}{17}\end{aligned}$

Solution to Activity 13

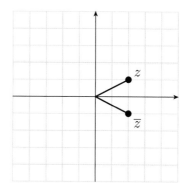

Solution to Activity 14

(The lines in the diagrams below are included to help you see how the answers are obtained. For example, in part (a) the parallelogram law is used to find $z+w$. Your solutions needn't include such lines.)

(a)

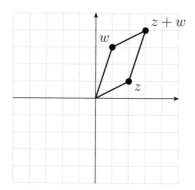

(b)

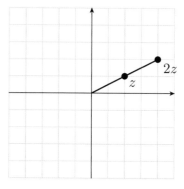

(c)

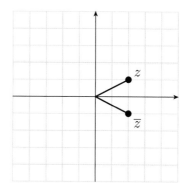

(d)

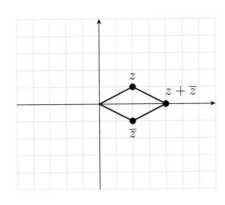

(e)

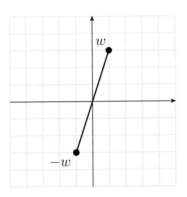

(f)

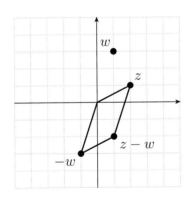

Solution to Activity 15

(a) $|3 + 4i| = \sqrt{3^2 + 4^2} = \sqrt{9 + 16} = \sqrt{25} = 5$

(b) $|-4 + 3i| = \sqrt{(-4)^2 + 3^2}$
$$= \sqrt{16 + 9}$$
$$= \sqrt{25}$$
$$= 5$$

(c) $|0| = 0$

(d) $|-31| = 31$

(e) $|17i| = \sqrt{17^2} = 17$

(f) $\left|7 - i\sqrt{15}\right| = \sqrt{7^2 + \left(-\sqrt{15}\right)^2}$
$$= \sqrt{49 + 15}$$
$$= \sqrt{64}$$
$$= 8$$

(g) $|1 + i| = \sqrt{1^2 + 1^2} = \sqrt{2}$

(h) $|19 + 19i| = \sqrt{19^2 + 19^2} = \sqrt{19^2 \times 2} = 19\sqrt{2}$

(i) $|-i| = \sqrt{(-1)^2} = 1$

(j) $\left|-\frac{1}{2} + \frac{\sqrt{3}}{2}i\right| = \sqrt{\left(-\frac{1}{2}\right)^2 + \left(\frac{\sqrt{3}}{2}\right)^2}$
$$= \sqrt{\frac{1}{4} + \frac{3}{4}}$$
$$= \sqrt{1}$$
$$= 1$$

Solution to Activity 16

Since $z = a + bi$, it follows that
$$-z = -a - bi$$
and
$$\overline{z} = a - bi.$$
Therefore $|z|$, $|-z|$ and $|\overline{z}|$ are all equal to $\sqrt{a^2 + b^2}$, so they are all equal.

Solution to Activity 17

(a) $\dfrac{1}{2 + i} = \dfrac{\overline{2 + i}}{|2 + i|^2} = \dfrac{2 - i}{2^2 + 1^2} = \dfrac{2 - i}{5}$

(b) $\dfrac{1}{-1 - 3i} = \dfrac{\overline{-1 - 3i}}{|-1 - 3i|^2}$
$$= \dfrac{-1 + 3i}{(-1)^2 + (-3)^2}$$
$$= \dfrac{-1 + 3i}{10}$$

(c) You could use the formula
$$\frac{1}{z} = \frac{\overline{z}}{|z|^2}$$
to find $1/2i$, but it's easier to multiply the top and bottom of the fraction $1/2i$ by i to give
$$\frac{1}{2i} = \frac{1}{2i} \times \frac{i}{i} = \frac{i}{2i^2} = -\frac{i}{2}.$$

Solution to Activity 18

(a)

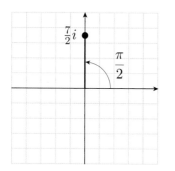

From the diagram, $\mathrm{Arg}(7i/2) = \pi/2$.

(b)

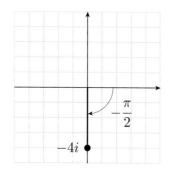

From the diagram, $\mathrm{Arg}(-4i) = -\pi/2$.

(c)

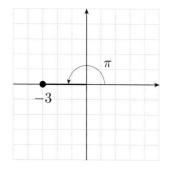

From the diagram, $\mathrm{Arg}(-3) = \pi$.

(d)

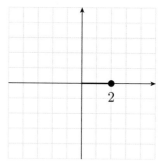

From the diagram, $\mathrm{Arg}(2) = 0$.

Solution to Activity 19

(a)

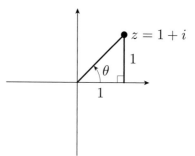

From the diagram,
$$\tan\theta = \frac{1}{1} = 1.$$
So the principal argument is $\theta = \pi/4$.

Alternatively, you may see immediately from the diagram that the principal argument is $\pi/4$, because it's half a right angle ($\pi/2$ radians).

(b)

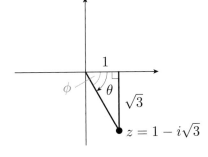

From the diagram,
$$\tan\phi = \frac{\sqrt{3}}{1} = \sqrt{3}.$$
Therefore $\phi = \pi/3$. So the principal argument is
$$\theta = -\phi = -\frac{\pi}{3}.$$

(c)

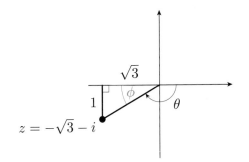

From the diagram,
$$\tan\phi = \frac{1}{\sqrt{3}}.$$
Therefore $\phi = \pi/6$. So the principal argument is
$$\theta = -(\pi - \phi) = -\left(\pi - \frac{\pi}{6}\right) = -\frac{5\pi}{6}.$$

(d)

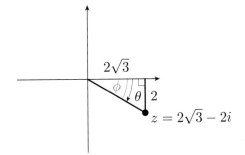

From the diagram,
$$\tan\phi = \frac{2}{2\sqrt{3}} = \frac{1}{\sqrt{3}}.$$
Therefore $\phi = \pi/6$. So the principal argument is
$$\theta = -\phi = -\frac{\pi}{6}.$$

Solution to Activity 20

(a) $3(\cos 0 + i \sin 0) = 3(1 + 0) = 3$

(b) $7\left(\cos\left(\frac{\pi}{2}\right) + i\sin\left(\frac{\pi}{2}\right)\right) = 7(0 + i) = 7i$

(c) $6(\cos\pi + i\sin\pi) = 6(-1 + 0) = -6$

(d) $\cos\left(-\frac{\pi}{2}\right) + i\sin\left(-\frac{\pi}{2}\right) = 0 - i = -i$

(e) $5(\cos(-\pi) + i\sin(-\pi)) = 5(-1 + 0) = -5$

(f) $4\left(\cos\left(\frac{\pi}{3}\right) + i\sin\left(\frac{\pi}{3}\right)\right) = 4\left(\frac{1}{2} + i\frac{\sqrt{3}}{2}\right)$
$$= 2 + 2\sqrt{3}\,i$$

(g) $2\left(\cos\left(-\frac{\pi}{4}\right) + i\sin\left(-\frac{\pi}{4}\right)\right) = 2\left(\frac{1}{\sqrt{2}} - \frac{i}{\sqrt{2}}\right)$
$$= \sqrt{2} - i\sqrt{2}$$

(h) $\sqrt{3}\left(\cos\left(\frac{5\pi}{6}\right) + i\sin\left(\frac{5\pi}{6}\right)\right)$
$$= \sqrt{3}\left(-\frac{\sqrt{3}}{2} + \frac{i}{2}\right)$$
$$= -\frac{3}{2} + i\frac{\sqrt{3}}{2}$$

Solution to Activity 21

(a) The modulus is $7/2$. From Activity 18(a), the principal argument is $\pi/2$. Therefore
$$\frac{7}{2}i = \frac{7}{2}\left(\cos\left(\frac{\pi}{2}\right) + i\sin\left(\frac{\pi}{2}\right)\right).$$

(b) The modulus is 4. From Activity 18(b), the principal argument is $-\pi/2$. Therefore
$$-4i = 4\left(\cos\left(-\frac{\pi}{2}\right) + i\sin\left(-\frac{\pi}{2}\right)\right).$$

(c) The modulus is 3. From Activity 18(c), the principal argument is π. Therefore
$$-3 = 3(\cos\pi + i\sin\pi).$$

(d) The modulus is 2. From Activity 18(d), the principal argument is 0. Therefore
$$2 = 2(\cos 0 + i\sin 0).$$

(e) The modulus is
$$r = \sqrt{1^2 + 1^2} = \sqrt{1+1} = \sqrt{2}.$$
From Activity 19(a), the principal argument is $\pi/4$. Therefore
$$1 + i = \sqrt{2}\left(\cos\left(\frac{\pi}{4}\right) + i\sin\left(\frac{\pi}{4}\right)\right).$$

(f) The modulus is
$$r = \sqrt{1^2 + (-\sqrt{3})^2} = \sqrt{1+3} = \sqrt{4} = 2.$$
From Activity 19(b), the principal argument is $-\pi/3$. Therefore
$$1 - i\sqrt{3} = 2\left(\cos\left(-\frac{\pi}{3}\right) + i\sin\left(-\frac{\pi}{3}\right)\right).$$

(g) The modulus is
$$r = \sqrt{(-\sqrt{3})^2 + (-1)^2} = \sqrt{3+1} = \sqrt{4} = 2.$$
From Activity 19(c), the principal argument is $-5\pi/6$. Therefore
$$-\sqrt{3} - i = 2\left(\cos\left(-\frac{5\pi}{6}\right) + i\sin\left(-\frac{5\pi}{6}\right)\right).$$

(h) The modulus is
$$r = \sqrt{(2\sqrt{3})^2 + (-2)^2} = \sqrt{12+4} = \sqrt{16} = 4.$$
From Activity 19(d), the principal argument is $-\pi/6$. Therefore
$$2\sqrt{3} - 2i = 4\left(\cos\left(-\frac{\pi}{6}\right) + i\sin\left(-\frac{\pi}{6}\right)\right).$$

Solution to Activity 22

(a)
$$zw = 48\left(\cos\left(\frac{\pi}{5} + \frac{\pi}{10}\right) + i\sin\left(\frac{\pi}{5} + \frac{\pi}{10}\right)\right)$$
$$= 48\left(\cos\left(\frac{3\pi}{10}\right) + i\sin\left(\frac{3\pi}{10}\right)\right)$$

(b)
$$zw = 40\left(\cos\left(\frac{7\pi}{8} + \frac{3\pi}{4}\right) + i\sin\left(\frac{7\pi}{8} + \frac{3\pi}{4}\right)\right)$$
$$= 40\left(\cos\left(\frac{13\pi}{8}\right) + i\sin\left(\frac{13\pi}{8}\right)\right)$$
The angle $13\pi/8$ lies outside the interval $(-\pi, \pi]$, so it isn't the principal argument of zw. The principal argument is given by
$$\frac{13\pi}{8} - 2\pi = \frac{13\pi}{8} - \frac{16\pi}{8} = -\frac{3\pi}{8}.$$
Therefore
$$zw = 40\left(\cos\left(-\frac{3\pi}{8}\right) + i\sin\left(-\frac{3\pi}{8}\right)\right).$$

(c)
$$zw = \cos\left(\frac{8\pi}{9} + \frac{8\pi}{9}\right) + i\sin\left(\frac{8\pi}{9} + \frac{8\pi}{9}\right)$$
$$= \cos\left(\frac{16\pi}{9}\right) + i\sin\left(\frac{16\pi}{9}\right)$$
The angle $16\pi/9$ lies outside the interval $(-\pi, \pi]$, so it isn't the principal argument of zw. The principal argument is given by
$$\frac{16\pi}{9} - 2\pi = \frac{16\pi}{9} - \frac{18\pi}{9} = -\frac{2\pi}{9}.$$
Therefore
$$zw = \cos\left(-\frac{2\pi}{9}\right) + i\sin\left(-\frac{2\pi}{9}\right).$$

Solution to Activity 23

The product uvw equals
$$8\left(\cos\left(\frac{3\pi}{7} + \frac{\pi}{7} + \frac{5\pi}{7}\right) + i\sin\left(\frac{3\pi}{7} + \frac{\pi}{7} + \frac{5\pi}{7}\right)\right)$$
$$= 8\left(\cos\left(\frac{9\pi}{7}\right) + i\sin\left(\frac{9\pi}{7}\right)\right)$$
$$= 8\left(\cos\left(-\frac{5\pi}{7}\right) + i\sin\left(-\frac{5\pi}{7}\right)\right).$$

Solution to Activity 24

(a)
$$\frac{z}{w} = 3\left(\cos\left(\frac{\pi}{5} - \frac{\pi}{10}\right) + i\sin\left(\frac{\pi}{5} - \frac{\pi}{10}\right)\right)$$
$$= 3\left(\cos\left(\frac{\pi}{10}\right) + i\sin\left(\frac{\pi}{10}\right)\right)$$

(b)
$$\frac{z}{w} = 2\left(\cos\left(\frac{3\pi}{8} - \frac{5\pi}{8}\right) + i\sin\left(\frac{3\pi}{8} - \frac{5\pi}{8}\right)\right)$$
$$= 2\left(\cos\left(-\frac{2\pi}{8}\right) + i\sin\left(-\frac{2\pi}{8}\right)\right)$$
$$= 2\left(\cos\left(-\frac{\pi}{4}\right) + i\sin\left(-\frac{\pi}{4}\right)\right)$$

(c)
$$\frac{z}{w} = \cos\left(\frac{8\pi}{9} - \frac{8\pi}{9}\right) + i\sin\left(\frac{8\pi}{9} - \frac{8\pi}{9}\right)$$
$$= \cos 0 + i\sin 0$$
In this case, the Cartesian form of z/w is 1 (as you would expect since $z = w$), which is simpler than the polar form.

Solution to Activity 25

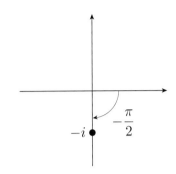

From the diagram,
$$-i = \cos\left(-\frac{\pi}{2}\right) + i\sin\left(-\frac{\pi}{2}\right).$$
Let $z = r(\cos\theta + i\sin\theta)$. Then
$$z \times (-i)$$
$$= r(\cos\theta + i\sin\theta) \times \left(\cos\left(-\frac{\pi}{2}\right) + i\sin\left(-\frac{\pi}{2}\right)\right)$$
$$= r\left(\cos\left(\theta - \frac{\pi}{2}\right) + i\sin\left(\theta - \frac{\pi}{2}\right)\right).$$

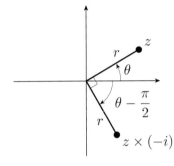

Therefore multiplying z by $-i$ corresponds to a clockwise rotation through a quarter turn ($-\pi/2$ radians).

Solution to Activity 26

(a) The modulus of $1 + i$ is
$$\sqrt{1^2 + 1^2} = \sqrt{1+1} = \sqrt{2}.$$
The principal argument of $1 + i$ was found to be $\pi/4$ in Activity 19(a). Therefore
$$1 + i = \sqrt{2}\left(\cos\left(\frac{\pi}{4}\right) + i\sin\left(\frac{\pi}{4}\right)\right).$$

Hence
$$(1+i)^3 = (\sqrt{2})^3\left(\cos\left(3 \times \frac{\pi}{4}\right) + i\sin\left(3 \times \frac{\pi}{4}\right)\right)$$
$$= 2\sqrt{2}\left(\cos\left(\frac{3\pi}{4}\right) + i\sin\left(\frac{3\pi}{4}\right)\right)$$
$$= 2\sqrt{2}\left(-\frac{1}{\sqrt{2}} + \frac{i}{\sqrt{2}}\right)$$
$$= -2 + 2i.$$

(b) $\left(2^{1/3}\left(\cos\left(\frac{\pi}{9}\right) + i\sin\left(\frac{\pi}{9}\right)\right)\right)^{12}$
$$= 2^{12/3}\left(\cos\left(\frac{12\pi}{9}\right) + i\sin\left(\frac{12\pi}{9}\right)\right)$$
$$= 2^4\left(\cos\left(\frac{4\pi}{3}\right) + i\sin\left(\frac{4\pi}{3}\right)\right)$$
$$= 16\left(-\frac{1}{2} - i\frac{\sqrt{3}}{2}\right)$$
$$= -8 - 8\sqrt{3}\,i.$$

(c) The modulus of $-1 + i\sqrt{3}$ is
$$\sqrt{(-1)^2 + (\sqrt{3})^2} = \sqrt{1+3} = \sqrt{4} = 2.$$
The principal argument of $-1 + i\sqrt{3}$ was found to be $2\pi/3$ in Example 5. Therefore
$$-1 + i\sqrt{3} = 2\left(\cos\left(\frac{2\pi}{3}\right) + i\sin\left(\frac{2\pi}{3}\right)\right).$$
Hence
$$(-1 + i\sqrt{3})^7$$
$$= 2^7\left(\cos\left(7 \times \frac{2\pi}{3}\right) + i\sin\left(7 \times \frac{2\pi}{3}\right)\right)$$
$$= 128\left(\cos\left(\frac{14\pi}{3}\right) + i\sin\left(\frac{14\pi}{3}\right)\right).$$
Since
$$\frac{14\pi}{3} = 4\pi + \frac{2\pi}{3},$$
we obtain
$$(-1 + i\sqrt{3})^7 = 128\left(\cos\left(\frac{2\pi}{3}\right) + i\sin\left(\frac{2\pi}{3}\right)\right)$$
$$= 128\left(-\frac{1}{2} + i\frac{\sqrt{3}}{2}\right)$$
$$= 64(-1 + i\sqrt{3}).$$

(d) The modulus of $\sqrt{3}+i$ is

$$\sqrt{(\sqrt{3})^2+1^2}=\sqrt{3+1}=\sqrt{4}=2.$$

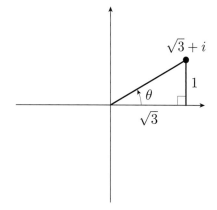

From the diagram,

$$\tan\theta=\frac{1}{\sqrt{3}}.$$

Therefore the principal argument is $\theta=\pi/6$. So

$$\sqrt{3}+i=2\left(\cos\left(\frac{\pi}{6}\right)+i\sin\left(\frac{\pi}{6}\right)\right).$$

Therefore

$$\begin{aligned}(\sqrt{3}+i)^{-6}&=2^{-6}\left(\cos\left(-6\times\frac{\pi}{6}\right)+i\sin\left(-6\times\frac{\pi}{6}\right)\right)\\&=\frac{1}{64}(\cos(-\pi)+i\sin(-\pi))\\&=\frac{1}{64}(-1+0)\\&=-\frac{1}{64}.\end{aligned}$$

(e) The modulus of $2+2i$ is

$$\sqrt{2^2+2^2}=\sqrt{4+4}=\sqrt{8}=2\sqrt{2}.$$

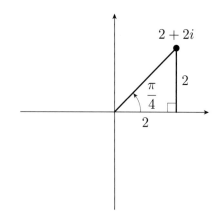

From the diagram, the principal argument is $\pi/4$. Therefore

$$2+2i=2\sqrt{2}\left(\cos\left(\frac{\pi}{4}\right)+i\sin\left(\frac{\pi}{4}\right)\right).$$

Hence

$$\begin{aligned}&(2+2i)^{-5}\\&=(2\sqrt{2})^{-5}\left(\cos\left(-\frac{5\pi}{4}\right)+i\sin\left(-\frac{5\pi}{4}\right)\right).\end{aligned}$$

Since

$$-\frac{5\pi}{4}+2\pi=\frac{3\pi}{4},$$

we obtain

$$\begin{aligned}&(2+2i)^{-5}\\&=(2\sqrt{2})^{-5}\left(\cos\left(\frac{3\pi}{4}\right)+i\sin\left(\frac{3\pi}{4}\right)\right)\\&=\frac{1}{(2\sqrt{2})^5}\left(-\frac{1}{\sqrt{2}}+\frac{i}{\sqrt{2}}\right)\\&=\frac{1}{256}(-1+i).\end{aligned}$$

Solution to Activity 28

(a) Completing the square on the left-hand side gives

$$(z-1)^2+1=0;$$

that is,

$$(z-1)^2=-1.$$

Taking square roots of both sides gives

$$z-1=\pm i,\quad\text{so}\quad z=1\pm i.$$

(b) Completing the square on the left-hand side gives

$$(z+2)^2+9=0;$$

that is,

$$(z+2)^2=-9.$$

Taking square roots of both sides gives

$$z+2=\pm3i,\quad\text{so}\quad z=-2\pm3i.$$

(c) Subtracting 25 from both sides gives

$$z^2=-25.$$

Taking square roots of both sides gives

$$z=\pm5i.$$

Solution to Activity 29

(a)
$$z = \frac{-2 \pm \sqrt{2^2 - 4 \times 1 \times 2}}{2 \times 1}$$
$$= \frac{-2 \pm \sqrt{-4}}{2}$$
$$= \frac{-2 \pm 2i}{2}$$
$$= -1 \pm i$$

(b) You could solve this quadratic equation by using the quadratic formula, but it's easier to solve it by factorising, as follows:
$$z^2 + 6z + 9 = 0$$
$$(z+3)^2 = 0$$
$$z + 3 = 0$$
$$z = -3.$$

(c) You could solve this quadratic equation by using the quadratic formula, but it's easier to solve it by using a simple rearrangement.

Subtract 5 from both sides of the equation to give
$$3z^2 = -5; \quad \text{that is} \quad z^2 = -\frac{5}{3}.$$
Therefore
$$z = \pm i\sqrt{\frac{5}{3}} = \pm i\frac{\sqrt{5}}{\sqrt{3}}.$$
Rationalising the denominator gives
$$z = \pm i\frac{\sqrt{5}}{\sqrt{3}} \times \frac{\sqrt{3}}{\sqrt{3}} = \pm i\frac{\sqrt{15}}{3}.$$

(d)
$$z = \frac{4 \pm \sqrt{(-4)^2 - 4 \times 1 \times 8}}{2 \times 1}$$
$$= \frac{4 \pm \sqrt{-16}}{2}$$
$$= \frac{4 \pm 4i}{2}$$
$$= 2 \pm 2i$$

(e) You could solve this quadratic equation by using the quadratic formula, but it's easier to solve it by factorising, as follows:
$$z^2 + 3z = 0$$
$$z(z + 3) = 0$$
$$z = 0 \quad \text{or} \quad z + 3 = 0$$
$$z = 0 \quad \text{or} \quad z = -3.$$

(f)
$$z = \frac{3 \pm \sqrt{(-3)^2 - 4 \times 2 \times 5}}{2 \times 2}$$
$$= \frac{3 \pm \sqrt{-31}}{4}$$
$$= \frac{3 \pm i\sqrt{31}}{4}$$

Solution to Activity 30

(a) A suitable quadratic equation is
$$(z - (1 + 2i))(z - (1 - 2i)) = 0.$$
Simplifying gives
$$((z-1) - 2i)((z-1) + 2i) = 0$$
$$(z-1)^2 - (2i)^2 = 0$$
$$z^2 - 2z + 1 + 4 = 0$$
$$z^2 - 2z + 5 = 0.$$

(b) A suitable quadratic equation is
$$(z - (-3 + 4i))(z - (-3 - 4i)) = 0.$$
Simplifying gives
$$((z+3) - 4i)((z+3) + 4i) = 0$$
$$(z+3)^2 - (4i)^2 = 0$$
$$z^2 + 6z + 9 + 16 = 0$$
$$z^2 + 6z + 25 = 0.$$

(c) A suitable quadratic equation is
$$(z - 7i)(z - (-7i)) = 0.$$
Simplifying gives
$$z^2 - (7i)^2 = 0$$
$$z^2 + 49 = 0.$$

(d) A suitable quadratic equation is
$$(z - (1 + \tfrac{1}{2}i))(z - (1 - \tfrac{1}{2}i)) = 0.$$
Simplifying gives
$$((z-1) - \tfrac{1}{2}i)((z-1) + \tfrac{1}{2}i) = 0$$
$$(z-1)^2 - (\tfrac{1}{2}i)^2 = 0$$
$$z^2 - 2z + 1 + \tfrac{1}{4} = 0$$
$$z^2 - 2z + \tfrac{5}{4} = 0$$
$$4z^2 - 8z + 5 = 0.$$

Solution to Activity 32

$$\left(-1-i\sqrt{3}\right)^2 = 1 + 2i\sqrt{3} + i^2\left(\sqrt{3}\right)^2$$
$$= 1 + 2i\sqrt{3} - 3$$
$$= -2 + 2i\sqrt{3}.$$

Therefore

$$\left(-1-i\sqrt{3}\right)^3 = \left(-1-i\sqrt{3}\right)^2\left(-1-i\sqrt{3}\right)$$
$$= \left(-2+2i\sqrt{3}\right)\left(-1-i\sqrt{3}\right)$$
$$= 2 + 2i\sqrt{3} - 2i\sqrt{3} - 2i^2\left(\sqrt{3}\right)^2$$
$$= 2 + 6$$
$$= 8.$$

Hence

$$\left(\frac{-1-i\sqrt{3}}{2}\right)^3 = \frac{\left(-1-i\sqrt{3}\right)^3}{2^3} = \frac{8}{8} = 1.$$

(There's another, quicker solution to this activity. Let $w = \frac{1}{2}\left(-1+i\sqrt{3}\right)$, so that $\overline{w} = \frac{1}{2}\left(-1-i\sqrt{3}\right)$. You've already seen that w is a cube root of unity, and now you're asked to show that $\overline{w}$ is also a cube root of unity. To do this, take the complex conjugate of each side of the equation

$$w^3 = 1$$

to give

$$\overline{w^3} = 1.$$

Since

$$\overline{w^3} = \overline{w \times w \times w} = \overline{w} \times \overline{w} \times \overline{w} = \overline{w}^3,$$

it follows that

$$\overline{w}^3 = 1.)$$

Solution to Activity 33

(a) Let $z = r(\cos\theta + i\sin\theta)$. Then

$$r^3(\cos 3\theta + i\sin 3\theta) = \cos 0 + i\sin 0.$$

Comparing moduli gives $r^3 = 1$, so $r = 1$.

Comparing arguments gives

$$3\theta = 0 + 2m\pi = 2m\pi, \quad \text{where } m \text{ is an integer.}$$

Hence

$$\theta = \frac{2m\pi}{3}, \quad \text{where } m \text{ is an integer.}$$

Taking $m = 0, 1, 2$ gives the solutions

$$z_0 = \cos 0 + i\sin 0 = 1$$
$$z_1 = \cos\left(\frac{2\pi}{3}\right) + i\sin\left(\frac{2\pi}{3}\right) = -\frac{1}{2} + i\frac{\sqrt{3}}{2}$$
$$z_2 = \cos\left(\frac{4\pi}{3}\right) + i\sin\left(\frac{4\pi}{3}\right) = -\frac{1}{2} - i\frac{\sqrt{3}}{2}.$$

All other values of m give repetitions of these three solutions.

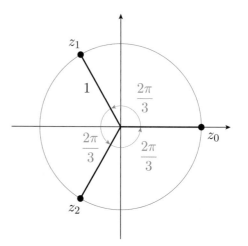

(b) Let $z = r(\cos\theta + i\sin\theta)$. Then
$$r^4(\cos 4\theta + i\sin 4\theta) = \cos 0 + i\sin 0.$$
Comparing moduli gives $r^4 = 1$, so $r = 1$.

Comparing arguments gives
$$4\theta = 0 + 2m\pi = 2m\pi, \quad \text{where } m \text{ is an integer.}$$
Hence
$$\theta = \frac{m\pi}{2}, \quad \text{where } m \text{ is an integer.}$$
Taking $m = 0, 1, 2, 3$ gives the solutions
$$z_0 = \cos 0 + i\sin 0 = 1$$
$$z_1 = \cos\left(\frac{\pi}{2}\right) + i\sin\left(\frac{\pi}{2}\right) = i$$
$$z_2 = \cos\pi + i\sin\pi = -1$$
$$z_3 = \cos\left(\frac{3\pi}{2}\right) + i\sin\left(\frac{3\pi}{2}\right) = -i.$$
All other values of m give repetitions of these four solutions.

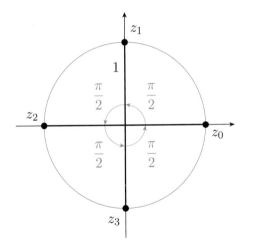

(c) Let $z = r(\cos\theta + i\sin\theta)$. Then
$$r^6(\cos 6\theta + i\sin 6\theta) = \cos 0 + i\sin 0.$$
Comparing moduli gives $r^6 = 1$, so $r = 1$.

Comparing arguments gives
$$6\theta = 0 + 2m\pi = 2m\pi, \quad \text{where } m \text{ is an integer.}$$
Hence
$$\theta = \frac{m\pi}{3}, \quad \text{where } m \text{ is an integer.}$$
Taking $m = 0, 1, 2, 3, 4, 5$ gives the solutions
$$z_0 = \cos 0 + i\sin 0 = 1$$
$$z_1 = \cos\left(\frac{\pi}{3}\right) + i\sin\left(\frac{\pi}{3}\right) = \frac{1}{2} + i\frac{\sqrt{3}}{2}$$
$$z_2 = \cos\left(\frac{2\pi}{3}\right) + i\sin\left(\frac{2\pi}{3}\right) = -\frac{1}{2} + i\frac{\sqrt{3}}{2}$$
$$z_3 = \cos\pi + i\sin\pi = -1$$
$$z_4 = \cos\left(\frac{4\pi}{3}\right) + i\sin\left(\frac{4\pi}{3}\right) = -\frac{1}{2} - i\frac{\sqrt{3}}{2}$$
$$z_5 = \cos\left(\frac{5\pi}{3}\right) + i\sin\left(\frac{5\pi}{3}\right) = \frac{1}{2} - i\frac{\sqrt{3}}{2}.$$
All other values of m give repetitions of these six solutions.

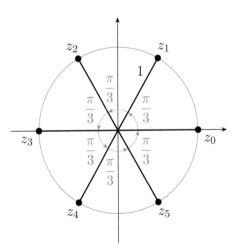

Solution to Activity 34

(a) A polar form of the complex number 64 is $64(\cos 0 + i \sin 0)$. Let $z = r(\cos \theta + i \sin \theta)$. Then

$$r^6(\cos 6\theta + i \sin 6\theta) = 64(\cos 0 + i \sin 0).$$

Comparing moduli gives $r^6 = 64$, so $r = 2$.

Comparing arguments gives

$$6\theta = 0 + 2m\pi, \quad \text{where } m \text{ is an integer.}$$

Hence

$$\theta = \frac{m\pi}{3}, \quad \text{where } m \text{ is an integer.}$$

Taking $m = 0, 1, 2, 3, 4, 5$ gives the solutions

$$z_0 = 2(\cos 0 + i \sin 0) = 2$$

$$z_1 = 2\left(\cos\left(\frac{\pi}{3}\right) + i \sin\left(\frac{\pi}{3}\right)\right) = 1 + i\sqrt{3}$$

$$z_2 = 2\left(\cos\left(\frac{2\pi}{3}\right) + i \sin\left(\frac{2\pi}{3}\right)\right) = -1 + i\sqrt{3}$$

$$z_3 = 2\left(\cos \pi + i \sin \pi\right) = -2$$

$$z_4 = 2\left(\cos\left(\frac{4\pi}{3}\right) + i \sin\left(\frac{4\pi}{3}\right)\right) = -1 - i\sqrt{3}$$

$$z_5 = 2\left(\cos\left(\frac{5\pi}{3}\right) + i \sin\left(\frac{5\pi}{3}\right)\right) = 1 - i\sqrt{3}.$$

All other values of m give repetitions of these six solutions.

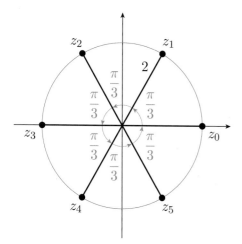

(b) A polar form of the complex number -8 is $8(\cos \pi + i \sin \pi)$. Let $z = r(\cos \theta + i \sin \theta)$. Then

$$r^3(\cos 3\theta + i \sin 3\theta) = 8(\cos \pi + i \sin \pi).$$

Comparing moduli gives $r^3 = 8$, so $r = 2$.

Comparing arguments gives

$$3\theta = \pi + 2m\pi = (2m + 1)\pi,$$

where m is an integer.

Hence

$$\theta = \frac{(2m + 1)\pi}{3}, \quad \text{where } m \text{ is an integer.}$$

Taking $m = 0, 1, 2$ gives the solutions

$$z_0 = 2\left(\cos\left(\frac{\pi}{3}\right) + i \sin\left(\frac{\pi}{3}\right)\right) = 1 + i\sqrt{3}$$

$$z_1 = 2(\cos \pi + i \sin \pi) = -2$$

$$z_2 = 2\left(\cos\left(\frac{5\pi}{3}\right) + i \sin\left(\frac{5\pi}{3}\right)\right) = 1 - i\sqrt{3}.$$

All other values of m give repetitions of these three solutions.

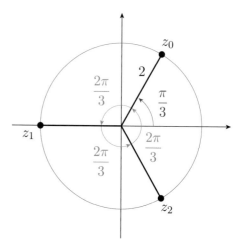

(c) The modulus of $-1-i$ is
$$\sqrt{(-1)^2 + (-1)^2} = \sqrt{1+1} = \sqrt{2}.$$

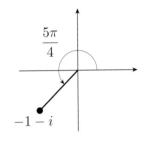

From the diagram,
$$\mathrm{Arg}(-1-i) = \frac{5\pi}{4}.$$
Therefore
$$-1-i = \sqrt{2}\left(\cos\left(\frac{5\pi}{4}\right) + i\sin\left(\frac{5\pi}{4}\right)\right).$$
Let $z = r(\cos\theta + i\sin\theta)$. Then
$$r^5(\cos 5\theta + i\sin 5\theta)$$
$$= \sqrt{2}\left(\cos\left(\frac{5\pi}{4}\right) + i\sin\left(\frac{5\pi}{4}\right)\right).$$
Comparing moduli gives $r^5 = \sqrt{2}$, so $r = 2^{1/10}$.

Comparing arguments gives
$$5\theta = 5\pi/4 + 2m\pi, \quad \text{where } m \text{ is an integer.}$$
Hence
$$\theta = \frac{\pi}{4} + \frac{2m\pi}{5}, \quad \text{where } m \text{ is an integer.}$$
Taking $m = 0, 1, 2, 3, 4$ gives the solutions
$$z_0 = 2^{1/10}\left(\cos\left(\frac{\pi}{4}\right) + i\sin\left(\frac{\pi}{4}\right)\right)$$
$$z_1 = 2^{1/10}\left(\cos\left(\frac{13\pi}{20}\right) + i\sin\left(\frac{13\pi}{20}\right)\right)$$
$$z_2 = 2^{1/10}\left(\cos\left(\frac{21\pi}{20}\right) + i\sin\left(\frac{21\pi}{20}\right)\right)$$
$$z_3 = 2^{1/10}\left(\cos\left(\frac{29\pi}{20}\right) + i\sin\left(\frac{29\pi}{20}\right)\right)$$
$$z_4 = 2^{1/10}\left(\cos\left(\frac{37\pi}{20}\right) + i\sin\left(\frac{37\pi}{20}\right)\right).$$
All other values of m give repetitions of these five solutions.

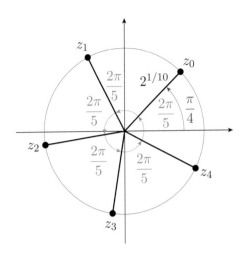

Solution to Activity 36

(a) $3e^{i0} = 3(\cos 0 + i\sin 0)$
$$= 3(1+0)$$
$$= 3$$

(b) $7e^{i\pi/2} = 7\left(\cos\left(\frac{\pi}{2}\right) + i\sin\left(\frac{\pi}{2}\right)\right)$
$$= 7(0+i)$$
$$= 7i$$

(c) $6e^{i\pi} = 6(\cos\pi + i\sin\pi)$
$$= 6(-1+0)$$
$$= -6$$

(d) $e^{-i\pi/2} = \cos(-\pi/2) + i\sin(-\pi/2)$
$$= 0 - i$$
$$= -i$$

(e) $5e^{-i\pi} = 5(\cos(-\pi) + i\sin(-\pi))$
$$= 5(-1+0)$$
$$= -5$$

(f) $4e^{i\pi/3} = 4\left(\cos\left(\frac{\pi}{3}\right) + i\sin\left(\frac{\pi}{3}\right)\right)$
$$= 4\left(\frac{1}{2} + i\frac{\sqrt{3}}{2}\right)$$
$$= 2 + 2\sqrt{3}\,i$$

(g) $2e^{-i\pi/4} = 2\left(\cos\left(-\frac{\pi}{4}\right) + i\sin\left(-\frac{\pi}{4}\right)\right)$
$$= 2\left(\frac{1}{\sqrt{2}} - \frac{i}{\sqrt{2}}\right)$$
$$= \sqrt{2} - i\sqrt{2}$$

(h) $\sqrt{3}e^{5\pi i/6} = \sqrt{3}\left(\cos\left(\dfrac{5\pi}{6}\right) + i\sin\left(\dfrac{5\pi}{6}\right)\right)$

$= \sqrt{3}\left(-\dfrac{\sqrt{3}}{2} + \dfrac{i}{2}\right)$

$= -\dfrac{3}{2} + i\dfrac{\sqrt{3}}{2}$

Solution to Activity 37

(a) From Activity 21(a), the modulus is $7/2$ and the principal argument is $\pi/2$. Therefore
$$\frac{7}{2}i = \frac{7}{2}e^{i\pi/2}.$$

(b) From Activity 21(b), the modulus is 4 and the principal argument is $-\pi/2$. Therefore
$$-4i = 4e^{-i\pi/2}.$$

(c) From Activity 21(c), the modulus is 3 and the principal argument is π. Therefore
$$-3 = 3e^{i\pi}.$$

(d) From Activity 21(d), the modulus is 2 and the principal argument is 0. Therefore
$$2 = 2e^{i0}.$$

(e) From Activity 21(e), the modulus is $\sqrt{2}$ and the principal argument is $\pi/4$. Therefore
$$1 + i = \sqrt{2}e^{i\pi/4}.$$

(f) From Activity 21(f), the modulus is 2 and the principal argument is $-\pi/3$. Therefore
$$1 - i\sqrt{3} = 2e^{-i\pi/3}.$$

(g) From Activity 21(g), the modulus is 2 and the principal argument is $-5\pi/6$. Therefore
$$-\sqrt{3} - i = 2e^{-5\pi i/6}.$$

(h) From Activity 21(h), the modulus is 4 and the principal argument is $-\pi/6$. Therefore
$$2\sqrt{3} - 2i = 4e^{-i\pi/6}.$$

Solution to Activity 38

Because
$$r(\cos\theta + i\sin\theta) = re^{i\theta}$$
$$s(\cos\phi + i\sin\phi) = se^{i\phi}$$
$$\frac{r}{s}(\cos(\theta - \phi) + i\sin(\theta - \phi)) = \frac{r}{s}e^{i(\theta-\phi)},$$
the formula for the quotient of two complex numbers in polar form can be written as
$$\frac{re^{i\theta}}{se^{i\phi}} = \frac{r}{s}e^{i(\theta-\phi)}.$$

Solution to Activity 39

We use the formulas in the boxes above the activity, and the formula from Activity 38. That is, we use the usual index laws.

(a) $e^{i\pi/8} \times e^{3\pi i/8} = e^{i(\pi/8 + 3\pi/8)}$

$= e^{i(4\pi/8)}$

$= e^{i\pi/2}$

(b) $\left(e^{i\pi/8}\right)^4 = e^{i(4\times\pi/8)} = e^{i\pi/2}$

(c) $\dfrac{e^{3\pi i/8}}{e^{\pi i/8}} = e^{i(3\pi/8 - \pi/8)}$

$= e^{i(2\pi/8)}$

$= e^{i\pi/4}$

(d) $\dfrac{e^{i\pi/8}}{e^{3\pi i/8}} = e^{i(\pi/8 - 3\pi/8)}$

$= e^{i(-2\pi/8)}$

$= e^{-i\pi/4}$

Solution to Activity 40

Euler's formula gives
$$e^{i(\theta+2\pi)} = \cos(\theta + 2\pi) + i\sin(\theta + 2\pi).$$
Since
$$\cos(\theta + 2\pi) = \cos\theta \quad \text{and} \quad \sin(\theta + 2\pi) = \sin\theta,$$
it follows that
$$e^{i(\theta+2\pi)} = \cos\theta + i\sin\theta = e^{i\theta}.$$

Solution to Activity 41

For brevity, write $c = \cos\theta$ and $s = \sin\theta$. Then, by de Moivre's formula and the binomial theorem,

$$\cos 4\theta + i\sin 4\theta = (\cos\theta + i\sin\theta)^4$$
$$= (c + is)^4$$
$$= c^4 + 4c^3(is) + 6c^2(is)^2$$
$$+ 4c(is)^3 + (is)^4$$
$$= c^4 + 4ic^3 s - 6c^2 s^2 - 4ics^3 + s^4$$
$$= (c^4 - 6c^2 s^2 + s^4) + 4ics(c^2 - s^2).$$

Comparing real and imaginary parts, and using the identity $c^2 + s^2 = 1$, gives

$$\cos 4\theta = c^4 - 6c^2 s^2 + s^4$$
$$= c^4 - 6c^2(1 - c^2) + (1 - c^2)(1 - c^2)$$
$$= c^4 - 6c^2 + 6c^4 + 1 - 2c^2 + c^4$$
$$= 8c^4 - 8c^2 + 1$$
$$= 8\cos^4\theta - 8\cos^2\theta + 1$$

and

$$\sin 4\theta = 4sc(c^2 - s^2)$$
$$= 4\sin\theta\cos\theta(\cos^2\theta - \sin^2\theta),$$

which are the required identities.

(Another way to obtain the identities in this activity is to apply the double-angle identities

$$\sin 2\theta = 2\sin\theta\cos\theta \quad \text{and} \quad \cos 2\theta = \cos^2\theta - \sin^2\theta$$

repeatedly. For example,

$$\sin 4\theta = \sin(2(2\theta))$$
$$= 2\sin 2\theta\cos 2\theta$$
$$= 2(2\sin\theta\cos\theta)(\cos^2\theta - \sin^2\theta)$$
$$= 4\sin\theta\cos\theta(\cos^2\theta - \sin^2\theta).)$$

Solution to Activity 42

(a) By the given formula for $\sin\theta$ and the binomial theorem,

$$\sin^3\theta = \frac{1}{(2i)^3}\left(e^{i\theta} - e^{-i\theta}\right)^3$$
$$= \frac{1}{-8i}\left((e^{i\theta})^3 + 3(e^{i\theta})^2(-e^{-i\theta})\right.$$
$$\left. + 3e^{i\theta}(-e^{-i\theta})^2 + (-e^{-i\theta})^3\right)$$
$$= \frac{1}{-8i}\left(e^{3i\theta} - 3e^{2i\theta}e^{-i\theta} + 3e^{i\theta}e^{-2i\theta} - e^{-3i\theta}\right)$$
$$= -\frac{1}{8i}\left(e^{3i\theta} - 3e^{i\theta} + 3e^{-i\theta} - e^{-3i\theta}\right)$$
$$= \frac{1}{8i}\left(3(e^{i\theta} - e^{-i\theta}) - (e^{3i\theta} - e^{-3i\theta})\right)$$
$$= \frac{1}{4}\left(3\left(\frac{e^{i\theta} - e^{-i\theta}}{2i}\right) - \frac{e^{3i\theta} - e^{-3i\theta}}{2i}\right)$$
$$= \frac{1}{4}\left(3\sin\theta - \sin 3\theta\right).$$

(b) By the given formula for $\cos\theta$ and the binomial theorem,

$$\cos^4\theta = \frac{1}{2^4}\left(e^{i\theta} + e^{-i\theta}\right)^4$$
$$= \frac{1}{16}\left((e^{i\theta})^4 + 4(e^{i\theta})^3 e^{-i\theta} + 6(e^{i\theta})^2(e^{-i\theta})^2\right.$$
$$\left. + 4e^{i\theta}(e^{-i\theta})^3 + (e^{-i\theta})^4\right)$$
$$= \frac{1}{16}\left(e^{4i\theta} + 4e^{3i\theta}e^{-i\theta} + 6e^{2i\theta}e^{-2i\theta}\right.$$
$$\left. + 4e^{i\theta}e^{-3i\theta} + e^{-4i\theta}\right)$$
$$= \frac{1}{16}\left(e^{4i\theta} + 4e^{2i\theta} + 6 + 4e^{-2i\theta} + e^{-4i\theta}\right)$$
$$= \frac{1}{16}\left((e^{4i\theta} + e^{-4i\theta}) + 4(e^{2i\theta} + e^{-2i\theta}) + 6\right)$$
$$= \frac{1}{8}\left(\frac{e^{4i\theta} + e^{-4i\theta}}{2} + 4\left(\frac{e^{2i\theta} + e^{-2i\theta}}{2}\right) + 3\right)$$
$$= \frac{1}{8}\left(\cos 4\theta + 4\cos 2\theta + 3\right).$$

Acknowledgements

Grateful acknowledgement is made to the following sources:

Figure 1: Taken from: www.amazon.com

Figure 3: Taken from:
http://en.wikipedia.org/wiki/File:Julia_set_camp4_hi_rez.png. This file is
licensed under the Creative Commons Attribution-Share Alike Licence
http://creativecommons.org/licenses/by-sa/3.0/

Page 175: Smithsonian Institution

Page 236: Photodisc

Page 241: Taken from:
http://en.wikipedia.org/wiki/File:William_Rowan_Hamilton_Plaque_-
geograph.org.uk-_347941.jpg. This file is licensed under the Creative
Commons Attribution-Share Alike Licence
http://creativecommons.org/licenses/by-sa/3.0/

Page 243 (money): www.123royaltyfree.com

Page 243 (peregrine falcon): Mike Baird / This file is licensed under the
Creative Commons Attribution Licence
http://creativecommons.org/licenses/by/3.0/

Every effort has been made to contact copyright holders. If any have been
inadvertently overlooked the publishers will be pleased to make the
necessary arrangements at the first opportunity.

Index